Wooten S.C.

# SELECTIONS FROM
# ROBERT LOUIS STEVENSON

# SELECTIONS FROM

# ROBERT LOUIS STEVENSON

EDITED BY

## HENRY SEIDEL CANBY

AND

## FREDERICK ERASTUS PIERCE

Assistant Professors of English in Yale University

CHARLES SCRIBNER'S SONS

NEW YORK     CHICAGO     BOSTON

# CONTENTS

# INTRODUCTION

## I.—LIFE OF STEVENSON

THE life of Robert Louis Stevenson is almost coextensive with the last half of the nineteenth century. He was born in the middle of that century (Nov. 13, 1850), and died a little before its end (Dec. 3, 1894). His birthplace was Edinburgh; and in spite of many journeys hither and thither, this city may be considered his permanent home until he left Scotland for the Western Hemisphere.

Almost from the cradle he showed that tendency to physical weakness and insidious disease which pursued him all his life. As a result of delicate health his schooling was irregular, and his early education chiefly drawn from wide general reading at home. Furthermore, in that harsh northern climate he was forced to spend much of his time indoors. This restriction must have been a heavy disappointment to the boy; for his spirit was as ambitious as his body was frail, and more than one clever prank of his boyhood shows the love of adventure which later produced *Treasure Island*.

Stevenson's father, uncle, and grandfather before him had been civil engineers, famous for their work in building lighthouses. The love of this bold, out-of-door life with its great possibilities of accomplishment had become a family tradition; and, as a result, Stevenson himself was intended for the same career. But though he was full of enthusiasm for his father's work and wondered later in life if he had not made a mistake in substituting literature for it, he never showed any strong inclination to become an engineer. Unquestionably Stevenson had some of the scientific ability hereditary in the family as well as some of the family love for danger and

vii

achievement and the mysterious fascination of the ocean; but his precarious health and inborn passion for writing drew him too powerfully another way. His attempt to become a lawyer was equally unsatisfactory. He was admitted to the Scottish Bar in 1875, but made almost no attempt to practice. His heart was elsewhere.

Fortunately, his family were in comfortable circumstances; and his father, though disappointed at the boy's attitude toward engineering, was loving and generous. Hence, Stevenson was not forced by want into a distasteful profession, but was allowed to mature at leisure his natural gift as an author. His first works were short essays, setting forth his own original views on the most widely differing topics, from the characteristics of a landscape to the dangers of falling in love. Although some of these essays have since won a high rank by their literary polish and vivid individuality, they attracted but little notice at the time. Then came a series of travel-sketches, in which the author's success was due to the very ill health that pursued him. His tendency to lung disease forced him frequently to flee out of the inclement air of Scotland to some warmer region, France, or Italy, or Belgium These trips not only fulfilled his romantic longings to see men and countries, they also gave him a great fund of interesting material, which he worked up into such delightfully picturesque narratives as the *Inland Voyage* and *Travels with a Donkey*, his first published books. Gradually various essays and stories of his found places in different magazines; and, although they won little notice from the general public, they did make an impression on a few discerning critics, and thereby laid a foundation for Stevenson's future success. By degrees, also, he made the acquaintance of literary men older and more prominent than himself, who by their criticism aided him in his work and by their influence helped him to find publishers and readers. Among these was Sidney Colvin, recently elected Slade professor of Fine Arts at Cambridge University, who later became Stevenson's lifelong friend; the poet, W. E. Henley; and the well-known critics and authors, Edmund Gosse and Andrew Lang.

Before he was thirty, Stevenson began to drift away from essays and travel-sketches into the field of story-writing. No doubt this change was partly a step to meet the demands of the public; but partly also it was a response to the man's own nature. There was, as one American critic has put it, a troll in his blood, a restless, adventurous, romance-loving spirit, which was debarred from its natural development by the weakness of his body and found expression instead in the exciting creations of his mind. It must not be assumed that he abandoned his old field of work altogether; on the contrary some of his finest essays had still to be written; but from now on their number dwindles, and narrative forms more and more the bulk of the author's output.

In France, in 1876, Stevenson first met the woman who was to be his future wife. She was a Mrs. Osbourne, an American, who after an unhappy marriage had left her Californian home to live with her two children in a foreign country. Acquaintance soon deepened into friendship; but on account of financial and other reasons it was nearly four years before they were married. The marriage finally took place May 19, 1880, in California, whither Stevenson had gone to join his future wife. It was while sailing from Scotland to New York on this trip that the author encountered those experiences which he afterward embodied in *The Amateur Emigrant.*

Shortly after their marriage Mr. and Mrs. Stevenson returned to Scotland. But it soon became evident that if Stevenson was to live long he could not remain permanently in that bleak and trying climate. Consequently, during the next seven years we find them experimenting with temporary homes in various parts of Europe. Two years were spent mainly at Davos in the Swiss Alps, two more in Southern France near Marseilles, neither residence proving wholly satisfactory, and finally three years at Bournemouth on the English coast. During all this time the strong affection between Stevenson and his parents brought the young people on frequent trips to the Stevenson home in Edinburgh. In the middle of this period (1883) appeared *Treasure Island,* the first of its author's books which became really popular and brought in a substantial income. In 1886, shortly before leaving Bournemouth, he published the *Strange Case of Dr. Jekyll and Mr. Hyde*, which gained a sale and a popularity far beyond that of anything that he had previously produced. From this time on Stevenson had an international reputation and a comfortable income from his writings. From this time on, also, his productions were no longer mainly essays, as they had been during his first period, or mainly short stories, as they had been more recently, but chiefly novels and tales of considerable length, like *The Wrecker* and *The Beach of Falesá*.

In 1885 appeared *A Child's Garden of Verse*, Stevenson's first published volume of poetry. Two other volumes of verse came out during his life, and one after his death. Each of these contained poems written within a period of several years. As a whole Stevenson's poetry does not rank as high as his prose; it seldom has the subtle melody or inexplicable charm of the great masters. But his songs for children have a sunny kindliness and his other poems a narrative swing which lift them far above mediocrity and reveal the same gifted story-teller and loving friend who delights us in his tales.

In 1887 his father, Thomas Stevenson, died. That death snapped one of the strongest links which bound the son to his birthplace; and in a few months he left Europe, planning, perhaps, to return, but destined never to do so. The demand of his invalid body for health and the craving of his adventurous spirit for new experience alike drew him to the Western Hemisphere. The rest of his life was a series of wanderings or short sojourns in America and the islands of the Pacific. His companions were his wife, his step-son, Lloyd Osbourne, to whom he was deeply attached, and part of the time his mother.

Stevenson entered America the second time, not obscurely, as he had come ten years before, but as an author whose reputation was assured. Several of his works had already been published by Scribner; now almost immediately he was engaged by them to furnish twelve monthly articles for their magazine. From this time on he was in close relation with that well-known house. For the sake of the bracing climate, he spent the winter of 1887–88 at Saranac among the Adirondack Mountains of New York State. It is in this region that the tragic end of *The Master of Ballantrae* is pictured as occurring; and Stevenson tells us that he conceived that dramatic scene at this time, amid scenery as wild and on a night as cold as when Secundra dug up his buried master. But, although Saranac proved bracing for the invalid and convenient for the author it did not keep him long. Deep in his nature was the love of the ocean with its excitement and mystery, that ocean with which his ancestors had wrestled for generations; and he tells us that he would gladly have exchanged his fame as an author for a yacht and a voyage at sea. Consequently, the following summer the party crossed the continent, and, chartering the yacht *Casco* at San Francisco, sailed out into the romantic island world of the Pacific.

For nearly three years after this Stevenson and his companions voyaged to and fro between different groups of islands which lie hundreds of miles apart, now visiting the Hawaiian group far north of the equator, where he saw the dreary leper settlement at Molokai, now, as far south of the equator, to the Society Islands and New Caledonia. It was a changing panorama of differing surroundings and differing peoples, a life of variety and novel experience. It had its spice of danger, too; for more than once nothing but good luck and the utmost efforts of the crew prevented shipwreck. Finally, more by accident than design, the wanderers made themselves a permanent home at Apia in the Samoan group.

Almost four years, the last four of his life, Stevenson lived at Samoa. He built his home, called Vailima, or the Five Rivers, a little outside of the town of Apia, and not far from the mountain where he was afterward buried. He was never an indolent man, and his life here was one of surprising activity. Not only did he turn out an amount of literary work astonishing in a man of such frail physique, but he also took an active and unselfish part in the politics of the island, fearlessly criticised the misgovernment of the European representatives there, and won the love and respect of the natives as few white men have done. A monument to the affection which he inspired in the Samoans is found in the road which their chiefs built to his house, built by their own toil and at their own expense, and which they significantly christened Ala Loto Alofa, The Road of the Loving Heart. Here at Vailima he died suddenly and almost painlessly, December 3, 1894. He had been working hard all day on the last (and what would have been the greatest) of his novels, *Weir of Hermiston.* At sunset he had come downstairs for rest and the company of his wife, when the blow fell. He lost consciousness almost immediately; and in an hour or two all was over. He was buried by his loving friends, Europeans and Samoans, on the summit of Mt. Vaea, a narrow ledge of rock, which from a height of thirteen hundred feet overlooks Samoa and the sea. On one of the panels of his tomb is engraved the *Requiem* which he himself composed years before:

> Under the wide and starry sky,
> Dig the grave and let me lie.
> Glad did I live and gladly die,
> And I laid me down with a will.
>
> This be the verse you grave for me:
> *Here he lies where he longed to be;*
> *Home is the sailor, home from sea,*
> *And the hunter home from the hill.*

The character of Stevenson is one which deservedly commands not only respect but love. The gentle kindliness of his nature was unalterable, except by occasional outbursts of righteous indignation at some act of cruelty. And these outbursts themselves came from the warmth of his heart. Yet, though tactful and sympathetic as a woman, he was essentially a masculine spirit, strong and courageous. The buoyant cheerfulness with which he laughed aside the disease that he never could conquer, and the determination with which he clung to his work when stronger men were idle is evidence enough of this. Though chivalrous always and an affectionate son and husband, he usually cared less for the society of women than for that of men. His novels, too, appeal more to men than women. Much of the charm of his writing is due to a childlike freshness in his feeling, which he never lost. It was his rare good fortune to outgrow the immaturity of boyhood without losing its romance and its enthusiasm in the process. Genius, according to the definition of a French critic, is nothing but the power to live over our childhood at will; and it is this quality in Stevenson which has immortalised *Treasure Island*. Furthermore, as he appeals to our hearts by his boyishness and sympathy, so he appeals to our minds by his ingenious and versatile brain. True, he never saw into life as deeply as Shakespeare or Browning; but he saw life from many points of view, and hence all that he says has the fascination of variety and novelty. He said once that he was fifty-five per cent artist and forty-five per cent adventurer; and both artists and adventurers are interesting people. They may have a dash of the Bohemian in them, as Stevenson himself did; but their very eccentricities are refreshing. In one sense of the word, his genius was made rather than born, for it was only by long and patient effort that he made himself a better writer than those around him. But this fact merely increases our respect for him as a man, for it brings him into the list of that gallant army who are using all their efforts to make the world happier. While other writers have too often wasted the splendid gifts that nature gave them in dissipation or inaction, Stevenson can claim our affection and reverence because all his natural powers were used bravely and to the utmost for the good of humanity.

F. E. P.

## II.—OUTLINE OF THE MAIN EVENTS IN STEVENSON'S LIFE

1850.     Stevenson born.
1859–67.  Attends various schools, mostly in Edinburgh.
1863.     Trip to Italy with parents.

1865–66. Part of the time spent at Torquay in Devonshire, England.

1867–73. Studies at Edinburgh University.

1873. First published work (*Roads*) printed in *Portfolio* magazine.

" Goes to Southern France for health.

1874–79. Various trips to the continent of Europe.

1875. Called to the Scottish Bar.

1876. First meets his future wife in France.

1877. His first story (*A Lodging for the Night*) printed in *Temple Bar* magazine.

1878. His first book (*Inland Voyage*) published.

1879. First voyage to America.

1880. Married.

" Returns to Scotland.

1880–82. At Davos in the Swiss Alps.

1882–84. In Southern France.

1883. *Treasure Island* (Stevenson's first popular success) published.

1884–87. At Bournemouth.

1886. *Dr. Jekyll and Mr. Hyde* published, giving the author an international reputation.

1887. Stevenson's father dies.

1887–88. Second journey to America.

1883–91. Voyages in the Pacific.

1891–94. Life at Samoa.

1894. Stevenson's death.

## III.—LIST OF STEVENSON'S PUBLICATIONS

This list includes all of Stevenson's more important publications, with the date of their first appearance in book form, and also a few less important works which help to give an idea of the author's versatility.

1878. An Inland Voyage.
1879. Travels with a Donkey.
1881. Virginibus Puerisque.
1882. Familiar Studies of Men and Books.
1882. New Arabian Nights.
1883. The Silverado Squatters.

## IV.—BIBLIOGRAPHY

The following editions and biographical studies should be
first consulted by those wishing to gain more knowledge of
Stevenson than these Selections can give.

### EDITIONS

The Thistle Edition, 26 vols.   A complete collection of
Stevenson's writings.

The Biographical Edition, 32 vols.   These volumes are of
especial interest because of the introductions by Mrs. Stevenson.

The Scribner Popular Edition, 10 vols.

Life of Robert Louis Stevenson, 2 vols. By Graham Balfour. Published in the Thistle Edition but sold separately.

The Vailima Letters, 2 vols. Edited by Sidney Colvin, published separately and in the Thistle Edition.

The Letters of Robert Louis Stevenson, 4 vols. Edited by Sidney Colvin.

A Chronicle of Friendships, by Will H. Low. Especially valuable for its account of Stevenson's life in Paris and Fontainebleau.

## V.—STEVENSON THE WRITER

Sargent's well-known portrait of the slender Stevenson, in his velveteen jacket, with cigarette in hand, while a whimsical look softens the glow of his cavernous eyes, emphasises too strongly perhaps the Bohemian in Stevenson's nature, and yet suggests unforgettably his most characteristic traits. The air of one who seeks the romantic in life breathes from the figure; the serious eyes and the glance belong to a humourist who loves a world which both pains and amuses him; and "artist" is as indelibly imprinted upon the whole as if it had been written in upon the picture. Romanticist, humourist, artist,—these, in truth, were the attributes of Robert Louis Stevenson.

First, last, and always he was a romanticist in the good, broad sense of the word; that is, he was a lover of all that stirs the imagination. Romantic ages such as the fifteenth century in France; romantic men like the Stuart Pretenders; romantic moments like the terrible hours after a great crime, or a momentous resolution;—all these interested him and found their way into his books. Love, which makes the most romantic romance of them all, did not, strangely enough, appeal so strongly, perhaps because, as with many men who lack physical strength, it was the masculine in life which stirred his fancy. But he fed his mind upon everything else that was strange, or splendid, and his acts and works were often moulded by romantic desires. He loved the sea better than the land; the mountains more than the plains; when he set out upon his exile it was to the uttermost islands of the Pacific; even when most discouraged he would not let life seem trivial, or otherwise than full of the possibilities of charm and wonder. Few men have been so sure of the eternal value of whatsoever frees the imagination from the commonplace, and so convinced that nothing pushes back the horizons, nothing stirs the heart like romance.

Next to romance humour was the quality which Stevenson best understood, and this is not surprising, for the great romanticists have all been humourists. Humour is not the same as wit. Humour is a power which comes to kindly people who can grasp the truth about human nature, yet still retain their love for it. They see the inconsistencies, the incongruities, the weaknesses of mankind, and since they love their fellow-men can make these follies a cause of mirth, a reason for comprehension and sympathy. Without humour a writer of romances loses touch with human nature, and we, his readers, feel ill at ease in his world, where there is little humanity and only stage-laughs.

This saving grace of humour was Stevenson's, but it did more than sweeten his romance; it made him a preacher. All great humourists are preachers. They cannot avoid preaching except by silence, for they have only to describe the world as they see it to give the liveliest perceptions of its errors and mistakes. And they are often the best of preachers because they are content to make clear the absurdity of error, leaving the remedy to time who takes care of proved absurdities. Indeed, as one reads certain essays in this volume, for example the throbbing *Aes Triplex*, where the writer wars upon all cowardly fear of death, Stevenson's preaching is so serious that one may easily overlook the humour underlying it. But *Aes Triplex*, like nearly all the rest, is fundamentally humorous. It was the work of a thinker who saw the man-flock scurrying hither and thither in trivial terror, though the grass was tender, the water sweet, and little time at best to enjoy them; a thinker who saw man, like a blind horse in a cider-press, plodding on and on, unconscious that he never left his appointed rut. These sights filled him with mingled pity and mirth. He spoke out, and such fine preaching as is to be found in the essays of this volume resulted. But very rarely, and only when the tragic entered his stories, or when, as in his more sombre essays, his native cheerfulness fought for its right to exist, did Stevenson cease to be essentially humorous in his attitude toward the world.

Such humourist's preaching differs, of course, in a very important fashion from the usual pulpit variety. It is tolerant, it is never dogmatic. Stevenson could not be intolerant of other men's opinions for he saw but too clearly how fallible are all opinions; he could not be dogmatic for he knew that all programmes of conduct might lead somewhere or somehow to error. He pitied, or smiled at, the follies of the world instead of abusing them. One sees this in *An Apology for Idlers*, where he holds up for mirth the sordid individual who thinks that his own business is the only thing that matters, or in *Aes Triplex*, where he pictures Death creeping upon a life so shaken by fear of him as to be scarcely worth ending. One sees it also in work where he was not preaching; somewhat grimly, for example, in his story, *The Merry Men*, where the conscience-stricken uncle is haunted by his fears; more lightly in *Will o' the Mill*, when the sluggish youth who gives to that story its title decides that it is better to be comfortable than in love. His travel-sketches, too, are full of this humorous spirit; his charming letters are alight with the keenest, but the most sympathetic perceptions of mortal folly, mortal weakness (his own as much as anybody's), and mortal shame. There have been far greater humourists than Stevenson, men, who, better than he, saw deeply, felt truly, and gave us human nature with the lovable and unlovable qualities of the flesh. But no writer in English of our period has done all these things so well for the readers of this generation.

And, finally, R. L. S., as he liked to sign himself, was to the finger-tips an artist. The true artist, whether painter, musician, or writer of literature, is content only when his work is as true as he can make it to the conceptions shaped by his imagination. He labours incessantly at what he calls his technique. Stevenson was a true artist, who never willingly and knowingly did less than his best. He wrote for money, as all artists should, since the need of making one's work desirable is the best preventive of morbid, unnatural, useless art; but he wrote, as he says in one of his letters, first of all for himself. The results are to be seen in the dignity, depth, and sincerity of his books, but most of all in his style. Stevenson's style, which, at its finest, is of remarkable force and beauty, was the product of a determination to express his ideas in the best possible manner. It is like the glaze which the potter bakes upon his already modelled clay, or the colour and final form which the painter gives to his sketch for a picture. Stevenson's carefully chosen words, his delicately modulated sentences, the melodious rhythm of his paragraphs serve to express to perfection the nicety, or the profundity, or the beauty of his thought. His style, therefore, is the best result as well as the best evidence of a lifelong devotion to the highest ideals of art.

Stevenson is so much a part of our own generation that we cannot, even if it were desirable, label him, and place him upon his proper shelf in literary history. Nevertheless, it is already evident that he was a leader in some very definite tendencies of his times.

The first of these was the swing toward romance. In the seventies and eighties, when R. L. S. began to write, science, much more than now, was affecting men's imaginations. Discoveries in physics, in chemistry, and in mechanics, most of all the then new theories of man's evolution from lower forms of life were emphasising the importance of *facts*. Fiction speedily responded to this scientific movement. In France, Zola was writing his careful studies of the ills of humanity; in England, Hardy was pessimistically narrating the truth, as he saw it, of country life, and (for all realistic fiction is not either squalid or pessimistic) Trollope was pouring out matter-of-fact stories of amusing but very commonplace people. Romance is a reaction against this realistic attitude. It is a protest that the soul needs to dream as well as to understand. Romance does not deny the ugly and the commonplace, it temporarily ignores them. Stevenson was unfamiliar neither with science nor with misery and pain, but in such books as *Kidnapped, Treasure Island,* and *The Master of Ballantrae,* such stories as *The Sire de Malétroit's Door* and *A Lodging for the Night* he led away from them into regions where a man could be a boy again, could let loose his fancy, and give his heart a chance to beat. In these narratives Stevenson headed the romantic reaction, which has given us a series of tales of adventure or strange situation to place beside the novels of scientific realism that have also been produced throughout our period. But Stevenson's followers have none of them equalled the master. Indeed, no writer, since the great romanticists of an earlier generation, has flung himself with Stevenson's ardour into the pursuit of romance. "You just indulge the pleasure of your heart," he said of writing *Treasure Island,* "just drive along as the words come and the pen will scratch!"

*Treasure Island* is pure romance, like *Ivanhoe,* or *As You Like It,* but elsewhere Stevenson did more than revive romance, he linked it to the scientific spirit of the time. *Dr. Jekyll and Mr. Hyde,* for example, is conducted like an experiment in the new science of psychology; *The Merry Men* is first of all a romantic picture of the landsman's terror of the sea, but it is also a psychological study of a guilty imagination. And in such essays as *Pulvis et Umbra* those problems with which scientists were wrestling are fearlessly handled by a romanticist, with admirable results.

. Stevenson reacts against opposing tendencies not only in his romance but also in his humour. He came from Scotland, where Puritanical dogmatism kept the tightest of grips upon belief and conscience. In his youth he broke away in agony from the dogma of his father's church, suffering and giving pain in order to be free. And in his manhood he not less decisively broke away from the writers who still dominated English literature. The great preacher-essayists, Carlyle, Arnold, Ruskin, had made laws for conduct, for culture, for art. Stevenson, though never in dispute with them, presents the other side. Being humourist, he deprecates taking oneself too seriously; he points to the good things of God, the dawn, the forest, friendship, love, and even a pipe of tobacco, which may be forgotten while men are pulling one another's ears; he leads the way to tolerance, and a cheerful determination to get the best from living. This is humour of the kind that Charles Lamb practised before the days of reform and modern science. It is most useful as an offset to the overpositive preachers of the middle of the century.

In this, strangely enough, Stevenson is at one with those same scientists whose matter-of-fact theories of life had driven him to romance. His tolerance, his distrust of dogmatism would meet with their approval, for they experiment before they assert. But his distrust of dogma goes deeper than theirs. If he smiles at the philosopher or theologian who, from his little pin-head in the universe, declares that only thus or so shall a man's life be led or his soul be saved, his humour makes him smile no less at the pretensions of the scientist who deduces from experiments that man is a machine and life a chemical compound of dust.

Stevenson's position and his influence as an artist are by no means so clear as his place in humour and romance. A great refiner of language, a perfecter of phrases even to the verge of affectation, it is true that he gave to English prose a solemn and beautiful music. It is true that he gave to the short story, which he among British authors of our period was the first to write with success, a dignity and a beauty which it had not been given since the days of Hawthorne and Poe. But, after all, the chief importance of Stevenson's art is to be sought elsewhere. It is chiefly valuable not so much for its possible influence as because, by means of it, form and expression were given to the romantic imaginings and the humorous thoughts of a very rare, very sweet, and very wise spirit embodied in one of the most lovable of men.

H. S. C.

# LETTERS

# LETTERS

## STUDENT DAYS AT EDINBURGH[1]

### To Alison Cunningham

The following is the first of many letters to the admirable nurse whose care, during his ailing childhood, had done so much both to preserve Stevenson's life and awaken his love of tales and poetry, and of whom until his death he thought with the utmost constancy of affection. The letter bears no sign of date or place, but by the handwriting would seem to belong to this year.

[1871?]

MY DEAR CUMMY,—I was greatly pleased by your letter in many ways. Of course, I was glad to hear from you; you know you and I have so many old stories between us, that even if there was nothing else, even if there was not a very sincere respect and affection, we

[1] Stevenson's published correspondence has until recently been chiefly contained in three volumes, *Letters*, vols. I and II, and the *Vailima Letters*. The latter comprises all those sent from Samoa, during the author's residence there, to Sidney Colvin. As mail steamers are rare in the Pacific islands, Stevenson wrote these letters to Colvin in the form of a journal, sending out long consignments at rare intervals. They were written after he had become famous and when he knew that much of his personal MSS. would eventually be published; hence the contents of the Vailima volume are more polished and less frankly informal, as a whole, than the rest. The remaining letters, including those sent from Vailima to other friends than Colvin, were published chronologically in the two volumes already referred to. Our selections include extracts from all three volumes, arranged in the order in which they were written, only those dating from Samoa and addressed to Sidney Colvin being from the *Vailima Letters*. A new and revised edition of Stevenson's letters has just appeared in four volumes. All the letters are arranged in chronological order, and these new volumes will be the definitive and complete form of the collection.

should always be glad to pass a nod. I say "even if there was not." But you know right well there is. Do not suppose that I shall ever forget those long, bitter nights, when I coughed and coughed and was so unhappy, and you were so patient and loving with a poor, sick child. Indeed, Cummy, I wish I might become a man worth talking of, if it were only that you should not have thrown away your pains.

Happily, it is not the result of our acts that makes them brave and noble, but the acts themselves and the unselfish love that moved us to do them. "Inasmuch as you have done it unto one of the least of these." My dear old nurse, and you know there is nothing a man can say nearer his heart except his mother or his wife— my dear old nurse, God will make good to you all the good that you have done, and mercifully forgive you all the evil. And next time when the spring comes round, and everything is beginning once again, if you should happen to think that you might have had a child of your own, and that it was hard you should have spent so many years taking care of some one else's prodigal, just you think this—you have been for a great deal in my life; you have made much that there is in me, just as surely as if you had conceived me; and there are sons who are more ungrateful to their own mothers than I am to you. For I am not ungrateful, my dear Cummy, and it is with a very sincere emotion that I write myself your little boy,

LOUIS.

# FIRST JOURNEY TO AMERICA

## To Edmund Gosse[1]

With reference to the "term of reproach," it must be explained that Mr. Gosse, who now signs with only one initial, used in these days to sign with two, E. W. G. The nickname Weg was fastened on him by Stevenson, partly under a false impression as to the order of these initials, partly in friendly derision of a passing fit of lameness, which called up the memory of Silas Wegg, the immortal literary gentleman "*with* a wooden leg" of *Our Mutual Friend*.

17 Heriot Row,[2] Edinburgh [*July* 29, 1879].

My Dear Gosse,—Yours was delicious; you are a young person of wit; one of the last of them; wit being quite out of date, and humour confined to the Scotch Church and the *Spectator* in unconscious survival. You will probably be glad to hear that I am up again in the world; I have breathed again, and had a frolic on the strength of it. The frolic was yesterday, Sawbath; the scene, the Royal Hotel, Bathgate; I went there with a humorous friend to lunch. The maid soon showed herself a lass of character. She was looking out of window. On being asked what she was after, "I 'm lookin' for my lad," says she. "Is that him?" "Weel, I 've been lookin' for him a' my life, and I 've never seen him yet," was the response. I wrote her some verses in the vernacular; she read them. "They 're no bad for a beginner," said she. The landlord's daughter, Miss Stewart, was present in oil colour; so I wrote her a declaration in verse, and sent it by the handmaid. She (Miss S.) was present on the stair to witness our departure, in a

---

[1] See page viii.
[2] The home of Stevenson's parents, where most of his boyhood had been passed. This letter was written less than a fortnight before the author's first voyage to America.

warm, suffused condition.    Damn it, Gosse, you needn't
suppose that you 're the only poet in the world.

Your statement about your initials, it will be seen, I pass
over in contempt and silence.    When once I have made up
my mind, let me tell you, sir, there lives no pock-pudding
who can change it.    Your anger I defy.    Your unmanly
reference to a well-known statesman I puff from me, sir,
like so much vapour.    Weg is your name; Weg.    W E G.

My enthusiasm has kind of dropped from me.    I
envy you your wife, your home, your child—I was
going to say your cat.    There would be cats in my
home too if I could but get it.    I may seem to you
"the impersonation of life," but my life is the impersonation of waiting, and that 's a poor creature.    God
help us all, and the deil be kind to the hindmost!    Upon
my word, we are a brave, cheery crew, we human beings, and my admiration increases daily—primarily for
myself, but by a roundabout process for the whole
crowd; for I dare say they have all their poor little secrets and anxieties.    And here am I, for instance, writing to you as if you were in the seventh heaven, and
yet I know you are in a sad anxiety yourself.    I hope
earnestly it will soon be over, and a fine pink Gosse
sprawling in a tub, and a mother in the best of health
and spirits, glad and tired, and with another interest in
life.    Man, you are out of the trouble when this is
through.    A first child is a rival, but a second is only
a rival to the first; and the husband stands his ground
and may keep married all his life—a consummation
heartily to be desired.    Good-bye, Gosse.    Write me a
witty letter with good news of the mistress.

R. L. S.

To Edmund Gosse

A poetical counterpart to this letter will be found in the piece beginning "Not yet, my soul, these friendly fields desert," which was composed at the same time and is printed in *Underwoods*, p. 30.

San Francisco, Cal., *April* 16 [1880].[1]

My Dear Gosse,—You have not answered my last; and I know you will repent when you hear how near I have been to another world. For about six weeks I have been in utter doubt; it was a toss-up for life or death all that time; but I won the toss, sir, and Hades went off once more discomfited. This is not the first time, nor will it be the last, that I have a friendly game with that gentleman. I know he will end by cleaning me out; but the rogue is insidious, and the habit of that sort of gambling seems to be a part of my nature; it was, I suspect, too much indulged in youth; break your children of this tendency, my dear Gosse, from the first. It is, when once formed, a habit more fatal than opium —I speak, as St. Paul says, like a fool. I have been very very sick; on the verge of a galloping consumption, cold sweats, prostrating attacks of cough, sinking fits in which I lost the power of speech, fever, and all the ugliest circumstances of the disease; and I have cause to bless God, my wife that is to be, and one Dr. Bamford (a name the Muse repels), that I have come out of all this, and got my feet once more upon a little hilltop, with a fair prospect of life and some new desire of living. Yet I did not wish to die, neither; only I felt unable to go on farther with that rough horseplay of human life: a man must be pretty well to take the business in good part. Yet I felt all the time that I had done nothing to entitle me to an honourable discharge;

[1] Written about a month before Stevenson's marriage.

that I had taken up many obligations and begun many friendships which I had no right to put away from me; and that for me to die was to play the cur and slinking sybarite, and desert the colours on the eve of the decisive fight. Of course I have done no work for I do not know how long; and here you can triumph. I have been reduced to writing verses for amusement. A fact. The whirligig of time brings in its revenges, after all. But I 'll have them buried with me, I think, for I have not the heart to burn them while I live. Do write. I shall go to the mountains as soon as the weather clears; on the way thither, I marry myself; then I set up my family altar among the pinewoods, 3000 feet, sir, from the disputatious sea.—I am, dear Weg, most truly yours,

R. L. S.


## DAVOS IN SWITZERLAND

### To Charles Baxter [1]

[Chalet am Stein], Davos, *December* 5, 1881.

My Dear Charles,—We have been in miserable case here; my wife worse and worse; and now sent away with Lloyd [2] for sick-nurse, I not being allowed to go down. I do not know what is to become of us; and you may imagine how rotten I have been feeling, and feel now, alone with my weasel-dog and my German maid, on the top of a hill here, heavy mist and thin snow all about me, and the devil to pay in general. I don't care so much for solitude as I used to; results, I suppose, of marriage.

Pray write me something cheery. A little Edinburgh

---

[1] A friend of the author's student days. Stevenson speaks very highly of his tact and judgment as an adviser.

[2] Lloyd Osbourne, his step-son, to whom he was much attached.

gossip, in Heaven's name. Ah! what would I not give to steal this evening with you through the big, echoing college archway, and away south under the street lamps, and away to dear Brash's,[1] now defunct! But the old time is dead also, never, never to revive. It was a sad time too, but so gay and so hopeful, and we had such sport with all our low spirits and all our distresses, that it looks like a kind of lamplit fairyland behind me. O for ten Edinburgh minutes—sixpence between us, and the ever-glorious Lothian Road, or dear mysterious Leith Walk! But here, a sheer hulk, lies poor Tom Bowling; here in this strange place, whose very strangeness would have been heaven to him then; and aspires, yes, C. B., with tears, after the past. See what comes of being left alone. Do you remember Brash? the sheet of glass that we followed along George Street? Granton? the night at Bonny mainhead? the compass near the sign of the *Twinkling Eye?* the night I lay on the pavement in misery?

> I swear it by the eternal sky
> Johnson—nor Thomson—ne'er shall die !

Yet I fancy they are dead too; dead like Brash.

R. L. S.

[1] Peter Brash, an innkeeper of Edinburgh, the subject of many of Stevenson's early jokes.

## SOUTHERN FRANCE

### To W. E. Henley [1]

The "new dictionary" means, of course, the first instalments of the great Oxford Dictionary of the English Language, edited by Dr. J. A. H. Murray.

Hyères [2] [*June*, 1883].

Dear Lad,—I was delighted to hear the good news about ——. Bravo, he goes uphill fast. Let him beware of vanity, and he will go higher; let him be still discontented, and let him (if it might be) see the merits and not the faults of his rivals, and he may swarm at last to the topgallant. There is no other way. Admiration is the only road to excellence; and the critical spirit kills, but envy and injustice are putrefaction on its feet.

Thus far the moralist. The eager author now begs to know whether you may have got the other Whistles, and whether a fresh proof is to be taken; also whether in that case the dedication should not be printed therewith; *B*ulk *D*elights *P*ublishers (original aphorism; to be said sixteen times in succession as a test of sobriety).

Your wild and ravening commands were received; but cannot be obeyed. And anyway, I do assure you I am getting better every day; and if the weather would but turn, I should soon be observed to walk in hornpipes. Truly I am on the mend. I am still very careful. I have the new dictionary; a joy, a thing of beauty, and —bulk. I shall be raked i' the mools [3] before it 's finished; that is the only pity; but meanwhile I sing.

I beg to inform you that I, Robert Louis Stevenson,

[1] See page viii.
[2] Stevenson's home for nine months during his two years' residence in Southern France after leaving Davos.
[3] Buried under the earth.

author of *Brashiana*[1] and other works, am merely beginning to commence to prepare to make a first start
at trying to understand my profession. O the height
and depth of novelty and worth in any art! and O that
I am privileged to swim and shoulder through such
oceans ! Could one get out of sight of land—all in the
blue? Alas not, being anchored here in flesh, and the
bonds of logic being still about us.

But what a great space and a great air there is in these
small shallows where alone we venture ! and how new
each sight, squall, calm, or sunrise! An art is a fine
fortune, a palace in a park, a band of music, health,
and physical beauty; all but love—to any worthy prac-
tiser. I sleep upon my art for a pillow; I waken in my
art; I am unready for death, because I hate to leave
it. I love my wife, I do not know how much, nor
can, nor shall, unless I lost her; but while I can conceive my being widowed, I refuse the offering of life without my art. I *am* not but in my art; it is me; I am
the body of it merely.

And yet I produce nothing, am the author of *Brashiana* and other works: tiddy-iddity—as if the works one
wrote were anything but prentice's experiments. Dear
reader, I deceive you with husks, the real works and all
the pleasure are still mine and incommunicable. After
this break in my work, beginning to return to it, as
from light sleep, I wax exclamatory, as you see.

> Sursum Corda:[2]
> Heave ahead:
> Here 's luck.
> Art and Blue Heaven,
> April and God's Larks.
> Green reeds and the sky-scattering river.
> A stately music.
> Enter God !                                     R. L. S.

[1] Writings on Brash.     [2] Upward with our hearts, *i. e.*, be cheerful

Ay, but you know, until a man can write that "Enter God," he has made no art! None! Come, let us take counsel together and make some!

---

## To W. H. Low[1]

*Manhattan,* mentioned below, is the name of a short-lived New York magazine, the editor of which had asked through Mr. Low for a contribution from R. L. S.

LA SOLITUDE,[2] HYÈRES, *October* [1883].

MY DEAR LOW,— . . . Some day or other, in Cassell's *Magazine of Art,* you will see a paper which will interest you, and where your name appears. It is called "Fontainebleau: Village Communities of Artists," and the signature of R. L. Stevenson will be found annexed.[3]

Please tell the editor of *Manhattan* the following secrets for me: 1*st,* That I am a beast; 2*nd,* that I owe him a letter; 3*rd,* that I have lost his, and cannot recall either his name or address; 4*th,* that I am very deep in engagements, which my absurd health makes it hard for me to overtake; but 5*th,* that I will bear him in mind; 6*th* and last, that I am a brute.

My address is still the same, and I live in a most sweet corner of the universe, sea and fine hills before me, and a rich, variegated plain; and at my back a craggy hill, loaded with vast feudal ruins. I am very quiet; a person passing by my door half startles me: but I enjoy the most aromatic airs, and at night the most wonderful view into a moonlit garden. By day this garden fades into nothing, overpowered by its sur-

[1] American painter and illustrator. Stevenson and he had been good friends since the days they spent together in Paris and the forest of Fontainebleau, an account of which is given in Low's *A Chronicle of Friendships.*

[2] The name of Stevenson's cottage at Hyères.

[3] Published May, June, 1884.

roundings and the luminous distance; but at night and when the moon is out, that garden, the arbour, the flight of stairs that mount the artificial hillock, the plumed blue gum-trees that hang trembling, become the very skirts of Paradise. Angels I know frequent it; and it thrills all night with the thrills of silence. Damn that garden;—and by day it is gone.

Continue to testify boldly against realism. Down with Dagon, the fish god![1] All art swings down towards imitation, in these days, fatally. But the man who loves art with wisdom sees the joke; it is the lustful that tremble and respect her ladyship; but the honest and romantic lovers of the Muse can see a joke and sit down to laugh with Apollo.

The prospect of your return to Europe is very agreeable; and I was pleased by what you said about your parents. One of my oldest friends died recently, and this has given me new thoughts of death.[2] Up to now I had rather thought of him as a mere personal enemy of my own; but now that I see him hunting after my friends, he looks altogether darker. My own father is not well; and Henley, of whom you must have heard me speak, is in a questionable state of health. These things are very solemn, and take some of the colour out of life. It is a great thing, after all, to be a man of reasonable honour and kindness. Do you remember once consulting me in Paris whether you had not better sacrifice honesty to art; and how, after much confabulation, we agreed that your art would suffer if you did? We decided better than we knew. In this strange welter where we live, all hangs together by a million filaments;

[1] Used by Stevenson to denote unimaginative art and pedantry. See his letter to Colvin, July 28, 1879.

[2] Walter Ferrier, a comrade of Stevenson's Edinburgh days, and the first of his close friends to be removed by death. His memory is preserved in the essay, *Old Mortality*, 1884.

and to do reasonably well by others, is the first prerequisite of art.    Art is a virtue; and if I were the man I should be, my art would rise in the proportion of my life.

If you were privileged to give some happiness to your parents, I know your art will gain by it.    *By God, it will!* *Sic subscribitur,*[2]

R. L. S.

--------

## To W. H. Low

The paper referred to at the beginning of the second paragraph is one on R. L. S. in the *Century Magazine,* the first seriously critical notice, says Mr. Low, which appeared of him in the States.

[CHALET LA SOLITUDE, HYÈRES, *Oct.* 23, 1883.]

MY DEAR LOW,—*C'est d'un bon camarade,*[3] and I am much obliged to you for your two letters and the enclosure.    Times are a lityle changed with all of us since the ever memorable days of Lavenue:[4] hallowed be his name! hallowed his old Fleury!—of which you did not see—I think—as I did—the glorious apotheosis: advanced on a Tuesday to three francs, on the Thursday to six, and on Friday swept off, holus bolus, for the proprietor's private consumption.    Well, we had the start of that proprietor.    Many a good bottle came our way, and was, I think, worthily made welcome.

I am pleased that Mr. Gilder[5] should like my literature ; and I ask you particularly to thank Mr. Bunner (have I the name right?) for his notice, which was of that friendly, headlong sort that really pleases an author like what the French call a "shake-hands."    It pleased

---

[1] The reference is to himself.        [2] Thus subscribing.
[3] It is the part of a good friend.
[4] A famous restaurant in the Mont Parnasse district of Paris; a gathering place for artists.
[5] R. W. Gilder, for many years editor of *The Century Magazine.*

me the more coming from the States, where I have met
not much recognition, save from the buccaneers, and
above all from pirates who misspell my name. I saw
my book advertised in a number of the *Critic* as the
work of one R. L. Stephenson; and, I own, I boiled.
It is so easy to know the name of a man whose book
you have stolen; for there it is, at full length, on the
title-page of your booty. But no, damn him, not he!
He calls me Stephenson. These woes I only refer to by
the way, as they set a higher value on the *Century* notice.

I am now a person with an established ill-health—a
wife—a dog possessed with an evil, a Gadarene spirit—
a chalet on a hill, looking out over the Mediterranean—
a certain reputation—and very obscure finances. Otherwise, very much the same, I guess; and were a bottle
of Fleury a thing to be obtained, capable of developing
theories along with a fit spirit even as of yore. Yet I
now draw near to the Middle Ages; nearly three years
ago, that fatal Thirty struck; and yet the great work
is not yet done—not yet even conceived. But so, as
one goes on, the wood seems to thicken, the footpath to
narrow, and the House Beautiful on the hill's summit
to draw further and further away. We learn, indeed, to
use our means; but only to learn, along with it, the
paralysing knowledge that these means are only applica-
ble to two or three poor commonplace motives. Eight
years ago, if I could have slung ink as I can now, I
should have thought myself well on the road after
Shakespeare; and now—I find I have only got a pair
of walking-shoes and not yet begun to travel. And art
is still away there on the mountain summit. But I
need not continue; for, of course, this is your story just
as much as it is mine; and, strange to think, it was
Shakespeare's too, and Beethoven's, and Phidias's. It
is a blessed thing that, in this forest of art, we can pur-

sue our wood-lice and sparrows, *and not catch them*, with almost the same fervour of exhilaration as that with which Sophocles hunted and brought down the Mastodon.

Tell me something of your work, and your wife.— My dear fellow, I am yours ever,

R. L. STEVENSON.

My wife begs to be remembered to both of you; I cannot say as much for my dog, who has never seen you, but he would like, on general principles, to bite you.

---

## To Mr. Dick

This correspondent was for many years head clerk and confidential assistant in the family firm at Edinburgh.

LA SOLITUDE, HYÈRES, VAR, 12*th March*, 1884.

MY DEAR MR. DICK,—I have been a great while owing you a letter, but I am not without excuses, as you have heard. I overworked to get a piece of work finished before I had my holiday, thinking to enjoy it more; and instead of that, the machinery near hand came sundry in my hands! like Murdie's uniform. However, I am now, I think, in a fair way of recovery; I think I was made, what there is of me, of whipcord and thorn-switches; surely I am tough! But I fancy I shall not overdrive again, or not so long. It is my theory that work is highly beneficial, but that it should, if possible, and certainly for such partially broken-down instruments as the thing I call my body, be taken in batches, with a clear break and breathing space between. I always do vary my work, laying one thing aside to take up another, not merely because I believe it rests the brain, but because I have found it most beneficial to the result. Reading,

Bacon says, makes a full man, but what makes me full on any subject is to banish it for a time from all my thoughts. However, what I now propose is, out of every quarter, to work two months and rest the third. I believe I shall get more done, as I generally manage, on my present scheme, to have four months' impotent illness and two of imperfect health—one before, one after, I break down. This, at least, is not an economical division of the year.

I re-read the other day that heart-breaking book, the *Life of Scott*. One should read such works now and then, but O, not often. As I live, I feel more and more that literature should be cheerful and brave-spirited, even if it cannot be made beautiful and pious and heroic. We wish it to be a green place; the *Waverley Novels* are better to re-read than the over-true Life, fine as dear Sir Walter was. The Bible, in most parts, is a cheerful book; it is our little piping theologies, tracts, and sermons that are dull and dowie; [1] and even the Shorter Catechism, which is scarcely a work of consolation, opens with the best and shortest and completest sermon ever written—upon Man's chief end.—Believe me, my dear Mr. Dick, very sincerely yours,

ROBERT LOUIS STEVENSON.

*P. S.*—You see I have changed my hand. I was threatened apparently with scrivener's cramp, and at any rate had got to write so small that the revisal of my MS. tried my eyes, hence my signature alone remains upon the old model; for it appears that if I changed that, I should be cut off from my "vivers." [2]

R. L. S.

[1] Doleful.  [2] Means of living.

## BOURNEMOUTH, ENGLAND

### To W. E. Henley

There is no certain clue to the date of the following ; neither has it been possible to make sure what was the enclosure mentioned. The special illness referred to seems to be that of the preceding May at Hyères.

[WENSLEYDALE, BOURNEMOUTH, *October*, 1884 ?]

DEAR BOY,—I trust this finds you well; it leaves me so-so. The weather is so cold that I must stick to bed, which is rotten and tedious, but can't be helped.

I find in the blotting-book the enclosed, which I wrote to you the eve of my blood.[1] Is it not strange? That night, when I naturally thought I was coopered, the thought of it was much in my mind ; I thought it had gone; and I thought what a strange prophecy I had made in jest, and how it was indeed like to be the end of many letters. But I have written a good few since, and the spell is broken. I am just as pleased, for I earnestly desire to live. This pleasant middle age into whose port we are steering is quite to my fancy. I would cast anchor here, and go ashore for twenty years, and see the manners of the place. Youth was a great time, but somewhat fussy. Now in middle age (bar lucre) all seems mighty placid. It likes me; I spy a little bright café in one corner of the port, in front of which I now propose we should sit down. There is just enough of the bustle of the harbour and no more; and the ships are close in, regarding us with stern-windows—the ships that bring deals from Norway and parrots from the Indies. Let us sit down here for twenty years, with a packet of tobacco and a drink, and talk of

[1] That is, of a recent attack of hemorrhage.

art and women. By and by, the whole city will sink, and the ships too, and the table, and we also; but we shall have sat for twenty years and had a fine talk; and by that time, who knows? exhausted the subject.

I send you a book which (or I am mistook) will please you; it pleased me. But I do desire a book of adventure—a romance—and no man will get or write me one. Dumas I have read and re-read too often; Scott, too, and I am short. I want to hear swords clash. I want a book to begin in a good way; a book, I guess, like *Treasure Island*, alas! which I have never read, and cannot though I live to ninety. I would God that some one else had written it! By all that I can learn, it is the very book for my complaint. I like the way I hear it opens; and they tell me John Silver is good fun. And to me it is, and must ever be, a dream unrealised, a book unwritten. O my sighings after romance, or even Skeltery,[1] and O! the weary age which will produce me neither!

### CHAPTER I

The night was damp and cloudy, the ways foul. The single horseman, cloaked and booted, who pursued his way across Willesden Common, had not met a traveller, when the sound of wheels——

### CHAPTER I

"Yes, sir," said the old pilot, "she must have dropped into the bay a little afore dawn. A queer craft she looks."

"She shows no colours," returned the young gentleman, musingly.

---

[1] Cheap and sensational romance, so-called from *Skelt's Juvenile Drama*, a series of melodramatic plays for a toy theatre, which made a great impression on Stevenson as a boy. See his *A Penny Plain and Twopence Coloured*.

"They 're a-lowering of a quarter-boat, Mr. Mark," resumed the old salt. "We shall soon know more of her."

"Ay," replied the young gentleman called Mark, "and here, Mr. Seadrift, comes your sweet daughter Nancy tripping down the cliff."

"God bless her kind heart, sir," ejaculated old Seadrift.

### CHAPTER I

The notary, Jean Rossignol, had been summoned to the top of a great house in the Isle St. Louis to make a will; and now, his duties finished, wrapped in a warm roquelaure[1] and with a lantern swinging from one hand, he issued from the mansion on his homeward way. Little did he think what strange adventures were to befall him!——

That is how stories should begin. And I am offered HUSKS instead.

| What should be: | What is: |
|---|---|
| The Filibuster's Cache. | Aunt Anne's Tea Cosy. |
| Jerry Abershaw. | Mrs. Brierly's Niece. |
| Blood Money: A Tale. | Society: A Novel. |

R. L. S.

---

### To Edmund Gosse

Skerryvore, Bournemouth, *Jan. 2nd*, 1886.
MY DEAR GOSSE,—Thank you for your letter, so interesting to my vanity. There is a review in the *St. James's*, which, as it seems to hold somewhat of your opinions, and is besides written with a pen and not a

---

[1] An old-fashioned type of cloak once used in France.

poker, we think may possibly be yours. The *Prince*[1] has done fairly well in spite of the reviews, which have been bad: he was, as you doubtless saw, well slated in the *Saturday;* one paper received it as a child's story; another (picture my agony) described it as a "Gilbert comedy." It was amusing to see the race between me and Justin M'Carthy:[2] the Milesian[3] has won by a length.

That is the hard part of literature. You aim high, and you take longer over your work, and it will not be so successful as if you had aimed low and rushed it. What the public likes is work (of any kind) a little loosely executed; so long as it is a little wordy, a little slack, a little dim and knotless, the dear public likes it; it should (if possible) be a little dull into the bargain. I know that good work sometimes hits; but, with my hand on my heart, I think it is by an accident. And I know also that good work must succeed at last; but that is not the doing of the public; they are only shamed into silence or affectation. I do not write for the public; I do write for money, a nobler deity; and most of all for myself, not perhaps any more noble, but both more intelligent and nearer home.

Let us tell each other sad stories of the bestiality of the beast whom we feed. What he likes is the newspaper; and to me the press is the mouth of a sewer, where lying is professed as from an university chair, and everything prurient, and ignoble, and essentially dull, finds its abode and pulpit. I do not like mankind; but men, and not all of these—and fewer women. As for respecting the race, and, above all, that fatuous rabble of burgesses called "the public," God save me from such irreligion!—that way lies disgrace and dishonour.

---

[1] *Prince Otto.*
[2] Irish novelist and political leader.
[3] A name sometimes applied to the Irish.

There must be something wrong in me, or I would not be popular.

This is perhaps a trifle stronger than my sedate and permanent opinion. Not much, I think. As for the art that we practise, I have never been able to see why its professors should be respected. They chose the primrose path; when they found it was not all primroses, but some of it brambly, and much of it uphill, they began to think and to speak of themselves as holy martyrs. But a man is never martyred in any honest sense in the pursuit of his pleasure; and *delirium tremens* has more of the honour of the cross. We were full of the pride of life, and chose, like prostitutes, to live by a pleasure. We should be paid if we give the pleasure we pretend to give; but why should we be honoured?

I hope some day you and Mrs. Gosse will come for a Sunday; but we must wait till I am able to see people. I am very full of Jenkin's[1] life; it is painful, yet very pleasant, to dig into the past of a dead friend, and find him, at every spadeful, shine brighter. I own, as I read, I wonder more and more why he should have taken me to be a friend. He had many and obvious faults upon the face of him; the heart was pure gold. I feel it little pain to have lost him, for it is a loss in which I cannot believe; I take it, against reason, for an absence; if not to-day, then to-morrow, I still fancy I shall see him in the door; and then, now when I know him better, how glad a meeting! Yes, if I could believe in the immortality business, the world would indeed be too good to be true; but we were put here to do what service we can, for honour and not for hire: the sods cover

[1] Fleeming Jenkin, Professor of Engineering at Edinburgh, where he and Stevenson first formed their life-long friendship. He had been dead about six months when this letter was written. Stevenson has preserved his memory in the *Memoir of Fleeming Jenkin.*

us, and the worm that never dies, the conscience, sleeps well at last; these are the wages, besides what we receive so lavishly day by day; and they are enough for a man who knows his own frailty and sees all things in the proportion of reality. The soul of piety was killed long ago by that idea of reward. Nor is happiness, whether eternal or temporal, the reward that mankind seeks. Happinesses are but his wayside campings; his soul is in the journey; he was born for the struggle, and only tastes his life in effort and on the condition that he is opposed. How, then, is such a creature, so fiery, so pugnacious, so made up of discontent and aspiration, and such noble and uneasy passions—how can he be rewarded but by rest? I would not say it aloud; for man's cherished belief is that he loves that happiness which he continually spurns and passes by; and this belief in some ulterior happiness exactly fits him. He does not require to stop and taste it; he can be about the rugged and bitter business where his heart lies; and yet he can tell himself this fairy tale of an eternal tea-party, and enjoy the notion that he is both himself and something else; and that his friends will yet meet him, all ironed out and emasculate, and still be lovable,—as if love did not live in the faults of the beloved only, and draw its breath in an unbroken round of forgiveness! But the truth is, we must fight until we die; and when we die there can be no quiet for mankind but complete resumption into—what?—God, let us say—when all these desperate tricks will lie spellbound at last.

Here came my dinner and cut this sermon short—*excusez.*

R. L. S.

## SECOND JOURNEY TO AMERICA

### To WILLIAM ARCHER

In early days in Paris, Stevenson's chivalrous feelings were once shocked by the scene in the *Demi-Monde* of Dumas *fils* where Suzanne d'Auge is trapped by Olivier de Jalin. His correspondent had asked to know exactly what was the sequel.

[SARANAC LAKE, *Spring*, 1888?]

MY DEAR ARCHER,—It happened thus.   I came forth from that performance in a breathing heat of indignation.   (Mind, at this distance of time and with my increased knowledge, I admit there is a problem in the piece; but I saw none then, except a problem in brutality; and I still consider the problem in that case not established.)   On my way down the *Français*[1] stairs, I trod on an old gentleman's toes, whereupon, with that suavity that so well becomes me, I turned about to apologise, and on the instant, repenting me of that intention, stopped the apology midway, and added something in French to this effect: No, you are one of the *lâches*[2] who have been applauding that piece.   I retract my apology. Said the old Frenchman, laying his hand on my arm, and with a smile that was truly heavenly in temperance, irony, good nature, and knowledge of the world, "Ah, monsieur, vous êtes bien jeune!" [3]

Yours very truly,    ROBERT LOUIS STEVENSON.

[1] The Théâtre Français, the most noted theatre in Paris.
[2] Cowards.
[3] Ah, sir, you are very young.

## PACIFIC VOYAGES

### To Charles Baxter

Yacht "Casco," at Sea, near the Paumotus,[1]
7 a. m., *September 6th*, 1888, *with a dreadful pen*.

My Dear Charles,—Last night as I lay under my blanket in the cockpit, courting sleep, I had a comic seizure. There was nothing visible but the southern stars, and the steersman there out by the binnacle lamp; we were all looking forward to a most deplorable landfall on the morrow, praying God we should fetch a tuft of palms which are to indicate the Dangerous Archipelago; the night was as warm as milk, and all of a sudden I had a vision of—Drummond Street. It came on me like a flash of lightning: I simply returned thither, and into the past. And when I remember all I hoped and feared as I pickled about Rutherford's in the rain and the east wind; how I feared I should make a mere shipwreck, and yet timidly hoped not; how I feared I should never have a friend, far less a wife, and yet passionately hoped I might; how I hoped (if I did not take to drink) I should possibly write one little book, etc. etc. And then now—what a change! I feel somehow as if I should like the incident set upon a brass plate at the corner of that dreary thoroughfare for all students to read, poor devils, when their hearts are down. And I felt I must write one word to you. Excuse me if I write little: when I am at sea, it gives me a headache; when I am in port, I have my diary crying "Give, give." I shall have a fine book of travels, I feel sure; and will tell you more of the South Seas after very few months than

[1] Island dependencies of France, about longitude 140° W, and latitude 20° S.

any other writer has done—except Herman Melville[1] perhaps, who is a howling cheese. Good luck to you, God bless you.—Your affectionate friend,

R. L. S.

---

## To R. A. M. Stevenson [2]

Honolulu, Hawaiian Islands, *February*, 1889.

My Dear Bob,—My extremely foolhardy venture is practically over. How foolhardy it was I don't think I realised. We had a very small schooner, and, like most yachts, over-rigged and over-sparred, and like many American yachts on a very dangerous sail plan. The waters we sailed in are, of course, entirely unlighted, and very badly charted; in the Dangerous Archipelago, through which we were fools enough to go, we were perfectly in ignorance of where we were for a whole night and half the next day, and this in the midst of invisible islands and rapid and variable currents; and we were lucky when we found our whereabouts at last. We have twice had all we wanted in the way of squalls: once, as I came on deck, I found the green sea over the cockpit coamings and running down the companion like a brook to meet me; at that same moment the foresail sheet jammed and the captain had no knife; this was the only occasion on the cruise that ever I set a hand to a rope, but I worked like a Trojan, judging the possibility of hæmorrhage better than the certainty of drowning. Another time I saw a rather singular thing: our whole ship's

---

[1] An American novelist (1819–1891) who wrote stories of life on the Pacific.

[2] Cousin and intimate friend of Stevenson. An art critic noted for his conversational powers. See W. H. Low's *A Chronicle of Friendships* for an account of the relationship between the cousins. His conversation is described in the latter portion of Stevenson's *Talks and Talkers* (omitted in these selections).

company as pale as paper from the captain to the cook; we had a black squall astern on the port side and a white squall ahead to starboard; the complication passed off innocuous, the black squall only fetching us with its tail, and the white one slewing off somewhere else. Twice we were a long while (days) in the close vicinity of hurricane weather, but again luck prevailed, and we saw none of it. These are dangers incident to these seas and small craft. What was an amazement, and at the same time a powerful stroke of luck, both our masts were rotten, and we found it out—I was going to say in time, but it was stranger and luckier than that. The head of the mainmast hung over so that hands were afraid to go to the helm; and less than three weeks before—I am not sure it was more than a fortnight—we had been nearly twelve hours beating off the lee shore of Eimeo (or Moorea, next island to Tahiti) in half a gale of wind with a violent head sea: she would neither tack nor wear once, and had to be boxed off with the mainsail—you can imagine what an ungodly show of kites we carried—and yet the mast stood. The very day after that, in the southern bight of Tahiti, we had a near squeak, the wind suddenly coming calm; the reefs were close in with, my eye! what a surf! The pilot thought we were gone, and the captain had a boat cleared, when a lucky squall came to our rescue. My wife, hearing the order given about the boats, remarked to my mother, "Is n't that nice? We shall soon be ashore!" Thus does the female mind unconsciously skirt along the verge of eternity. Our voyage up here was most disastrous—calms, squalls, head sea, waterspouts of rain, hurricane weather all about, and we in the midst of the hurricane season, when even the hopeful builder and owner of the yacht had pronounced these seas unfit for her. We ran out of food, and were quite given up for lost in Honolulu: people had ceased to speak to Belle[1] about the *Casco*, as a deadly subject.

But the perils of the deep were part of the programme; and though I am very glad to be done with them for a while and comfortably ashore, where a squall does not matter a snuff to any one, I feel pretty sure I shall want to get to sea again ere long. The dreadful risk I took was financial, and double-headed. First, I had to sink a lot of money in the cruise, and if I did n't get health, how was I to get it back? I have got health to a wonderful extent; and as I have the most interesting matter for my book, bar accidents, I ought to get all I have laid out and a profit. But, second (what I own I never consider till too late), there was the danger of collisions, of damages and heavy repairs, of disablement, towing, and salvage; indeed, the cruise might have turned round and cost me double. Nor will this danger be quite over till I hear the yacht is in San Francisco; for though I have shaken the dust of her deck from my feet, I fear (as a point of law) she is still mine till she gets there.

From my point of view, up to now the cruise has been a wonderful success. I never knew the world was so amusing. On the last voyage we had grown so used to sea-life that no one wearied, though it lasted a full month, except Fanny, who is always ill. All the time our visits to the islands have been more like dreams than realities: the people, the life, the beach-combers, the old stories and songs I have picked up, so interesting; the climate, the scenery, and (in some places) the women, so beautiful. The women are handsomest in Tahiti, the men in the Marquesas; both as fine types as can be imagined. Lloyd reminds me, I have not told you one characteristic incident of the cruise from a semi-naval

---

[1] Stevenson's step-daughter, Mrs. Strong, who was at this time living at Honolulu.

point of view.   One night we were going ashore in Anaho Bay; the most awful noise on deck; the breakers distinctly audible in the cabin; and there I had to sit below,
entertaining in my best style a negroid native chieftain,
much the worse for rum!   You can imagine the evening's pleasure.

This naval report on cruising in the South Seas would
be incomplete without one other trait.   On our voyage
up here I came one day into the dining-room, the hatch
in the floor was open, the ship's boy was below with a
baler, and two of the hands were carrying buckets as for
a fire; this meant that the pumps had ceased working.

One stirring day was that in which we sighted Hawaii.   It blew fair, but very strong; we carried jib, foresail, and mainsail, all single-reefed, and she carried her
lee rail under water and flew.   The swell, the heaviest I
have ever been out in—I tried in vain to estimate the
height, *at least* fifteen feet—came tearing after us about
a point and a half off the wind.   We had the best hand
—old Louis—at the wheel; and, really, he did nobly,
and had noble luck, for it never caught us once.   At
times it seemed we must have it; Louis would look over
his shoulder with the queerest look and dive down his
neck into his shoulders; and then it missed us somehow,
and only sprays came over our quarter, turning the little
outside lane of deck into a mill race as deep as to the
cockpit coamings.   I never remember anything more delightful and exciting.   Pretty soon after we were lying
absolutely becalmed under the lee of Hawaii, of which
we had been warned; and the captain never confessed
he had done it on purpose, but when accused, he smiled.
Really, I suppose he did quite right, for we stood committed to a dangerous race, and to bring her to the wind
would have been rather a heart-sickening manœuvre.

R. L. S.

To Mrs. R. L. Stevenson

KALAWAO, MOLOKAI [*May*, 1889].[1]

DEAR FANNY,—I had a lovely sail up. Captain Cameron and Mr. Gilfillan, both born in the States, yet the first still with a strong Highland, and the second still with a strong Lowland accent, were good company; the night was warm, the victuals plain but good. Mr. Gilfillan gave me his berth, and I slept well, though I heard the sisters sick in the next state-room, poor souls. Heavy rolling woke me in the morning; I turned in all standing, so went right on the upper deck. The day was on the peep out of a low morning bank, and we were wallowing along under stupendous cliffs. As the lights brightened, we could see certain abutments and buttresses on their front where wood clustered and grass grew brightly. But the whole brow seemed quite impassable, and my heart sank at the sight. Two thousand feet of rock making 19° (the Captain guesses) seemed quite beyond my powers. However, I had come so far; and, to tell you the truth, I was so cowed with fear and disgust that I dared not go back on the adventure in the interests of my own self-respect. Presently we came up with the leper promontory: lowland, quite bare and bleak and harsh, a little town of wooden houses, two churches, a landing-stair, all unsightly, sour, northerly, lying athwart the sunrise, with the great wall of the pali [2] cutting the world out on the south. Our lepers were sent on the first boat, about a dozen, one poor child very horrid, one white man, leaving a large grown family behind him in Honolulu, and then into the second stepped the sisters

---

[1] The two following letters were written during and immediately after Stevenson's visit to Molokai, the noted leper settlement and scene of Father Damien's labours.

[2] Precipice.

and myself. I do not know how it would have been with me had the sisters not been there. My horror of the horrible is about my weakest point; but the moral loveliness at my elbow blotted all else out; and when I found that one of them was crying, poor soul, quietly under her veil, I cried a little myself; then I felt as right as a trivet, only a little crushed to be there so uselessly. I thought it was a sin and a shame she should feel unhappy; I turned round to her, and said something like this: "Ladies, God Himself is here to give you welcome. I'm sure it is good for me to be beside you; I hope it will be blessed to me; I thank you for myself and the good you do me." It seemed to cheer her up; but indeed I had scarce said it when we were at the landing-stairs, and there was a great crowd, hundreds of (God save us!) pantomime masks in poor human flesh, waiting to receive the sisters and the new patients.

Every hand was offered: I had gloves, but I had made up my mind on the boat's voyage *not* to give my hand, that seemed less offensive than the gloves. So the sisters and I went up among that crew, and presently I got aside (for I felt I had no business there) and set off on foot across the promontory, carrying my wrap and the camera. All horror was quite gone from me: to see these dread creatures smile and look happy was beautiful. On my way through Kalaupapa I was exchanging cheerful *alohas*[1] with the patients coming galloping over on their horses; I was stopping to gossip at house-doors; I was happy, only ashamed of myself that I was here for no good. One woman was pretty, and spoke good English, and was infinitely engaging and (in the old phrase) towardly; she thought I was the new white patient; and when she found I was only a visitor, a curious change came in her face and voice—the only sad thing—morally

[1] The customary Hawaiian greeting.

sad, I mean—that I met that morning.   But for all that, they tell me none want to leave.   Beyond Kalaupapa the houses became rare; dry stone dykes, grassy, stony land, one sick pandanus;[1] a dreary country; from overhead in the little clinging wood shogs of the pali chirruping of birds fell; the low sun was right in my face; the trade blew pure and cool and delicious; I felt as right as nine-pence, and stopped and chatted with the patients whom I still met on their horses, with not the least disgust. About half-way over, I met the superintendent (a leper) with a horse for me, and O, was n't I glad!   But the horse was one of those curious, dogged, cranky brutes that always dully want to go somewhere else, and my traffic with him completed my crushing fatigue.   I got to the guest-house, an empty house with several rooms, kitchen, bath, etc.   There was no one there, and I let the horse go loose in the garden, lay down on the bed, and fell asleep.

Dr. Swift woke me and gave me breakfast, then I came back and slept again while he was at the dispensary, and he woke me for dinner; and I came back and slept again, and he woke me about six for supper; and then in about an hour I felt tired again, and came up to my solitary guest-house, played the flageolet, and am now writing to you.   As yet, you see, I have seen nothing of the settlement, and my crushing fatigue (though I believe that was moral and a measure of my coward-ice) and the doctor's opinion make me think the pali hopeless.   "You don't look a strong man," said the doctor; "but are you sound?"   I told him the truth; then he said it was out of the question, and if I were to get up at all, I must be carried up.   But, as it seems, men as well as horses continually fall on this ascent: the doctor

[1] A Malayan plant with palm-like stem and sword-shaped, spiny leaves.

goes up with a change of clothes—it is plain that to be carried would in itself be very fatiguing to both mind and body; and I should then be at the beginning of thirteen miles of mountain road to be ridden against time. How should I come through? I hope you will think me right in my decision: I mean to stay, and shall not be back in Honolulu till Saturday, June first. You must all do the best you can to make ready.

Dr. Swift has a wife and an infant son, beginning to toddle and run, and they live here as composed as brick and mortar—at least the wife does, a Kentucky German, a fine enough creature, I believe, who was quite amazed at the sisters shedding tears! How strange is mankind! Gilfillan too, a good fellow I think, and far from a stupid, kept up his hard Lowland Scottish talk in the boat while the sister was covering her face; but I believe he knew, and did it (partly) in embarrassment, and part perhaps in mistaken kindness. And that was one reason, too, why I made my speech to them. Partly, too, I did it, because I was ashamed to do so, and remembered one of my golden rules, "When you are ashamed to speak, speak up at once." But, mind you, that rule is only golden with strangers; with your own folks, there are other considerations. This is a strange place to be in. A bell has been sounded at intervals while I wrote, now all is still but a musical humming of the sea, not unlike the sound of telegraph wires; the night is quite cool and pitch dark, with a small fine rain; one light over in the leper settlement, one cricket whistling in the garden, my lamp here by my bedside, and my pen cheeping between my inky fingers.

Next day, lovely morning, slept all night, 80° in the shade, strong, sweet Anaho trade-wind.

LOUIS.

To Sidney Colvin.[1]

[Honolulu, *May or June*, 1889.]

My Dear Colvin,—I am just home after twelve days' journey to Molokai, seven of them at the leper settlement, where I can only say that the sight of so much courage, cheerfulness, and devotion strung me too high to mind the infinite pity and horror of the sights. I used to ride over from Kalawao to Kalaupapa (about three miles across the promontory, the cliff-wall, ivied with forest and yet inaccessible from steepness, on my left), go to the Sisters' home, which is a miracle of neatness, play a game of croquet with seven leper girls (90° in the shade), get a little old-maid meal served me by the Sisters, and ride home again, tired enough, but not too tired. The girls have all dolls, and love dressing them. You who know so many ladies delicately clad, and they who know so many dressmakers, please make it known it would be an acceptable gift to send scraps for doll dressmaking to the Reverend Sister Maryanne, Bishop Home, Kalaupapa, Molokai, Hawaiian Islands.

I have seen sights that cannot be told, and heard stories that cannot be repeated: yet I never admired my poor race so much, nor (strange as it may seem) loved life more than in the settlement. A horror of moral beauty broods over the place: that's like bad Victor Hugo, but it is the only way I can express the sense that lived with me all these days. And this even though it was in great part Catholic, and my sympathies flew never with so much difficulty as towards Catholic virtues. The pass-book kept with heaven stirs me to anger and laughter. One of the sisters calls the place "the ticket office to heaven." Well, what is the odds? They do their darg,[2] and do it with kindness and efficiency in-

---

[1] See page viii.  [2] Day's work.

credible; and we must take folk's virtues as we find them, and love the better part. Of old Damien,[1] whose weaknesses and worse perhaps I heard fully, I think only the more. It was a European peasant: dirty, bigotted, untruthful, unwise, tricky, but superb with generosity, residual candour and fundamental good-humour: convince him he had done wrong (it might take hours of insult) and he would undo what he had done and like his corrector better. A man, with all the grime and paltriness of mankind, but a saint and hero all the more for that. The place as regards scenery is grand, gloomy, and bleak. Mighty mountain walls descending sheer along the whole face of the island into a sea unusually deep; the front of the mountain ivied and furred with clinging forest, one viridescent cliff: about half-way from east to west, the low, bare, stony promontory edged in between the cliff and the ocean; the two little towns (Kalawao and Kalaupapa) seated on either side of it, as bare almost as bathing machines upon a beach; and the population—gorgons and chimæras dire. All this tear of the nerves I bore admirably; and the day after I got away, rode twenty miles along the opposite coast and up into the mountains: they call it twenty, I am doubtful of the figures: I should guess it nearer twelve; but let me take credit for what residents allege; and I was riding again the day after, so I need say no more about health. Honolulu does not agree with me at all: I am always out of sorts there, with slight headache, blood to the head, etc. I had a good deal of work to do and did it with miserable difficulty; and yet all the time I have been gaining strength, as you see, which is highly encouraging. By the time I am done with this cruise I shall have the material for a very singular book of travels: names of strange stories and characters, cannibals, pirates, ancient

[1] See *Father Damien*, p. 193.

legends, old Polynesian poetry,—never was so generous
a farrago. I am going down now to get the story of a
shipwrecked family, who were fifteen months on an
island with a murderer: there is a specimen. The Pacific is a strange place; the nineteenth century only ex-
ists there in spots: all round, it is a no man's land of the
ages, a stir-about of epochs and races, barbarisms and
civilisations, virtues and crimes.

It is good of you to let me stay longer, but if I had
known how ill you were, I should be now on my way
home. I had chartered my schooner and made all arrangements before (at last) we got definite news. I feel
highly guilty; I should be back to insult and worry you
a little. Our address till further notice is to be $^c/o$ R.
Towns and Co., Sydney. That is final: I only got the
arrangement made yesterday; but you may now publish
it abroad.—Yours ever,

R. L. S.

## LIFE IN SAMOA

### I

*In the Mountain, Apia, Samoa,*
*Monday, November 2d, 1890.*

MY DEAR COLVIN,—This is a hard and interesting
and beautiful life that we lead now. Our place is in a
deep cleft in Vaea Mountain, some six hundred feet above
the sea, embowered in forest, which is our strangling
enemy, and which we combat with axes and dollars. I
went crazy over out-door work, and had at last to con-
fine myself to the house, or literature must have gone by
the board. *Nothing* is so interesting as weeding, clearing, and path-making; the oversight of labourers becomes a disease; it is quite an effort not to drop into the

farmer; and it does make you feel so well. To come down covered with mud and drenched with sweat and rain after some hours in the bush, change, rub down, and take a chair in the verandah, is to taste a quiet conscience. And the strange thing that I mark is this: if I go out and make sixpence, bossing my labourers and plying the cutlass or the spade, idiot conscience applauds me; if I sit in the house and make twenty pounds, idiot conscience wails over my neglect and the day wasted. . . . Let me sketch my lads.—Henry—Henry has gone down to town or I could not be writing to you—this were the hour of his English lesson else, when he learns what he calls "long explesions" or "your chief's language" for the matter of an hour and a half—Henry is a chiefling from Savaii;[1] I once loathed, I now like and—pending fresh discoveries—have a kind of respect for Henry. He does good work for us; goes among the labourers, bossing and watching; helps Fanny; is civil, kindly, thoughtful; *O si sic semper!*[2] But will he be "his sometime self throughout the year"? Anyway, he has deserved of us, and he must disappoint me sharply ere I give him up.—Bene—or Peni—Ben, in plain English—is supposed to be my ganger;[3] the Lord love him! God made a truckling coward, there is his full history. He cannot tell me what he wants; he dares not tell me what is wrong; he dares not transmit my orders or translate my censures. And with all this, honest, sober, industrious, miserably smiling over the miserable issue of his own unmanliness,—Paul—a German—cook and steward—a glutton of work—a splendid fellow; drawbacks, three: (1) no cook; (2) an inveterate bungler, a man with twenty thumbs, continually falling in the dishes, throwing out the dinner, preserving the garbage; (3) a dr—, well, don't

---

[1] One of the Samoan Islands.
[2] If it were always thus!                    [3] Foreman.

let us say that—but we daren't let him go to town, and
he—poor, good soul—is afraid to be let go.—Lafaele
(Raphael), a strong, dull, deprecatory man; splendid
with an axe, if watched; the better for a rowing, when
he calls me "Papa" in the most wheedling tones; des-
perately afraid of ghosts, so that he dare not walk alone
up in the banana patch. . . . The rest are changing
labourers; and to-night, owing to the miserable cowar-
dice of Peni, who did not venture to tell me what the men
wanted—and which was no more than fair—all are gone
—and my weeding in the article of being finished! Pity
the sorrows of a planter.

I am, Sir, yours, and be jowned to you, The Planter,
R. L. S.

*Tuesday*, 3rd [*Nov.*, 1890].

I begin to see the whole scheme of letter-writing; you
sit down every day and pour out an equable stream of
twaddle.

This morning all my fears were fled, and all the trouble had fallen to the lot of Peni himself, who deserved
it; my field was full of weeders; and I am again able to
justify the ways of God. All morning I worked at the
South Seas, and finished the chapter I had stuck upon
on Saturday. Fanny, awfully hove-to with rheumatics
and injuries received upon the field of sport and glory,
chasing pigs, was unable to go up and down stairs, so
she sat upon the back verandah, and my work was
chequered by her cries. "Paul, you take a spade to do
that—dig a hole first. If you do that, you 'll cut your
foot off! Here, you boy, what you do there? You no
get work? You go find Simelé,[1] he give you work. Peni,
you tell this boy he go find Simelé; suppose Simelé no

---

[1] The "Henry" of the previous letter.

give him work, you tell him go 'way. I no want him
here. That boy no good."—*Peni* (from the distance in
reassuring tones), "All right, sir!"—*Fanny* (after a long
pause), "Peni, you tell that boy go find Simelé! I no
want him stand here all day. I no pay that boy. I see
him all day. He no do nothing."—Luncheon, beef,
soda-scones, fried bananas, pineapple in claret, coffee.
Try to write a poem; no go. Play the flageolet. Then
sneakingly off to farmering and pioneering. Four gangs
at work on our place; a lively scene; axes crashing
and smoke blowing; all the knives are out. But I rob
the garden party of one without a stock, and you should
see my hand—cut to ribbons. Now I want to do my
path up the Vaituliga[1] single-handed, and I want it to
burst on the public complete. Hence, with devilish ingenuity, I begin it at different places; so that if you stumble on one section, you may not even then suspect the
fulness of my labours. Accordingly, I started in a new
place, below the wire, and hoping to work up to it. It
was perhaps lucky I had so bad a cutlass, and my smarting hand bid me stay before I had got up to the wire, but
just in season, so that I was only the better of my activity, not dead beat as yesterday.

A strange business it was, and infinitely solitary; away
above, the sun was in the high tree-tops; the lianas noosed
and sought to hang me; the saplings struggled, and came
up with that sob of death that one gets to know so well;
great, soft, sappy trees fell at a lick of the cutlass, little
tough switches laughed at and dared my best endeavour.
Soon, toiling down in that pit of verdure, I heard blows
on the far side, and then laughter. I confess a chill settled on my heart. Being so dead alone, in a place where
by rights none should be beyond me, I was aware, upon
interrogation, if those blows had drawn nearer, I should

[1] One of the five rivers for which Vailima was named.

(of course quite unaffectedly) have executed a strategic movement to the rear; and only the other day I was lamenting my insensibility to superstition! Am I beginning to be sucked in? Shall I become a midnight twitterer like my neighbours? At times I thought the blows were echoes; at times I thought the laughter was from birds. For our birds are strangely human in their calls. Vaea mountain about sun-down sometimes rings with shrill cries, like the hails of merry, scattered children. As a matter of fact, I believe stealthy wood-cutters from Tanugamanono were above me in the wood and answerable for the blows; as for the laughter, a woman and two children had come and asked Fanny's leave to go up shrimp-fishing in the burn; beyond doubt, it was these I heard. Just at the right time I returned; to wash down, change, and begin this snatch of letter before dinner was ready, and to finish it afterwards, before Henry has yet put in an appearance for his lesson in "long explessions."

Dinner: stewed beef and potatoes, baked bananas, new loaf-bread hot from the oven, pineapple in claret. These are great days; we have been low in the past; but now are we as belly-gods, enjoying all things.

---

## II

*Dec. 2nd, afternoon* [1891].[1]

I have kept up the idleness; blew on the pipe[2] to Belle's piano; then had a ride in the forest all by my nainsel; back and piped again, and now dinner nearing. Take up this sheet with nothing to say. The weird figure of Faauma is in the room washing my windows, in a black

---

[1] To Sidney Colvin.　　　　　[2] His flageolet.

lavalava (kilt) with a red handkerchief hanging from round her neck between her breasts; not another stitch; her hair close cropped and oiled; when she first came here she was an angelic little stripling, but she is now in full flower—or half-flower—and grows buxom. As I write, I hear her wet cloth moving and grunting with some industry; for I had a word this day with her husband on the matter of work and meal-time, when she is always late. And she has a vague reverence for Papa, as she and her enormous husband address me when anything is wrong. Her husband is Lafaele, sometimes called the archangel, of whom I have writ you often. Rest of our household, Talolo, cook; Pulu, kitchen boy, good, steady, industrious lads; Henry, back again from Savaii, where his love affair seems not to have prospered, with what looks like a spear-wound in the back of his head, of which Mr. Reticence says nothing; Simi, Manulee, and two other labourers out-doors. Lafaele is provost of the live-stock, whereof now, three milk-cows, one bull-calf, one heifer, Jack, Macfarlane, the mare, Harold, Tifaga Jack, Donald and Edinburgh—seven horses—O, and the stallion—eight horses; five cattle; total, if my arithmetic be correct, thirteen head of beasts; I don't know how the pigs stand, or the ducks, or the chickens; but we get a good many eggs, and now and again a duckling or a chickling for the table; the pigs are more solemn and appear only on birthdays and sich.

---

## III

*Jan. 2nd* [1892].[1]

I woke this morning to find the blow quite ended. The heaven was all a mottled gray; even the east quite

[1] To Sidney Colvin.

colourless; the downward slope of the island veiled in
wafts of vapour, blue like smoke; not a leaf stirred on
the tallest tree; only, three miles away below me on the
barrier reef, I could see the individual breakers curl and
fall, and hear their conjunct roaring rise, as it still rises
at 1 P. M., like the roar of a thoroughfare close by. I did
a good morning's work, correcting and clarifying my
draft, and have now finished for press eight chapters,
ninety-one pages, of this piece of journalism. Four
more chapters, say fifty pages, remain to be done; I
should gain my wager and finish this volume in three
months, that is to say, the end should leave me per
February mail; I cannot receive it back till the mail of
April. Yes, it can be out in time; pray God that it be
in time to help.[1]

How do journalists fetch up their drivel? I aim only
at clearness and the most obvious finish, positively at no
higher degree of merit, not even at brevity—I am sure
it could have been all done, with double the time, in
two-thirds of the space. And yet it has taken me two
months to write 45,500 words; and be damned to my
wicked prowess, I am proud of the exploit! The real
journalist must be a man not of brass only, but bronze.
Chapter IX. gapes for me, but I shrink on the margin,
and go on chattering to you. . . . I estimate the whole
roughly at 70,000 words. Should anybody ever dream
of reading it, it would be found amusing. $\frac{70000}{300} = 233$
printed pages; a respectable little five-bob volume, to
bloom unread in shop windows. After that, I'll have a
spank at fiction. And rest? I shall rest in the grave, or
when I come to Italy. If only the public will continue
to support me! I lost my chance not dying; there seems
blooming little fear of it now. I worked close on five

[1] He was busy at the time with *A Foot-Note to History: Eight Years
of Trouble in Samoa.*

hours this morning; the day before, close on nine; and unless I finish myself off with this letter, I'll have another hour and a half, or *aiblins twa*,[1] before dinner. Poor man, how you must envy me, as you hear of these orgies of work, and you scarce able for a letter. But Lord Colvin how lucky the situations are not reversed, for I have no situation, nor am fit for any. Life is a steigh brae.[2] Here, have at Knappe,[3] and no more clavers![4]

---

## IV

*Thursday, April 5th* [1893].[5]

Well, there's no disguise possible; Fanny is not well, and we are miserably anxious. . . .

*Friday, 7th* [1893].

I am thankful to say the new medicine relieved her at once. A crape has been removed from the day for all of us. To make things better, the morning is ah! such a morning as you have never seen; heaven upon earth for sweetness, freshness, depth upon depth of unimaginable colour, and a huge silence broken at this moment only by the far-away murmur of the Pacific and the rich piping of a single bird. You can't conceive what a relief this is; it seems a new world. She has such extraordinary recuperative power that I do hope for the best. I am as tired as man can be. This is a great trial to a family, and I thank God it seems as if ours was going to bear it well. And oh! if it only lets up, it will be but a pleasant memory. We are all seedy, bar Lloyd;[6]

[1] Perhaps two.
[2] Steep hill.
[3] German consul in Samoa.
[4] Idle tales.
[5] To Sidney Colvin.
[6] See p. x.

Fanny, as per above; self nearly extinct; Belle, utterly overworked and bad toothache; Cook, down with a bad foot; Butler, prostrate with a bad leg. Eh, what a faim'ly!

*Sunday [April,* 1893].

Grey heaven, raining torrents of rain; occasional thunder and lightning. Everything to dispirit; but my invalids are really on the mend. The rain roars like the sea; in the sound of it there is a strange and ominous suggestion of an approaching tramp; something nameless and measureless seems to draw near, and strikes me cold, and yet is welcome. I lie quiet in bed today, and think of the universe with a good deal of equanimity. I have, at this moment, but the one objection to it; the *fracas* with which it proceeds. I do not love noise; I am like my grandfather in that; and so many years in these still islands has ingrained the sentiment perhaps. Here are no trains, only men pacing barefoot. No carts or carriages; at worst the rattle of a horse's shoes among the rocks. Beautiful silence; and so soon as this robustious rain takes off, I am to drink of it again by oceanfuls.

*April 16th* [1893].

Several pages of this letter destroyed as beneath scorn; the wailings of a crushed worm; matter in which neither you nor I can take stock. Fanny is distinctly better, I believe all right now; I too am mending, though I have suffered from crushed wormery, which is not good for the body, and damnation to the soul. I feel to-night a baseless anxiety to write a lovely poem *à propos des bottes de ma grandmère.*[1] I see I am idiotic. I'll try the poem.

[1] About nothing.

## To Alison Cunningham[1]

For a fuller account of the road-making affair here mentioned, see *Vailima Letters*, pp. 344, 360.

[VAILIMA], *October 8th*, 1894.

MY DEAR CUMMY,—So I hear you are ailing? Think shame to yourself! So you think there is nothing better to be done with time than that? and be sure we can all do much ourselves to decide whether we are to be ill, or well! like a man on the gymnastic bars. We are all pretty well. As for me, there is nothing the matter with me in the world, beyond the disgusting circumstance that I am not so young as once I was. Lloyd has a gymnastic machine, and practises upon it every morning for an hour: he is beginning to be a kind of young Samson. Austin[2] grows fat and brown, and gets on not so ill with his lessons, and my mother is in great price. We are having knock-me-down weather for heat; I never remember it so hot before, and I fancy it means we are to have a hurricane again this year, I think; since we came here, we have not had a single gale of wind! The Pacific is but a child to the North Sea; but when she does get excited, and gets up and girds herself, she can do something good. We have had a very interesting business here. I helped the chiefs who were in prison; and when they were set free, what should they do but offer to make a part of my road for me out of gratitude? Well, I was ashamed to refuse, and the trumps dug my road for me, and put up this inscription on a board:—

"*Considering the great love of His Excellency Tusitala in his loving care of us in our tribulation in the prison, we have made this great gift; it shall never be muddy, it*

---

[1] The faithful nurse of Stevenson's boyhood.
[2] Grandson of Mrs. R. L. Stevenson.

*shall go on for ever, this road that we have dug!"*   We had
a great feast when it was done, and I read them a kind
of lecture, which I dare say Auntie will have, and can
let you see.   Weel, guid-bye to ye, and joy be wi' ye!
I hae nae time to say mair.   They say I 'm gettin' *fat*
—a fact!—Your laddie, with all love,

ROBERT LOUIS STEVENSON.

# THE AMATEUR EMIGRANT

# THE AMATEUR EMIGRANT[1]

## THE SECOND CABIN

I FIRST encountered my fellow-passengers on the *Broomielaw*[2] in Glasgow. Thence we descended the Clyde in no familiar spirit, but looking askance on each other as on possible enemies. A few Scandinavians, who had already grown acquainted on the North Sea, were friendly and voluble over their long pipes; but among English speakers distance and suspicion reigned supreme. The sun was soon overclouded, the wind freshened and grew sharp as we continued to descend the widening estuary; and with the falling temperature the gloom among the passengers increased. Two of the women wept. Any one who had come aboard might have supposed we were all absconding from the law. There was scarce a word interchanged, and no common sentiment but that of cold united us, until at length, having touched at Greenock,[3] a pointing arm and a rush

---

[1] Written during the autumn and winter before Stevenson's marriage (1879–1880), while the author was in California. It is drawn direct from life, being based on Stevenson's experiences in crossing the Atlantic the previous summer. Preparations for printing it were made at once; but for various reasons publication was indefinitely postponed. The work was abridged and revised in 1894, and published in the Edinburgh Edition, January, 1895. Writing to Sidney Colvin when *The Amateur Emigrant* was about half done, Stevenson says, "I believe it will be more popular than any of my others; the canvas is so much more popular and larger too." This statement was, perhaps, too sanguine; but the last clause shows where the real strength of the *Emigrant* lies.

[2] A quay just below Glasgow bridge.

[3] A seaport on the Clyde nineteen miles northwest of Glasgow.

to starboard now announced that our ocean steamer was in sight. There she lay in mid-river, at the tail of the Bank, her sea-signal flying: a wall of bulwark, a street of white deck-houses, an aspiring forest of spars, larger than a church, and soon to be as populous as many an incorporated town in the land to which she was to bear us.

I was not, in truth, a steerage passenger. Although anxious to see the worst of emigrant life, I had some work to finish on the voyage, and was advised to go by the second cabin, where at least I should have a table at command. The advice was excellent; but to understand the choice, and what I gained, some outline of the internal disposition of the ship will first be necessary. In her very nose is Steerage No. 1, down two pair of stairs. A little abaft, another companion, labelled Steerage No. 2 and 3, gives admission to three galleries, two running forward towards Steerage No. 1, and the third aft towards the engines. The starboard forward gallery is the second cabin. Away abaft the engines and below the officers' cabins, to complete our survey of the vessel, there is yet a third nest of steerages, labelled 4 and 5. The second cabin, to return, is thus a modified oasis in the very heart of the steerages. Through the thin partition you can hear the steerage passengers being sick, the rattle of tin dishes as they sit at meals, the varied accents in which they converse, the crying of their children terrified by this new experience, or the clean flat smack of the parental hand in chastisement.

There are, however, many advantages for the inhabitant of this strip. He does not require to bring his own bedding or dishes, but finds berths and a table completely if somewhat roughly furnished. He enjoys a distinct superiority in diet; but this, strange to say, differs not only on different ships, but on the same ship according as her head is to the east or west. In my own experience, the principal difference between our table and that of the true steerage passenger was the table itself, and the crockery plates from which we ate. But lest I should show myself ungrateful, let me recapitulate every advantage. At breakfast, we had a choice between tea and coffee for beverage; a choice not easy to make, the two were so surprisingly alike. I found that I could sleep after the coffee and lay awake after the tea, which is proof conclusive of some chemical disparity; and even by the palate I could distinguish a smack of snuff in the former from a flavour of boiling and dish-cloths in the second. As a matter of fact, I have seen passengers, after many sips, still doubting which had been supplied them. In the way of eatables at the same meal we were gloriously favoured; for in addition to porridge, which was common to all, we had Irish stew, sometimes a bit of fish, and sometimes rissoles. The dinner of soup, roast fresh beef, boiled salt junk, and potatoes, was, I believe, exactly common to the steerage and the second cabin; only I have heard it rumoured that our potatoes were of a superior brand; and twice a week, on pudding-days, instead of duff, we had a saddle-bag filled with currants under the name of a plum-pudding. At tea we were served with some broken meat from the saloon; sometimes in the comparatively elegant form of spare patties or rissoles; but as a general thing, mere chicken-bones and flakes of fish, neither hot nor cold. If these were not the scrapings of plates their looks belied them sorely; yet we were all too hungry to be proud, and fell to these leavings greedily. These, the bread, which was excellent, and the soup and porridge which were both good, formed my whole diet throughout the voyage; so that except for the broken meat and the convenience of a table I might as well have been in the steerage outright. Had they given me porridge again in the evening, I should have been perfectly contented with the fare. As it was, with a few biscuits and some whisky and water before turning in, I kept my body going and my spirits up to the mark.

The last particular in which the second-cabin passenger remarkably stands ahead of his brother of the steerage is one altogether of sentiment. In the steerage there are males and females; in the second cabin ladies and gentlemen. For some time after I came aboard I thought I was only a male; but in the course of a voyage of discovery between decks, I came on a brass plate, and learned that I was still a gentleman. Nobody knew it, of course. I was lost in the crowd of males and females, and rigorously confined to the same quarter of the deck. Who could tell whether I housed on the port or starboard side of steerage No. 2 and 3? And it was only there that my superiority became practical; everywhere else I was incognito, moving among my inferiors with simplicity, not so much as a swagger to indicate that I was a gentleman after all, and had broken meat to tea. Still, I was like one with a patent of nobility in a drawer at home; and when I felt out of spirits I could go down and refresh myself with a look of that brass plate.

For all these advantages I paid but two guineas. Six guineas is the steerage fare; eight that by the second cabin; and when you remember that the steerage passenger must supply bedding and dishes, and, in five cases out of ten, either brings some dainties with him, or privately pays the steward for extra rations, the difference in price becomes almost nominal. Air comparatively fit to breathe, food comparatively varied, and the satisfaction of being still privately a gentleman, may thus be had almost for the asking. Two of my fellow-passengers in the second cabin had already made the passage by the cheaper fare, and declared it was an experiment not to be repeated. As I go on to tell about my steerage friends, the reader will perceive that they were not alone in their opinion. Out of ten with whom I was more or less intimate, I am sure not fewer than five vowed, if they returned, to travel second cabin; and all who had left their wives behind them assured me they would go without the comfort of their presence until they could afford to bring them by saloon.

Our party in the second cabin was not perhaps the most interesting on board. Perhaps even in the saloon there was as much good-will and character. Yet it had some elements of curiosity. There was a mixed group of Swedes, Danes, and Norsemen, one of whom, generally known by the name of "Johnny," in spite of his own protests, greatly diverted us by his clever, cross-country efforts to speak English, and became on the strength of that an universal favourite—it takes so little in this world of shipboard to create a popularity. There was, besides, a Scots mason, known from his favourite dish as "Irish Stew," three or four nondescript Scots, a fine young Irishman, O'Reilly, and a pair of young men who deserve a special word of condemnation. One of them was Scots; the other claimed to be American; admitted, after some fencing, that he was born in England; and ultimately proved to be an Irishman born and nurtured, but ashamed to own his country. He had a sister on board, whom he faithfully neglected throughout the voyage, though she was not only sick, but much his senior, and had nursed and cared for him in childhood. In appearance he was like an imbecile Henry the Third of France. The Scotsman, though perhaps as big an ass, was not so dead of heart; and I have only bracketed them together because they were fast friends, and disgraced themselves equally by their conduct at the table.

Next, to turn to topics more agreeable, we had a newly married couple, devoted to each other, with a pleasant story of how they had first seen each other years ago at a preparatory school, and that very afternoon he had carried her books home for her. I do not know if this story will be plain to Southern readers; but to me it recalls many a school idyll, with wrathful swains of eight and nine confronting each other stride-legs, flushed with jealousy; for to carry home a young lady's books was both a delicate attention and a privilege.

Then there was an old lady, or indeed I am not sure that she was as much old as antiquated and strangely out of place, who had left her husband, and was travelling all the way to Kansas by herself. We had to take her own word that she was married; for it was sorely contradicted by the testimony of her appearance. Nature seemed to have sanctified her for the single state; even the colour of her hair was incompatible with matrimony, and her husband, I thought, should be a man of saintly spirit and phantasmal bodily presence. She was ill, poor thing; her soul turned from the viands; the dirty tablecloth shocked her like an impropriety; and the whole strength of her endeavour was bent upon keeping her watch true to Glasgow time till she should reach New York. They had heard reports, her husband and she, of some unwarrantable disparity of hours between these two cities; and with a spirit commendably scientific, had seized on this occasion to put them to the proof. It was a good thing for the old lady; for she passed much leisure time in studying the watch. Once, when prostrated by sickness, she let it run down. It was inscribed on her harmless mind in letters of adamant that the hands of a watch must never be turned backwards; and so it behoved her to lie in wait for the exact moment ere she started it again. When she imagined this was about due, she sought out one of the young second-cabin Scotsmen, who was embarked on the same experiment as herself and had hitherto been less neglectful. She was in quest of two o'clock; and when she learned it was already seven on the shores of Clyde, she lifted up her voice and cried "Gravy!" I had not heard this innocent expletive since I was a young child; and I suppose it must have been the same with the other Scotsmen present, for we all laughed our fill.

Last but not least, I come to my excellent friend Mr. Jones. It would be difficult to say whether I was his right-hand man, or he mine, during the voyage. Thus at table I carved, while he only scooped gravy; but at our concerts, of which more anon, he was the president who called up performers to sing, and I but his messenger who ran his errands and pleaded privately with the over-modest. I knew I liked Mr. Jones from the moment I saw him. I thought him by his face to be Scottish; nor could his accent undeceive me. For as there is a *lingua franca*[1] of many tongues on the moles and in the feluccas of the Mediterranean, so there is a free or common accent among English-speaking men who follow the sea. They catch a twang in a New England port; from a cockney skipper, even a Scotsman sometimes learns to drop an *h;* a word of a dialect is picked up from another hand in the forecastle; until often the result is undecipherable, and you have to ask for the man's place of birth. So it was with Mr. Jones. I thought him a Scotsman who had been long to sea; and yet he was from Wales, and had been most of his life a blacksmith at an inland forge; a few years in America and half a score of ocean voyages having sufficed to modify his speech into the common pattern. By his

[1] A phrase applied to any mixed jargon formed from words of several languages and used as an international dialect.

own account he was both strong and skilful in his trade. A few years back, he had been married and after a fashion a rich man; now the wife was dead and the money gone. But his was the nature that looks forward, and goes on from one year to another and through all the extremities of fortune undismayed; and if the sky were to fall to-morrow, I should look to see Jones, the day following, perched on a step-ladder and getting things to rights. He was always hovering round inventions like a bee over a flower, and lived in a dream of patents. He had with him a patent medicine, for instance, the composition of which he had bought years ago for five dollars from an American peddler, and sold the other day for a hundred pounds (I think it was) to an English apothecary. It was called Golden Oil, cured all maladies without exception; and I am bound to say that I partook of it myself with good results. It is a character of the man that he was not only perpetually dosing himself with Golden Oil, but wherever there was a head aching or a finger cut, there would be Jones with his bottle.

If he had one taste more strongly than another, it was to study character. Many an hour have we two walked upon the deck dissecting our neighbours in a spirit that was too purely scientific to be called unkind; whenever a quaint or human trait slipped out in conversation, you might have seen Jones and me exchanging glances; and we could hardly go to bed in comfort till we had exchanged notes and discussed the day's experience. We were then like a couple of anglers comparing a day's kill. But the fish we angled for were of a metaphysical species, and we angled as often as not in one another's baskets. Once, in the midst of a serious talk, each found there was a scrutinising eye upon himself; I own I paused in embarrassment at this double detection; but

Jones, with a better civility, broke into a peal of unaf-
fected laughter, and declared, what was the truth, that
there was a pair of us indeed.


## EARLY IMPRESSIONS

We steamed out of the Clyde on Thursday night, and
early on the Friday forenoon we took in our last batch
of emigrants at Lough Foyle, in Ireland, and said farewell to Europe. The company was now complete, and
began to draw together, by inscrutable magnetisms,
upon the decks. There were Scots and Irish in plenty,
a few English, a few Americans, a good handful of Scandinavians, a German or two, and one Russian; all now
belonging for ten days to one small iron country on the
deep.

As I walked the deck and looked round upon my fellow-passengers, thus curiously assorted from all northern Europe, I began for the first time to understand the
nature of emigration. Day by day throughout the passage, and thenceforward across all the States, and on to
the shores of the Pacific, this knowledge grew more clear
and melancholy. Emigration, from a word of the most
cheerful import, came to sound most dismally in my ear.
There is nothing more agreeable to picture and nothing more pathetic to behold. The abstract idea, as conceived at home, is hopeful and adventurous. A young
man, you fancy, scorning restraints and helpers, issues
forth into life, that great battle, to fight for his own hand.
The most pleasant stories of ambition, of difficulties over-
come, and of ultimate success, are but as episodes to
this great epic of self-help. The epic is composed of
individual heroisms; it stands to them as the victorious
war which subdued an empire stands to the personal

act or bravery which spiked a single cannon and was adequately rewarded with a medal. For in emigration the young men enter direct and by the shipload on their heritage of work; empty continents swarm, as at the bo'sun's whistle, with industrious hands, and whole new empires are domesticated to the service of man.

This is the closet picture, and is found, on trial, to consist mostly of embellishments. The more I saw of my fellow-passengers, the less I was tempted to the lyric note. Comparatively few of the men were below thirty; many were married, and encumbered with families; not a few were already up in years; and this itself was out of tune with my imaginations, for the ideal emigrant should certainly be young. Again, I thought he should offer to the eye some bold type of humanity, with bluff or hawk-like features, and the stamp of an eager and pushing disposition. Now those around me were for the most part quiet, orderly, obedient citizens, family men broken by adversity, elderly youths who had failed to place themselves in life, and people who had seen better days. Mildness was the prevailing character; mild mirth and mild endurance. In a word, I was not taking part in an impetuous and conquering sally, such as swept over Mexico or Siberia, but found myself, like Marmion, "in the lost battle, borne down by the flying."

Labouring mankind had in the last years, and throughout Great Britain, sustained a prolonged and crushing series of defeats. I had heard vaguely of these reverses; of whole streets of houses standing deserted by the Tyne,[1] the cellar-doors broken and removed for firewood; of homeless men loitering at the street-corners of Glasgow with their chests beside them; of closed factories, useless strikes, and starving girls. But I had never taken them home to me or represented these distresses livingly to my

[1] A river in northern England.

Imagination. A turn of the market may be a calamity as disastrous as the French retreat from Moscow; but it hardly lends itself to lively treatment, and makes a trifling figure in the morning papers. We may struggle as we please, we are not born economists. The individual is more affecting than the mass. It is by the scenic accidents, and the appeal to the carnal eye, that for the most part we grasp the significance of tragedies. Thus it was only now, when I found myself involved in the rout, that I began to appreciate how sharp had been the battle. We were a company of the rejected; the drunken, the incompetent, the weak, the prodigal, all who had been unable to prevail against circumstances in the one land, were now fleeing pitifully to another; and though one or two might still succeed, all had already failed. We were a shipful of failures, the broken men of England. Yet it must not be supposed that these people exhibited depression. The scene, on the contrary, was cheerful. Not a tear was shed on board the vessel. All were full of hope for the future, and showed an inclination to innocent gaiety. Some were heard to sing, and all began to scrape acquaintance with small jests and ready laughter.

The children found each other out like dogs, and ran about the decks scraping acquaintance after their fashion also. "What do you call your mither?" I heard one ask. "Mawmaw," was the reply, indicating, I fancy, a shade of difference in the social scale. When people pass each other on the high seas of life at so early an age, the contact is but slight, and the relation more like what we may imagine to be the friendship of flies than that of men; it is so quickly joined, so easily dissolved, so open in its communications and so devoid of deeper human qualities. The children, I observed, were all in a band, and as thick as thieves at a fair, while their elders were

still ceremoniously manœuvring on the outskirts of acquaintance. The sea, the ship, and the seamen were
soon as familiar as home to these half-conscious little
ones. It was odd to hear them, throughout the voyage,
employ shore words to designate portions of the vessel.
"Go 'way doon to yon dyke," I heard one say, probably
meaning the bulwark. I often had my heart in my
mouth, watching them climb into the shrouds or on the
rails, while the ship went swinging through the waves;
and I admired and envied the courage of their mothers,
who sat by in the sun and looked on with composure at
these perilous feats. "He 'll maybe be a sailor," I heard
one remark; "now 's the time to learn." I had been on
the point of running forward to interfere, but stood back
at that, reproved. Very few in the more delicate classes
have the nerve to look upon the peril of one dear to them;
but the life of poorer folk, where necessity is so much
more immediate and imperious, braces even a mother to
this extreme of endurance. And perhaps, after all, it is
better that the lad should break his neck than that you
should break his spirit.

And since I am here on the chapter of the children, I
must mention one little fellow, whose family belonged
to Steerage No. 4 and 5, and who, wherever he went,
was like a strain of music round the ship. He was an
ugly, merry, unbreeched child of three, his lint white
hair in a tangle, his face smeared with suet and treacle;
but he ran to and fro with so natural a step, and fell and
picked himself up again with such grace and good-
humour, that he might fairly be called beautiful when he
was in motion. To meet him, crowing with laughter
and beating an accompaniment to his own mirth with
a tin spoon upon a tin cup, was to meet a little triumph
of the human species. Even when his mother and the
rest of his family lay sick and prostrate around him, he

sat upright in their midst and sang aloud in the pleasant heartlessness of infancy.

Throughout the Friday, intimacy among us men made but a few advances. We discussed the probable duration of the voyage, we exchanged pieces of information, naming our trades, what we hoped to find in the new world, or what we were fleeing from in the old; and, above all, we condoled together over the food and the vileness of the steerage. One or two had been so near famine that you may say they had run into the ship with the devil at their heels; and to these all seemed for the best in the best of possible steamers. But the majority were hugely discontented. Coming as they did from a country in so low a state as Great Britain, many of them from Glasgow, which commercially speaking was as good as dead, and many having long been out of work, I was surprised to find them so dainty in their notions. I myself lived almost exclusively on bread, porridge, and soup, precisely as it was supplied to them, and found it, if not luxurious, at least sufficient. But these working men were loud in their outcries. It was not "food for human beings," it was "only fit for pigs," it was "a disgrace." Many of them lived almost entirely upon biscuit, others on their own private supplies, and some paid extra for better rations from the ship. This marvellously changed my notion of the degree of luxury habitual to the artisan. I was prepared to hear him grumble, for grumbling is the traveller's pastime; but I was not prepared to find him turn away from a diet which was palatable to myself. Words I should have disregarded, or taken with a liberal allowance; but when a man prefers dry biscuit there can be no question of the sincerity of his disgust.

With one of their complaints I could most heartily sympathise. A single night of the steerage had filled them with horror. I had myself suffered, even in my decent second-cabin berth, from the lack of air; and as the night promised to be fine and quiet, I determined to sleep on deck, and advised all who complained of their quarters to follow my example. I daresay a dozen of others agreed to do so, and I thought we should have been quite a party. Yet, when I brought up my rug about seven bells, there was no one to be seen but the watch. That chimerical terror of good night-air, which makes men close their windows, list their doors, and seal themselves up with their own poisonous exhalations, had sent all these healthy workmen down below. One would think we had been brought up in a fever country; yet in England the most malarious districts are in the bedchambers.

I felt saddened at this defection, and yet half pleased to have the night so quietly to myself. The wind had hauled a little ahead on the starboard bow, and was dry but chilly. I found a shelter near the fire-hole, and made myself snug for the night. The ship moved over the uneven sea with a gentle and cradling movement. The ponderous, organic labours of the engine in her bowels occupied the mind, and prepared it for slumber. From time to time a heavier lurch would disturb me as I lay, and recall me to the obscure borders of consciousness; or I heard, as it were through a veil, the clear note of the clapper on the brass and the beautiful sea-cry, "All's well!" I know nothing, whether for poetry or music, that can surpass the effect of these two syllables in the darkness of a night at sea.

The day dawned fairly enough, and during the early part we had some pleasant hours to improve acquaintance in the open air; but towards nightfall the wind freshened, the rain began to fall, and the sea rose so high that it was difficult to keep one's footing on the deck.

I have spoken of our concerts. We were indeed a musical ship's company, and cheered our way into exile with the fiddle, the accordion, and the songs of all nations. Good, bad, or indifferent—Scottish, English, Irish, Russian, German or Norse,—the songs were received with generous applause. Once or twice, a recitation, very spiritedly rendered in a powerful Scottish accent, varied the proceedings; and once we sought in vain to dance a quadrille, eight men of us together, to the music of the violin. The performers were all humorous, frisky fellows, who loved to cut capers in private life; but as soon as they were arranged for the dance, they conducted themselves like so many mutes at a funeral. I have never seen decorum pushed so far; and as this was not expected, the quadrille was soon whistled down, and the dancers departed under a cloud. Eight Frenchmen, even eight Englishmen from another rank of society, would have dared to make some fun for themselves and the spectators; but the working man, when sober, takes an extreme and even melancholy view of personal deportment. A fifth-form school-boy is not more careful of dignity. He dares not be comical; his fun must escape from him unprepared, and above all, it must be unaccompanied by any physical demonstration. I like his society under most circumstances, but let me never again join with him in public gambols.

But the impulse to sing was strong, and triumphed over modesty and even the inclemencies of sea and sky. On this rough Saturday night, we got together by the main deck-house, in a place sheltered from the wind and rain. Some clinging to a ladder which led to the hurricane deck, and the rest knitting arms or taking hands, we made a ring to support the women in the violent lurching of the ship; and when we were thus disposed, sang to our heart's content. Some of the songs were appropriate to the scene; others strikingly the reverse. Bastard doggrel of the music-hall, such as, "Around her splendid form, I weaved the magic circle," sounded bald, bleak, and pitifully silly. "We don't want to fight, but, by Jingo, if we do," was in some measure saved by the vigour and unanimity with which the chorus was thrown forth into the night. I observed a Platt-Deutsch mason, entirely innocent of English, adding heartily to the general effect. And perhaps the German mason is but a fair example of the sincerity with which the song was rendered; for nearly all with whom I conversed upon the subject were bitterly opposed to war, and attributed their own misfortunes, and frequently their own taste for whisky, to the campaigns in Zululand and Afghanistan.

Every now and again, however, some song that touched the pathos of our situation was given forth; and you could hear by the voices that took up the burden how the sentiment came home to each. "The Anchor's Weighed" was true for us. We were indeed "Rocked on the bosom of the stormy deep." How many of us could say with the singer, "I'm lonely to-night, love, without you," or "Go, some one, and tell them from me, to write me a letter from home!" And when was there a more appropriate moment for "Auld Lang Syne" than now, when the land, the friends, and the affections of that mingled but beloved time were fading and fleeing behind us in the vessel's wake? It pointed forward to the hour when these labours should be overpast, to the return voyage, and to many a meeting in the sanded inn, when those who had parted in the spring of youth should again drink a cup of kindness in their age. Had not Burns contemplated emigration, I scarce believe he would have found that note.

All Sunday the weather remained wild and cloudy;

many were prostrated by sickness; only five sat down to tea in the second cabin, and two of these departed abruptly ere the meal was at an end. The Sabbath was observed strictly by the majority of the emigrants. I heard an old woman express her surprise that "the ship didna gae doon," as she saw some one pass her with a chess-board on the holy day. Some sang Scottish psalms. Many went to service, and in true Scottish fashion came back ill pleased with their divine. "I didna think he was an experienced preacher," said one girl to me.

It was a bleak, uncomfortable day; but at night, by six bells, although the wind had not yet moderated, the clouds were all wrecked and blown away behind the rim of the horizon, and the stars came out thickly overhead. I saw Venus burning as steadily and sweetly across this hurly-burly of the winds and waters as ever at home upon the summer woods. The engine pounded, the screw tossed out of the water with a roar, and shook the ship from end to end; the bows battled with loud reports against the billows: and as I stood in the lee-scuppers and looked up to where the funnel leaned out, over my head, vomiting smoke, and the black and monstrous topsails blotted, at each lurch, a different crop of stars, it seemed as if all this trouble were a thing of small account, and that just above the mast reigned peace unbroken and eternal.

## STEERAGE SCENES

Our companion (Steerage No. 2 and 3) was a favourite resort. Down one flight of stairs there was a comparatively large open space, the center occupied by a hatchway, which made a convenient seat for about twenty persons, while barrels, coils of rope, and the carpenter's bench afforded perches for perhaps as many more. The canteen, or steerage bar, was on one side of the stair; on the other, a no less attractive spot, the cabin of the indefatigable interpreter. I have seen people packed into this space like herrings in a barrel, and many merry evenings prolonged there until five bells, when the lights were ruthlessly extinguished and all must go to roost.

It had been rumoured since Friday that there was a fiddler aboard, who lay sick and unmelodious in Steerage No. 1; and on the Monday forenoon, as I came down the companion, I was saluted by something in Strathspey[1] time. A white-faced Orpheus was cheerily playing to an audience of white-faced women. It was as much as he could do to play, and some of his hearers were scarce able to sit; yet they had crawled from their bunks at the first experimental flourish, and found better than medicine in the music. Some of the heaviest heads began to nod in time, and a degree of animation looked from some of the palest eyes. Humanly speaking, it is a more important matter to play the fiddle, even badly, than to write huge works upon recondite subjects. What could Mr. Darwin have done for these sick women? But this fellow scraped away; and the world was positively a better place for all who heard him. We have yet to understand the economical value of these mere accomplishments. I told the fiddler he was a happy man, carrying happiness about with him in his fiddle-case, and he seemed alive to the fact.

"It is a privilege," I said. He thought a while upon the word, turning it over in his Scots head, and then answered with conviction, "Yes, a privilege."

That night I was summoned by "Merrily danced the

[1] A dance for two people, or a lively tune adapted to such a dance.

Quaker's wife" into the companion of Steerage No. 4 and 5. This was, properly speaking, but a strip across a deck-house, lit by a sickly lantern which swung to and fro with the motion of the ship. Through the open slide-door we had a glimpse of a grey night sea, with patches of phosphorescent foam flying, swift as birds, into the wake, and the horizon rising and falling as the vessel rolled to the wind. In the center the companion ladder plunged down sheerly like an open pit. Below, on the first landing, and lighted by another lamp, lads and lasses danced, not more than three at a time for lack of space, in jigs and reels and hornpipes. Above, on either side, there was a recess railed with iron, perhaps two feet wide and four long, which stood for orchestra and seats of honour. In the one balcony, five slatternly Irish lasses sat woven in a comely group. In the other was posted Orpheus, his body, which was convulsively in motion, forming an odd contrast to his somnolent, imperturbable Scots face. His brother, a dark man with a vehement, interested countenance, who made a god of the fiddler, sat by with open mouth, drinking in the general admiration and throwing out remarks to kindle it.

"That's a bonny hornpipe now," he would say, "it's a great favourite with performers; they dance the sand dance to it." And he expounded the sand dance. Then suddenly, it would be a long "Hush!" with uplifted finger and glowing, supplicating eyes; "he's going to play 'Auld Robin Gray' on one string!" And throughout this excruciating movement,—"On one string, that's on one string!" he kept crying. I would have given something myself that it had been on none; but the hearers were much awed. I called for a tune or two, and thus introduced myself to the notice of the brother, who directed his talk to me for some little while, keeping, I need hardly mention, true to his topic, like the seamen to the star. "He's grand of it," he said confidentially. "His master was a music-hall man." Indeed the music-hall man had left his mark, for our fiddler was ignorant of many of our best old airs; "Logie o' Buchan," for instance, he only knew as a quick, jigging figure in a set of quadrilles, and had never heard it called by name. Perhaps, after all, the brother was the more interesting performer of the two. I have spoken with him afterwards repeatedly, and found him always the same quick, fiery bit of a man, not without brains; but he never showed to such advantage as when he was thus squiring the fiddler into public note. There is nothing more becoming than a genuine admiration; and it shares this with love, that it does not become contemptible although misplaced.

The dancing was but feebly carried on. The space was almost impracticably small; and the Irish wenches combined the extreme of bashfulness about this innocent display with a surprising impudence and roughness of address. Most often, either the fiddle lifted up its voice unheeded, or only a couple of lads would be footing it and snapping fingers on the landing. And such was the eagerness of the brother to display all the acquirements of his idol, and such the sleepy indifference of the performer, that the tune would as often as not be changed, and the hornpipe expire into a ballad before the dancers had cut half a dozen shuffles.

In the meantime, however, the audience had been growing more and more numerous every moment; there was hardly standing-room round the top of the companion; and the strange instinct of the race moved some of the new-comers to close both the doors, so that the atmosphere grew insupportable. It was a good place, as the saying is, to leave.

The wind hauled ahead with a head sea. By ten at night heavy sprays were flying and drumming over the forecastle; the companion of Steerage No. 1 had to be closed, and the door of communication through the second cabin thrown open. Either from the convenience of the opportunity, or because we had already a number of acquaintances in that part of the ship, Mr. Jones and I paid it a late visit. Steerage No. 1 is shaped like an isosceles triangle, the sides opposite the equal angles bulging outward with the contour of the ship. It is lined with eight pens of sixteen bunks apiece, four bunks below and four above on either side. At night the place is lit with two lanterns, one to each table. As the steamer beat on her way among the rough billows, the light passed through violent phases of change, and was thrown to and fro and up and down with startling swiftness. You were tempted to wonder, as you looked, how so thin a glimmer could control and disperse such solid blackness. When Jones and I entered we found a little company of our acquaintances seated together at the triangular foremost table. A more forlorn party, in more dismal circumstances, it would be hard to imagine. The motion here in the ship's nose was very violent; the uproar of the sea often overpoweringly loud. The yellow flicker of the lantern spun round and round and tossed the shadows in masses. The air was hot, but it struck a chill from its fœtor. From all round in the dark bunks, the scarcely human noises of the sick joined into a kind of farmyard chorus. In the midst, these five friends of mine were keeping up what heart they could in company. Singing was their refuge from discomfortable thoughts and sensations. One piped, in feeble tones, "Oh why left I my hame?" which seemed a pertinent question in the circumstances. Another, from the invisible horrors of a pen where he lay dog-sick upon the upper shelf, found courage, in a blink of his sufferings, to give us several verses of the "Death of Nelson"; and it was odd and eerie to hear the chorus breathe feebly from all sorts of dark corners, and "this day has done his dooty" rise and fall and be taken up again in this dim *inferno*, to an accompaniment of plunging, hollow-sounding bows and the rattling spray-showers overhead.

All seemed unfit for conversation; a certain dizziness had interrupted the activity of their minds; and except to sing they were tongue-tied. There was present, however, one tall, powerful fellow of doubtful nationality, being neither quite Scotsman nor altogether Irish, but of surprising clearness of conviction on the highest problems. He had gone nearly beside himself on the Sunday, because of a general backwardness to indorse his definition of mind as "a living, thinking substance which cannot be felt, heard, or seen"—nor, I presume, although he failed to mention it, smelt. Now he came forward in a pause with another contribution to our culture.

"Just by way of change," said he, "I'll ask you a Scripture riddle. There's profit in them too," he added ungrammatically.

This was the riddle—

> C and P
> Did agree
> To cut down C;
> But C and P
> Could not agree
> Without the leave of G.
> All the people cried to see
> The crueltie
> Of C and P.

Harsh are the words of Mercury after the songs of Apollo! We were a long while over the problem, shaking our heads and gloomily wondering how a man could be such a fool; but at length he put us out of suspense and divulged the fact that C and P stood for Caiaphas and Pontius Pilate.

I think it must have been the riddle that settled us, but the motion and the close air likewise hurried our departure. We had not been gone long, we heard next morning, ere two or even three out of the five fell sick. We thought it little wonder on the whole, for the sea kept contrary all night. I now made my bed upon the second cabin floor, where, although I ran the risk of being stepped upon, I had a free current of air, more or less vitiated indeed, and running only from steerage to steerage, but at least not stagnant; and from this couch, as well as the usual sounds of a rough night at sea, the hateful coughing and retching of the sick and the sobs of children, I heard a man run wild with terror beseeching his friend for encouragement. "The ship's going down!" he cried with a thrill of agony. "The ship's going down!" he repeated, now in a blank whisper, now with his voice rising towards a sob; and his friend might reassure him, reason with him, joke at him—all was in vain, and the old cry came back, "The ship's going down!" There was something panicky and catching in the emotion of his tones; and I saw in a clear flash what an involved and hideous tragedy was a disaster to an emigrant ship. If this whole parishful of people came no more to land, into how many houses would the newspaper carry woe, and what a great part of the web of our corporate human life would be rent across for ever!

The next morning when I came on deck I found a new world indeed. The wind was fair; the sun mounted into a cloudless heaven; through great dark blue seas the ship cut a swath of curded foam. The horizon was dotted all day with companionable sails, and the sun shone pleasantly on the long, heaving deck.

We had many fine-weather diversions to beguile the time. There was a single chess-board and a single pack of cards. Sometimes as many as twenty of us would be playing dominoes for love. Feats of dexterity, puzzles for the intelligence, some arithmetical, some of the same order as the old problem of the fox and goose and cabbage, were always welcome; and the latter, I observed, more popular as well as more conspicuously well done than the former. We had a regular daily competition to guess the vessel's progress; and twelve o'clock, when the result was published in the wheel-house, came to be a moment of considerable interest. But the interest was unmixed. Not a bet was laid upon our guesses. From the Clyde to Sandy Hook I never heard a wager offered or taken. We had, besides, romps in plenty. Puss in the Corner, which we had rebaptized, in more manly style, Devil and four Corners, was my own favourite game; but there were many who preferred another, the humour of which was to box a person's ears until he found out who had cuffed him.

This Tuesday morning we were all delighted with the change of weather, and in the highest possible spirits. We got in a cluster like bees, sitting between each other's feet under lee of the deck-houses. Stories and laughter went around. The children climbed about the shrouds. White faces appeared for the first time, and began to take on colour from the wind. I was kept hard at work making cigarettes for one amateur after another, and my less than moderate skill was heartily admired. Lastly, down sat the fiddler in our midst and began to discourse his reels, and jigs, and ballads, with now and then a voice or two to take up the air and throw in the interest of human speech.

Through this merry and good-hearted scene there came three cabin passengers, a gentleman and two young ladies, picking their way with little gracious titters of indulgence, and a Lady-Bountiful air about nothing, which galled me to the quick. I have little of the radical in social questions, and have always nourished an idea that one person was as good as another. But I began to be troubled by this episode. It was astonishing what insults these people managed to convey by their presence. They seemed to throw their clothes in our faces. Their eyes searched us all over for tatters and incongruities. A laugh was ready at their lips; but they were too well-mannered to indulge it in our hearing. Wait a bit, till they were all back in the saloon, and then hear how wittily they would depict the manners of the steerage. We were in truth very innocently, cheerfully, and sensibly engaged, and there was no shadow of excuse for the swaying elegant superiority with which these damsels passed among us, or for the stiff and waggish glances of their squire. Not a word was said; only when they were gone Mackay sullenly damned their impudence under his breath; but we were all conscious of an icy influence and a dead break in the course of our enjoyment.


## STEERAGE TYPES


We had a fellow on board, an Irish-American, for all the world like a beggar in a print by Callot;[1] one-eyed, with great, splay crow's-feet round the sockets; a knotty squab nose coming down over his mustache; a miraculous hat; a shirt that had been white, ay, ages long ago; an alpaca coat in its last sleeves; and, without hyperbole, no buttons to his trousers. Even in these rags and tatters, the man twinkled all over with impudence like a piece of sham jewellery; and I have heard him offer a situ-

[1] A French engraver (1593–1635).

ation to one of his fellow-passengers with the air of a
lord. Nothing could overlie such a fellow; a kind of
base success was written on his brow. He was then in
his ill days; but I can imagine him in Congress with his
mouth full of bombast and sawder.[1] As we moved in
the same circle, I was brought necessarily into his society. I do not think I ever heard him say anything
that was true, kind, or interesting; but there was entertainment in the man's demeanour. You might call him
a half-educated Irish Tigg.[2]

Our Russian made a remarkable contrast to this impossible fellow. Rumours and legends were current in
the steerages about his antecedents. Some said he was
a Nihilist escaping; others set him down for a harmless
spendthrift, who had squandered fifty thousand roubles,
and whose father had now despatched him to America
by way of penance. Either tale might flourish in security; there was no contradiction to be feared, for the
hero spoke not one word of English. I got on with him
lumberingly enough in broken German, and learnt from
his own lips that he had been an apothecary. He carried the photograph of his betrothed in a pocket-book,
and remarked that it did not do her justice. The cut
of his head stood out from among the passengers with
an air of startling strangeness. The first natural instinct was to take him for a desperado; but although the
features, to our Western eyes, had a barbaric and un-
homely cast, the eye both reassured and touched. It
was large and very dark and soft, with an expression of
dumb endurance, as if it had often looked on desperate
circumstances and never looked on them without resolution.

---

[1] A slang expression, meaning flattery.
[2] Montague Tigg is a self-reliant but impecunious rascal in Dickens's *Martin Chuzzlewit.*

He cried out when I used the word. "No, no," he said, "not resolution."

"The resolution to endure," I explained.

And then he shrugged his shoulders, and said, "*Ach, ja,*" with gusto, like a man who had been flattered in his favourite pretensions. Indeed, he was always hinting at some secret sorrow; and his life, he said, had been one of unusual trouble and anxiety; so the legends of the steerage may have represented at least some shadow of the truth. Once, and once only, he sang a song at our concerts; standing forth without embarrassment, his great stature somewhat humped, his long arms frequently extended, his Kalmuck[1] head thrown backward. It was a suitable piece of music, as deep as a cow's bellow and wild like the White Sea. He was struck and charmed by the freedom and sociality of our manners. At home, he said, no one on a journey would speak to him, but those with whom he would not care to speak; thus unconsciously involving himself in the condemnation of his countrymen. But Russia was soon to be changed; the ice of the Neva was softening under the sun of civilization; the new ideas, "*wie eine jeine Violine,*"[2] were audible among the big empty drum notes of Imperial diplomacy; and he looked to see a great revival, though with a somewhat indistinct and childish hope.

We had a father and son who made a pair of Jacks-of-all-trades. It was the son who sang the "Death of Nelson" under such contrarious circumstances. He was by trade a shearer of ship plates; but he could touch the organ, had led two choirs, and played the flute and piccolo in a professional string band. His repertory of songs was, besides, inexhaustible, and ranged impartially from

[1] A broad, round head like those of the Kalmuck Tartars.
[2] Like the music of a fine violin.

the very best to the very worst within his reach. Nor did he seem to make the least distinction between these extremes, but would cheerfully follow up "Tom Bowling" with "Around her splendid form."

The father, an old, cheery, small piece of manhood, could do everything connected with tinwork from one end of the process to the other, use almost every carpenter's tool, and make picture frames to boot. "I sat down with silver plate every Sunday," said he, "and pictures on the wall. I have made enough money to be rolling in my carriage. But, sir," looking at me unsteadily with his bright rheumy eyes, "I was troubled with a drunken wife." He took a hostile view of matrimony in consequence. "It's an old saying," he remarked: "God made 'em, and the devil he mixed 'em."

I think he was justified by his experience. It was a dreary story. He would bring home three pounds on Saturday, and on Monday all the clothes would be in pawn. Sick of the useless struggle, he gave up a paying contract, and contented himself with small and ill-paid jobs. "A bad job was as good as a good job for me," he said; "it all went the same way." Once the wife showed signs of amendment; she kept steady for weeks on end; it was again worth while to labour and to do one's best. The husband found a good situation some distance from home, and, to make a little upon every hand, started the wife in a cook-shop; the children were here and there, busy as mice; savings began to grow together in the bank, and the golden age of hope had returned again to that unhappy family. But one week my old acquaintance, getting earlier through with his work, came home on the Friday instead of the Saturday, and there was his wife to receive him reeling drunk. He "took and gave her a pair o' black eyes," for which I pardon him, nailed up the cook-shop door, gave up his situation, and resigned himself to a life of poverty, with the workhouse at the end. As the children came to their full age they fled the house, and established themselves in other countries; some did well, some not so well; but the father remained at home alone with his drunken wife, all his sound-hearted pluck and varied accomplishments depressed and negatived.

Was she dead now? or, after all these years, had he broken the chain, and run from home like a school-boy? I could not discover which; but here at least he was out on the adventure, and still one of the bravest and most youthful men on board.

"Now, I suppose, I must put my old bones to work again," said he; "but I can do a turn yet."

And the son to whom he was going, I asked, was he not able to support him?

"Oh yes," he replied. "But I'm never happy without a job on hand. And I'm stout; I can eat a'most anything. You see no craze about me."

This tale of a drunken wife was paralleled on board by another of a drunken father. He was a capable man, with a good chance in life; but he had drunk up two thriving businesses like a bottle of sherry, and involved his sons along with him in ruin. Now they were on board with us, fleeing his disastrous neighbourhood.

Total abstinence, like all ascetical conclusions, is unfriendly to the most generous, cheerful, and human parts of man; but it could have adduced many instances and arguments from among our ship's company. I was one day conversing with a kind and happy Scotsman, running to fat and perspiration in the physical, but with a taste for poetry and a genial sense of fun. I had asked him his hopes in emigrating. They were like those of so many others, vague and unfounded; times were bad at home; they were said to have a turn for the better in the States; and a man could get on anywhere, he thought. That was precisely the weak point of his position; for if he could get on in America, why could he not do the same in Scotland? But I never had the courage to use that argument, though it was often on the tip of my tongue, and instead I agreed with him heartily, adding, with reckless originality, "If the man stuck to his work, and kept away from drink."

"Ah!" said he slowly, "the drink! You see, that's just my trouble."

He spoke with a simplicity that was touching, look-ing at me at the same time with something strange and timid in his eye, half-ashamed, half-sorry, like a good child who knows he should be beaten. You would have said he recognised a destiny to which he was born, and accepted the consequences mildly. Like the merchant Abudah,[1] he was at the same time fleeing from his destiny and carrying it along with him, the whole at an expense of six guineas.

As far as I saw, drink, idleness, and incompetency were the three great causes of emigration, and for all of them, and drink first and foremost, this trick of getting transported overseas appears to me the silliest means of cure. You cannot run away from a weakness; you must some time fight it out or perish; and if that be so, why not now, and where you stand? *Cœlum non animam.*[2] Change Glenlivet for Bourbon, and it is still whisky, only not so good. A sea-voyage will not give a man the nerve to put aside cheap pleasure; emigration has to be done before we climb the vessel; an aim in life is the

---

[1] A rich merchant in the Rev. James Ridley's *Tales of the Genii,* who, seeking a talisman for perfect happiness, finds it in love of God and submission to His will.

[2] *Cœlum non animum mutant qui trans mare currunt,* "Those who cross the sea change only the climate, not their character," a quota-tion from Horace.

only fortune worth the finding; and it is not to be found in foreign lands, but in the heart itself.

Speaking generally, there is no vice of this kind more contemptible than another; for each is but a result and outward sign of a soul tragically shipwrecked. In the majority of cases, cheap pleasure is resorted to by way of anodyne. The pleasure-seeker sets forth upon life with high and difficult ambitions; he meant to be nobly good and nobly happy, though at as little pains as possible to himself; and it is because all has failed in his celestial enterprise that you now behold him rolling in the garbage. Hence the comparative success of the tee-total pledge; because to a man who had nothing it sets at least a negative aim in life. Somewhat as prisoners beguile their days by taming a spider, the reformed drunkard makes an interest out of abstaining from intoxicating drinks, and may live for that negation. There is something, at least, *not to be done* each day; and a cold triumph awaits him every evening.

We had one on board with us, whom I have already referred to under the name of Mackay, who seemed to me not only a good instance of this failure in life of which we have been speaking, but a good type of the intelligence which here surrounded me. Physically he was a small Scotsman, standing a little back as though he were already carrying the elements of a corporation, and his looks somewhat marred by the smallness of his eyes. Mentally, he was endowed above the average. There were but few subjects on which he could not converse with understanding and a dash of wit; delivering himself slowly and with gusto, like a man who enjoyed his own sententiousness. He was a dry, quick, pertinent debater, speaking with a small voice, and swinging on his heels to launch and emphasise an argument. When he began a discussion, he could not bear to leave it off, but would pick the subject to the bone, without once relinquishing a point. An engineer by trade, Mackay believed in the unlimited perfectibility of all machines except the human machine. The latter he gave up with ridicule for a compound of carrion and perverse gases. He had an appetite for disconnected facts which I can only compare to the savage taste for beads. What is called information was indeed a passion with the man, and he not only delighted to receive it, but could pay you back in kind.

With all these capabilities, here was Mackay, already no longer young, on his way to a new country, with no prospects, no money, and but little hope. He was almost tedious in the cynical disclosures of his despair. "The ship may go down for me," he would say, "now or to-morrow. I have nothing to lose and nothing to hope." And again: "I am sick of the whole damned performance." He was, like the kind little man already quoted, another so-called victim of the bottle. But Mackay was miles from publishing his weakness to the world; laid the blame of his failure on corrupt masters and a corrupt State policy; and after he had been one night overtaken and had played the buffoon in his cups, sternly, though not without tact, suppressed all reference to his escapade. It was a treat to see him manage this; the various jesters withered under his gaze, and you were forced to recognise in him a certain steely force, and a gift of command which might have ruled a senate.

In truth it was not whisky that had ruined him; he was ruined long before for all good human purposes but conversation. His eyes were sealed by a cheap, schoolbook materialism. He could see nothing in the world out money and steam-engines. He did not know what you meant by the word happiness. He had forgotten the simple emotions of childhood, and perhaps never encountered the delights of youth. He believed in production, that useful figment of economy, as if it had been real like laughter; and production, without prejudice to liquor, was his god and guide. One day he took me to task—a novel cry to me—upon the overpayment of literature. Literary men, he said, were more highly paid than artisans; yet the artisan made threshing-machines and butter-churns, and the man of letters, except in the way of a few useful hand-books, made nothing worth the while. He produced a mere fancy article. Mackay's notion of a book was *Hoppus's Measurer*. Now in my time I have possessed and even studied that work; but if I were to be left to-morrow on Juan Fernandez,[1] Hoppus's is not the book that I should choose for my companion volume.

I tried to fight the point with Mackay. I made him own that he had taken pleasure in reading books otherwise, to his view, insignificant; but he was too wary to advance a step beyond the admission. It was in vain for me to argue that here was pleasure ready-made and running from the spring, whereas his ploughs and butter-churns were but means and mechanisms to give men the necessary food and leisure before they start upon the search for pleasure; he jibbed and ran away from such conclusions. The thing was different, he declared, and nothing was serviceable but what had to do with food. "Eat, eat, eat!" he cried; "that's the bottom and the top." By an odd irony of circumstance, he grew so much interested in this discussion that he let the hour slip by unnoticed and had to go without his tea. He had enough sense and humour, indeed he had no lack of either, to have chuckled over this himself in private; and even to me he referred to it with the shadow of a smile.

[1] A lonely island in the South Pacific, where Alexander Selkirk, the supposed original of Robinson Crusoe, remained alone for four years.

Mackay was a hot bigot. He would not hear of religion. I have seen him waste hours of time in argument with all sort of poor human creatures who understood neither him nor themselves, and he had had the
boyishness to dissect and criticise even so small a matter as the riddler's definition of mind. He snorted aloud
with zealotry and the lust for intellectual battle. Anything, whatever it was, that seemed to him likely to dis-
courage the continued passionate production of corn and
steam-engines he resented like a conspiracy against the
people. Thus, when I put in the plea for literature, that
it was only in good books, or in the society of the good,
that a man could get help in his conduct, he declared I
was in a different world from him. "Damn my conduct!" said he. "I have given it up for a bad job. My
question is, 'Can I drive a nail?'" And he plainly
looked upon me as one who was insidiously seeking to
reduce the people's annual bellyful of corn and steam-
engines.

It may be argued that these opinions spring from the
defect of culture; that a narrow and pinching way of life
not only exaggerates to a man the importance of material conditions, but indirectly, by denying him the necessary books and leisure, keeps his mind ignorant of larger
thoughts; and that hence springs this overwhelming concern about diet, and hence the bald view of existence professed by Mackay. Had this been an English peasant
the conclusion would be tenable. But Mackay had
most of the elements of a liberal education. He had
skirted metaphysical and mathematical studies. He had
a thoughtful hold of what he knew, which would be exceptional among bankers. He had been brought up in
the midst of hot-house piety, and told, with incongruous pride, the story of his own brother's death-bed ecstasies. Yet he had somehow failed to fulfil himself,

and was adrift like a dead thing among external circumstances, without hope or lively preference or shaping aim. And further, there seemed a tendency among many of his fellows to fall into the same blank and unlovely opinions. One thing, indeed, is not to be learned in Scotland, and that is the way to be happy. Yet that is the whole of culture, and perhaps two-thirds of morality. Can it be that the Puritan school, by divorcing a man from nature, by thinning out his instincts, and setting a stamp of its disapproval on whole fields of human activity and interest, leads at last directly to material greed?

Nature is a good guide through life, and the love of simple pleasures next, if not superior, to virtue; and we had on board an Irishman who based his claim to the widest and most affectionate popularity precisely upon these two qualities, that he was natural and happy. He boasted a fresh colour, a tight little figure, unquenchable gaiety, and indefatigable good-will. His clothes puzzled the diagnostic mind, until you heard he had been once a private coachman, when they became eloquent and seemed a part of his biography. His face contained the rest, and, I fear, a prophecy of the future; the hawk's nose above accorded so ill with the pink baby's mouth below. His spirit and his pride belonged, you might say, to the nose; while it was the general shiftlessness expressed by the other that had thrown him from situation to situation, and at length on board the emigrant ship. Barney ate, so to speak, nothing from the galley; his own tea, butter and eggs supported him throughout the voyage; and about mealtime you might often find him up to the elbows in amateur cookery. His was the first voice heard singing among all the passengers; he was the first who fell to dancing. From Loch Foyle to Sandy Hook, there was not a piece of fun undertaken but there was Barney in the midst.

You ought to have seen him when he stood up to sing at our concerts—his tight little figure stepping to and fro, and his feet shuffling to the air, his eyes seeking and bestowing encouragement—and to have enjoyed the bow, so nicely calculated between jest and earnest, between grace and clumsiness, with which he brought each song to a conclusion. He was not only a great favourite among ourselves, but his songs attracted the lords of the saloon, who often leaned to hear him over the rails of the hurricane-deck. He was somewhat pleased, but not at all abashed by this attention; and one night, in the midst of his famous performance of "Billy Keogh," I saw him spin half round in a pirouette and throw an audacious wink to an old gentleman above.

This was the more characteristic, as, for all his daffing[1], he was a modest and very polite little fellow among ourselves.

He would not have hurt the feelings of a fly, nor throughout the passage did he give a shadow of offence; yet he was always, by his innocent freedoms and love of fun, brought upon that narrow margin where politeness must be natural to walk without a fall. He was once seriously angry, and that in a grave, quiet manner, because they supplied no fish on Friday; for Barney was a conscientious Catholic. He had likewise strict notions of refinement; and when, late one evening, after the women had retired, a young Scotsman struck up an indecent song, Barney's drab clothes were immediately missing from the group. His taste was for the society of gentlemen, of whom, with the reader's permission, there was no lack in our five steerages and second cabin; and he avoided the rough and positive with a girlish shrinking. Mackay, partly from his superior powers of mind, which rendered him incomprehensible, partly

[1] Foolish gaiety.

from his extreme opinions, was especially distasteful to the Irishman. I have seen him slink off with backward looks of terror and offended delicacy, while the other, in his witty, ugly way, had been professing hostility to God, and an extreme theatrical readiness to be shipwrecked on the spot. These utterances hurt the little coachman's modesty like a bad word.

## THE SICK MAN

One night Jones, the young O'Reilly, and myself were walking arm-in-arm and briskly up and down the deck. Six bells had rung; a head-wind blew chill and fitful, the fog was closing in with a sprinkle of rain, and the fog-whistle had been turned on, and now divided time with its unwelcome outcries, loud like a bull, thrilling and intense like a mosquito. Even the watch lay somewhere snugly out of sight.

For some time we observed something lying black and huddled in the scuppers, which at last heaved a little and moaned aloud. We ran to the rails. An elderly man, but whether passenger or seaman it was impossible in the darkness to determine, lay grovelling on his belly in the wet scuppers, and kicking feebly with his outspread toes. We asked him what was amiss, and he replied incoherently, with a strange accent and in a voice unmanned by terror, that he had cramp in the stomach, that he had been ailing all day, had seen the doctor twice, and had walked the deck against fatigue till he was overmastered and had fallen where we found him.

Jones remained by his side, while O'Reilly and I hurried off to seek the doctor. We knocked in vain at the doctor's cabin; there came no reply; nor could we find any one to guide us. It was no time for delicacy; so we ran once more forward; and I, whipping up a ladder and touching my hat to the officer of the watch, addressed him as politely as I could:

"I beg your pardon, sir; but there is a man lying bad with cramp in the lee scuppers; and I can't find the doctor."

He looked at me peeringly in the darkness; and then, somewhat harshly, "Well, *I* can't leave the bridge, my man," said he.

"No, sir; but you can tell me what to do," I returned.

"Is it one of the crew?" he asked.

"I believe him to be a fireman," I replied.

I daresay officers are much annoyed by complaints and alarmist information from their freight of human creatures; but certainly, whether it was the idea that the sick man was one of the crew, or from something conciliatory in my address, the officer in question was immediately relieved and mollified; and speaking in a voice much freer from constraint, advised me to find a steward and despatch him in quest of the doctor, who would now be in the smoking-room over his pipe.

One of the stewards was often enough to be found about this hour down our companion, Steerage No. 2 and 3; that was his smoking-room of a night. Let me call him Blackwood. O'Reilly and I rattled down the companion, breathing hurry; and in his shirt-sleeves and perched across the carpenter's bench upon one thigh, found Blackwood; a neat, bright, dapper, Glasgow-looking man, with a bead of an eye and a rank twang in his speech. I forget who was with him, but the pair were enjoying a deliberate talk over their pipes. I dare say he was tired with his day's work, and eminently comfortable at that moment; and the truth is, I did not stop to consider his feelings, but told my story in a breath.

"Steward," said I, "there's a man lying bad with cramp, and I can't find the doctor."

He turned upon me as pert as a sparrow, but with a black look that is the prerogative of man; and taking his pipe out of his mouth——

"That's none of my business," said he. "I don't care."

I could have strangled the little ruffian where he sat. The thought of his cabin civility and cabin tips filled me with indignation. I glanced at O'Reilly; he was pale and quivering, and looked like assault and battery, every inch of him. But we had a better card than violence.

"You will have to make it your business," said I, "for I am sent to you by the officer on the bridge."

Blackwood was fairly tripped. He made no answer, but put out his pipe, gave me one murderous look, and set off upon his errand strolling. From that day forward, I should say, he improved to me in courtesy, as though he had repented his evil speech and were anxious to leave a better impression.

When we got on deck again, Jones was still beside the sick man; and two or three late stragglers had gathered round and were offering suggestions. One proposed to give the patient water, which was promptly negatived. Another bade us hold him up; he himself prayed to be let lie; but as it was at least as well to keep him off the streaming decks, O'Reilly and I supported him between us. It was only by main force that we did so, and neither an easy nor an agreeable duty; for he fought in his paroxysms like a frightened child, and moaned miserably when he resigned himself to our control.

"O let me lie!" he pleaded. "I'll no' get better anyway." And then, with a moan that went to my heart, "O why did I come upon this miserable journey?"

I was reminded of the song which I had heard a little

while before in the close, tossing steerage: "O why left I my hame?"

Meantime Jones, relieved of his immediate charge, had gone off to the galley, where we could see a light. There he found a belated cook scouring pans by the radiance of two lanterns, and one of these he sought to borrow. The scullion was backward. "Was it one of the crew?" he asked. And when Jones, smitten with my theory, had assured that it was a fireman, he reluctantly left his scouring and came towards us at an easy pace, with one of the lanterns swinging from his finger. The light, as it reached the spot, showed us an elderly man, thick-set, and grizzled with years; but the shifting and coarse shadows concealed from us the expression and even the design of his face.

So soon as the cook set eyes on him he gave a sort of whistle.

"*It's only a passenger!*" said he; and turning about, made, lantern and all, for the galley.

"He's a man anyway," cried Jones in indignation.

"Nobody said he was a woman," said a gruff voice, which I recognised for that of the bo's'un.

All this while there was no word of Blackwood or the doctor; and now the officer came to our side of the ship and asked, over the hurricane-deck rails, if the doctor were not yet come. We told him not.

"No?" he repeated with a breathing of anger; and we saw him hurry aft in person.

Ten minutes after the doctor made his appearance deliberately enough and examined our patient with the lantern. He made little of the case, had the man brought aft to the dispensary, dosed him, and sent him forward to his bunk. Two of his neighbours in the steerage had now come to our assistance, expressing loud sorrow that such "a fine cheery body" should be sick; and these, claiming a sort of possession, took him entirely under their own care. The drug had probably relieved him, for he struggled no more, and was led along plaintive and patient, but protesting. His heart recoiled at the thought of the steerage. "O let me lie down upon the bieldy[1] side," he cried; "O dinna take me down!" And again: "O why did ever I come upon this miserable voyage?" And yet once more, with a gasp and a wailing prolongation of the fourth word: "I had no *call* to come." But there he was, and by the doctor's orders and the kind force of his two shipmates disappeared down the companion of Steerage No. 1 into the den allotted him.

At the foot of our own companion, just where I found Blackwood, Jones and the bo's'un were now engaged in talk. This last was a gruff, cruel-looking seaman, who must have passed near half a century upon the seas; square-headed, goat-bearded, with heavy blond eyebrows, and an eye without radiance, but inflexibly steady and hard. I had not forgotten his rough speech; but I remembered also that he had helped us about the lantern; and now seeing him in conversation with Jones, and being choked with indignation, I proceeded to blow off my steam.

"Well," said I, "I make you my compliments upon your steward," and furiously narrated what had happened.

"I've nothing to do with him," replied the bo's'un. "They're all alike. They wouldn't mind if they saw you all lying dead one upon the top of another."

This was enough. A very little humanity went a long way with me after the experience of the evening. A sympathy grew up at once between the bo's'un and myself; and that night, and during the next few days, I learned to appreciate him better. He was a remarkable type, and not at all the kind of man you find in

[1] Sheltered.

books. He had been at Sebastopol[1] under English colours; and again in a States ship, "after the *Alabama*,[2] and praying God we shouldn't find her." He was a high Tory and a high Englishman. No manufacturer could have held opinions more hostile to the working-man and his strikes. "The workmen," he said, "think nothing of their country. They think of nothing but themselves. They're damned greedy, selfish fellows." He would not hear of the decadence of England. "They say they send us beef from America," he argued; "but who pays for it? All the money in the world's in England." The Royal Navy was the best of possible services, according to him. "Anyway the officers are gentlemen," said he; "and you can't get hazed to death by a damned non-commissioned —— as you can in the army." Among nations, England was the first; then came France. He respected the French navy and liked the French people; and if he were forced to make a new choice in life, "by God, he would try Frenchmen!" For all his looks and rough, cold manners, I observed that children were never frightened by him; they divined him at once to be a friend; and one night when he had chalked his hand and went about stealthily setting his mark on people's clothes, it was incongruous to hear this formidable old salt chuckling over his boyish monkey trick.

In the morning, my first thought was of the sick man. I was afraid I should not recognise him, so baffling had been the light of the lantern; and found myself unable to decide if he were Scots, English, or Irish. He had certainly employed north-country words and elisions; but the accent and the pronunciation seemed unfamiliar and incongruous in my ear.

---

[1] A Russian fortress, chief storm-centre of the Crimean war.
[2] A famous Confederate privateer which raised havoc with Northern commerce during the Civil War.

To descend on an empty stomach into Steerage No. 1, was an adventure that required some nerve. The stench was atrocious: each respiration tasted in the throat like some horrible kind of cheese; and the squalid aspect of the place was aggravated by so many people worming themselves into their clothes in the twilight of the bunks. You may guess if I was pleased, not only for him, but for myself also, when I heard that the sick man was better and had gone on deck.

The morning was raw and foggy, though the sun suffused the fog with pink and amber; the fog-horn still blew, stertorous and intermittent; and to add to the discomfort, the seamen were just beginning to wash down the decks. But for a sick man this was heaven compared to the steerage. I found him standing on the hot-water pipe, just forward of the saloon deck-house. He was smaller than I had fancied, and plain-looking; but his face was distinguished by strange and fascinating eyes, limpid grey from a distance, but, when looked into, full of changing colours and grains of gold. His manners were mild and uncompromisingly plain; and I soon saw that, when once started, he delighted to talk. His accent and language had been formed in the most natural way, since he was born in Ireland, had lived a quarter of a century on the banks of Tyne, and was married to a Scots wife. A fisherman in the season, he had fished the east coast from Fisherrow to Whitby. When the season was over, and the great boats, which required extra hands, were once drawn up on shore till the next spring, he worked as a labourer about chemical furnaces, or along the wharves unloading vessels. In this comparatively humble way of life he had gathered a competence, and could speak of his comfortable house, his hayfield, and his garden. On this ship, where so many accomplished artisans were fleeing from starvation, he was present on a pleasure trip to visit a brother in New York.

Ere he started, he informed me, he had been warned against the steerage and the steerage fare, and recommended to bring with him a ham and tea and a spice loaf. But he laughed to scorn such counsels. "*I 'm* not afraid," he had told his adviser; "*I 'll* get on for ten days. I 've not been a fisherman for nothing." For it is no light matter, as he reminded me, to be in an open boat, perhaps waist-deep with herrings, day breaking with a scowl, and for miles on every hand lee-shores, unbroken, iron-bound, surf-beat, with only here and there an anchorage where you dare not lie, or a harbour impossible to enter with the wind that blows. The life of a North Sea fisher is one long chapter of exposure and hard work and insufficient fare; and even if he makes land at some bleak fisher port, perhaps the season is bad or his boat has been unlucky, and after fifty hours' unsleeping vigilance and toil, not a shop will give him credit for a loaf of bread. Yet the steerage of the emigrant ship had been too vile for the endurance of a man thus rudely trained. He had scarce eaten since he came on board, until the day before, when his appetite was tempted by some excellent pea-soup. We were all much of the same mind on board, and beginning with myself, had dined upon pea-soup not wisely but too well; only with him the excess had been punished, perhaps because he was weakened by former abstinence, and his first meal had resulted in a cramp. He had determined to live henceforth on biscuit; and when, two months later, he should return to England, to make the passage by saloon. The second cabin, after due inquiry, he scouted as another edition of the steerage.

He spoke apologetically of his emotion when ill. "Ye see, I had no call to be here," said he; "and I thought it was by with me last night. I 've a good house at home, and plenty to nurse me, and I had no real call to leave them." Speaking of the attentions he had received from his shipmates generally, "they were all so kind," he said "that there's none to mention." And except in so far as I might share in this, he troubled me with no reference to my services.

But what affected me in the most lively manner was the wealth of this day-labourer, paying a two months' pleasure visit to the States, and preparing to return in the saloon, and the new testimony rendered by his story, not so much to the horrors of the steerage as to the habitual comfort of the working-classes. One foggy, frosty December evening, I encountered on Liberton Hill, near Edinburgh, an Irish labourer trudging homeward from the fields. Our roads lay together, and it was natural that we should fall into talk. He was covered with mud; an inoffensive, ignorant creature, who thought the Atlantic Cable was a secret contrivance of the masters the better to oppress labouring mankind; and I confess I was astonished to learn that he had nearly three hundred pounds in the bank. But this man had travelled over most of the world, and enjoyed wonderful opportunities on some American railroad, with two dollars a shift and double pay on Sunday and at night; whereas my fellow-passenger had never quitted Tyneside, and had made all that he possessed in that same accursed, down-falling England, whence skilled mechanics, engineers, millwrights, and carpenters were fleeing as from the native country of starvation.

Fitly enough, we slid off on the subject of strikes and wages and hard times. Being from the Tyne, and a man who had gained and lost in his own pocket by these fluctuations, he had much to say, and held strong opinions on the subject. He spoke sharply of the masters, and, when I led him on, of the men also. The masters had been selfish and obstructive; the men selfish, silly, and light-headed. He rehearsed to me the course of a meeting at which he had been present, and the somewhat

long discourse which he had there pronounced, calling
into question the wisdom and even the good faith of the
Union delegates; and although he had escaped himself
through flush times and starvation times with a hand-
somely provided purse, he had so little faith in either man
or master, and so profound a terror for the unerring
Nemesis of mercantile affairs, that he could think of no
hope for our country outside of a sudden and complete
political subversion.   Down must go Lords and Church
and Army; and capital, by some happy direction, must
change hands from worse to better, or England stood
condemned.   Such principles, he said, were growing
"like a seed."

From this mild, soft, domestic man, these words
sounded unusually ominous and grave.   I had heard
enough revolutionary talk among my workmen fellow-
passengers; but most of it was hot and turgid, and fell
discredited from the lips of unsuccessful men.   This man
was calm; he had attained prosperity and ease; he dis-
approved the policy which had been pursued by labour
in the past; and yet this was his panacea,—to rend the
old country from end to end, and from top to bottom,
and in clamour and civil discord remodel it with the hand
of violence.

## THE STOWAWAYS

On the Sunday, among a party of men who were talking in our companion, Steerage Nos. 2 and 3, we remarked
a new figure.   He wore tweed clothes, well enough made
if not very fresh, and a plain smoking-cap.   His face was
pale, with pale eyes, and spiritedly enough designed;
but though not yet thirty, a sort of blackguardly degen-
eration had already overtaken his features.   The fine
nose had grown fleshy towards the point, the pale eyes

were sunk in fat. His hands were strong and elegant; his experience of life evidently varied; his speech full of pith and verve; his manners forward, but perfectly presentable. The lad who helped in the second cabin told me, in answer to a question, that he did not know who he was, but thought, "by his way of speaking, and because he was so polite, that he was some one from the saloon."

I was not so sure, for to me there was something equivocal in his air and bearing. He might have been, I thought, the son of some good family who had fallen early into dissipation and run from home. But, making early allowance, how admirable was his talk! I wish you could have heard him tell his own stories. They were so swingingly set forth, in such dramatic language, and illustrated here and there by such luminous bits of acting that they could only lose in any reproduction. There were tales of the P. and O. Company,[1] where he had been an officer; of the East Indies, where in former years he had lived lavishly; of the Royal Engineers, where he had served for a period; and of a dozen other sides of life, each introducing some vigorous thumb-nail portrait. He had the talk to himself that night, we were all so glad to listen. The best talkers usually address themselves to some particular society; there they are kings, elsewhere camp-followers, as a man may know Russian and yet be ignorant of Spanish; but this fellow had a frank, headlong power of style, and a broad, human choice of subject, that would have turned any circle in the world into a circle of hearers. He was a Homeric talker, plain, strong, and cheerful; and the things and the people of which he spoke became readily and clearly present to the minds of those who heard him. This, with a certain

[1] Peninsular and Oriental steamship line running from England to India.

added colouring of rhetoric and rodomontade, must have been the style of Burns, who equally charmed the ears of duchesses and hostlers.

Yet freely and personally as he spoke, many points remained obscure in his narration. The Engineers, for instance, was a service which he praised highly; it is true there would be trouble with the sergeants; but then the officers were gentlemen, and his own, in particular, one among ten thousand. It sounded so far exactly like an episode in the rakish, topsy-turvy life of such an one as I had imagined. But then there came incidents more doubtful, which showed an almost impudent greed after gratuities, and a truly impudent disregard for truth. And then there was the tale of his departure. He had wearied, it seems, of Woolwich, and one fine day, with a companion, slipped up to London for a spree. I have a suspicion that spree was meant to be a long one; but God disposes all things; and one morning, near Westminster Bridge, whom should he come across but the very sergeant who had recruited him at first! What followed? He himself indicated cavalierly that he had then resigned. Let us put it so. But these resignations are sometimes very trying.

At length, after having delighted us for hours, he took himself away from the companion; and I could ask Mackay who and what he was. "That?" said Mackay. "Why, that's one of the stowaways."

"No man," said the same authority, "who has had anything to do with the sea, would ever think of paying for a passage." I give the statement as Mackay's, without endorsement; yet I am tempted to believe that it contains a grain of truth; and if you add that the man shall be impudent and thievish, or else dead-broke, it may even pass for a fair representation of the facts. We gentlemen of England who live at home at ease have, I suspect, very insufficient ideas on the subject. All the world over, people are stowing away in coal-holes and dark corners, and when ships are once out to sea, appearing again, begrimed and bashful, upon deck. The career of these sea-tramps partakes largely of the adventurous. They may be poisoned by coal-gas, or die by starvation in their place of concealment; or when found they may be clapped at once and ignominiously into irons, thus to be carried to their promised land, the port of destination, and alas! brought back in the same way to that from which they started, and there delivered over to the magistrates and the seclusion of a county jail. Since I crossed the Atlantic, one miserable stowaway was found in a dying state among the fuel, uttered but a word or two, and departed for a farther country than America.

When the stowaway appears on deck, he has but one thing to pray for: that he be set to work, which is the price and sign of his forgiveness. After half an hour with a swab or a bucket, he feels himself as secure as if he had paid for his passage. It is not altogether a bad thing for the company, who get more or less efficient hands for nothing but a few plates of junk and duff; and every now and again find themselves better paid than by a whole family of cabin passengers. Not long ago, for instance, a packet was saved from nearly certain loss by the skill and courage of a stowaway engineer. As was no more than just, a handsome subscription rewarded him for his success; but even without such exceptional good fortune, as things stand in England and America, the stowaway will often make a good profit out of his adventure. Four engineers stowed away last summer on the same ship, the *Circassia;* and before two days after their arrival each of the four had found a comfortable berth. This was the most hopeful tale of emigration that I heard from first to last; and as you see, the luck was for stowaways.

My curiosity was much inflamed by what I heard; and the next morning, as I was making the round of the ship, I was delighted to find the ex-Royal Engineer engaged in washing down the white paint of a deck house. There was another fellow at work beside him, a lad not more than twenty, in the most miraculous tatters, his handsome face sown with grains of beauty and lighted up by expressive eyes. Four stowaways had been found aboard our ship before she left the Clyde, but these two had alone escaped the ignominy of being put ashore. Alick, my acquaintance of last night, was Scots by birth, and by trade a practical engineer; the other was from Devonshire, and had been to sea before the mast. Two people more unlike by training, character, and habits, it would be hard to imagine; yet here they were together, scrubbing paint.

Alick had held all sorts of good situations, and wasted many opportunities in life. I have heard him end a story with these words: "That was in my golden days, when I used finger-glasses." Situation after situation failed him; then followed the depression of trade, and for months he had hung round with other idlers, playing marbles all day in the West Park, and going home at night to tell his landlady how he had been seeking for a job. I believe this kind of existence was not unpleasant to Alick himself, and he might have long continued to enjoy idleness and a life on tick; but he had a comrade, let us call him Brown, who grew restive. This fellow was continually threatening to slip his cable for the States, and at last, one Wednesday, Glasgow was left widowed of her Brown. Some months afterwards, Alick met another old chum in Sauchiehall Street.

"By the by, Alick," said he, "I met a gentleman in New York who was asking for you."

"Who was that?" asked Alick.

"The new second engineer on board the *So-and-so,*" was the reply.

"Well, and who is he?"

"Brown, to be sure."

For Brown had been one of the fortunate quartette aboard the *Circassia*. If that was the way of it in the States, Alick thought it was high time to follow Brown's example. He spent his last day, as he put it, "reviewing the yeomanry," and the next morning says he to his landlady, "Mrs. X., I'll not take porridge to-day, please; I'll take some eggs."

"Why, have you found a job?" she asked, delighted.

"Well, yes," returned the perfidious Alick; "I think I'll start to-day."

And so, well lined with eggs, start he did, but for America. I am afraid that landlady has seen the last of him.

It was easy enough to get on board in the confusion that attends a vessel's departure; and in one of the dark corners of Steerage No. 1, flat in a bunk and with an empty stomach, Alick made the voyage from the Broomielaw to Greenock. That night the ship's yeoman pulled him out by the heels and had him before the mate. Two other stowaways had already been found and sent ashore; but by this time darkness had fallen, they were out in the middle of the estuary, and the last steamer had left them till the morning.

"Take him to the forecastle and give him a meal," said the mate, "and see and pack him off the first thing to-morrow."

In the forecastle he had supper, a good night's rest, and breakfast; and was sitting placidly with a pipe, fancying all was over and the game up for good with that ship, when one of the sailors grumbled out an oath at him, with a "What are you doing there?" and "Do you call that hiding, anyway?" There was need of no more, Alick was in another bunk before the day was older. Shortly before the passengers arrived, the ship was cursorily inspected. He heard the round come down the companion and look into one pen after another, until they came within two of the one in which he lay concealed. Into these last two they did not enter, but merely glanced from without; and Alick had no doubt that he was personally favoured in this escape. It was the character of the man to attribute nothing to luck and but little to kindness; whatever happened to him he had earned in his own right amply; favours came to him from his singular attraction and adroitness, and misfortunes he had always accepted with his eyes open. Half an hour after the searchers had departed, the steerage began to fill with legitimate passengers, and the worst of Alick's troubles was at an end. He was soon making himself popular, smoking other people's tobacco, and politely sharing their private stock of delicacies, and when night came he retired to his bunk beside the others with composure.

Next day by afternoon, Lough Foyle being already far behind, and only the rough northwestern hills of Ireland within view, Alick appeared on deck to court inquiry and decide his fate. As a matter of fact, he was known to several on board, and even intimate with one of the engineers; but it was plainly not the etiquette of such occasions for the authorities to avow their information. Every one professed surprise and anger on his appearance, and he was led prisoner before the captain.

"What have you got to say for yourself?" inquired the captain.

"Not much," said Alick, "but when a man has been a long time out of a job, he will do things he would not under other circumstances."

"Are you willing to work?"

Alick swore he was burning to be useful.

"And what can you do?" asked the captain.

He replied composedly that he was a brass-fitter by trade.

"I think you will be better at engineering?" suggested the officer, with a shrewd look.

"No, sir," says Alick simply.—"There's few can beat me at a lie," was his engaging commentary to me as he recounted the affair.

"Have you been to sea?" again asked the captain.

"I've had a trip on a Clyde steamboat, sir, but no more," replied the unabashed Alick.

"Well, we must try and find some work for you," concluded the officer.

And hence we behold Alick, clear of the hot engine-room, lazily scraping paint and now and then taking a pull upon a sheet. "You leave me alone," was his deduction. "When I get talking to a man, I can get round him."

The other stowaway, whom I will call the Devonian —it was noticeable that neither of them told his name— had both been brought up and seen the world in a much smaller way. His father, a confectioner, died and was closely followed by his mother. His sisters had taken, I think, to dress-making. He himself had returned from sea about a year ago and gone to live with his brother, who kept the "George Hotel"—"it was not quite a real hotel," added the candid fellow—"and had a hired man to mind the horses." At first the Devonian was very welcome; but as time went on his brother not unnaturally grew cool towards him, and he began to find himself one too many at the "George Hotel." "I don't think brothers care much for you," he said, as a general reflection upon life. Hurt at this change, nearly penniless, and too proud to ask for more, he set off on foot and walked eighty miles to Weymouth, living on the journey as he could. He would have enlisted, but he was too small for the army and too old for the navy; and thought himself fortunate at last to find a berth on board a trading dandy.[1] Somewhere in the Bristol Channel, the dandy sprung a leak and went down; and though the crew were picked up and brought ashore by fishermen, they found themselves with nothing but the clothes upon their back. His next engagement was scarcely better starred; for the ship proved so leaky, and frightened them all so heartily during a short passage through the Irish Sea, that the entire crew deserted and remained behind upon the quays of Belfast.

Evil days were now coming thick on the Devonian. He could find no berth in Belfast, and had to work a passage to Glasgow on a steamer. She reached the Broomielaw on a Wednesday: the Devonian had a bellyful that morning, laying in breakfast manfully to provide against the future, and set off along the quays to seek employment. But he was now not only penniless, his clothes had begun to fall in tatters; he had begun to have the look of a street Arab; and captains will have nothing to say to a ragamuffin; for in that trade, as in all others, it is the coat that depicts the man. You may hand, reef, and steer like an angel, but if you have a hole in your trousers, it is like a millstone round your neck. The Devonian lost heart at so many refusals. He had not the impudence to beg; although, as he said, "when I had money of my own, I always gave it." It was only on Saturday morning, after three whole days of starvation, that he asked a scone[2] from a milk-woman, who added of her own accord a glass of milk. He had now made

---

[1] A vessel rigged as a sloop.
[2] A thin cake of wheat or barley-meal.

up his mind to stow away, not from any desire to see America, but merely to obtain the comfort of a place in the forecastle and a supply of familiar sea-fare. He lived by begging, always from milk-women, and always scones and milk and was not once refused. It was vile wet weather, and he could never have been dry. By night he walked the streets, and by day slept upon Glasgow Green, and heard, in the intervals of his dozing, the famous theologians of the spot clear up intricate points of doctrine and appraise the merits of the clergy. He had not much instruction; he could "read bills on the street," but was "main bad at writing"; yet these theologians seem to have impressed him with a genuine sense of amusement. Why he did not go to the Sailor's Home I know not; I presume there is in Glasgow one of these institutions, which are by far the happiest and the wisest effort of contemporaneous charity; but I must stand to my author, as they say in old books, and relate the story as I heard it. In the meantime, he had tried four times to stow away in different vessels, and four times had been discovered and handed back to starvation. The fifth time was lucky; and you may judge if he were pleased to be aboard ship again, at his old work, and with duff twice a week. He was, said Alick, "a devil for the duff." Or if devil was not the word, it was one if anything stronger.

The difference in the conduct of the two was remarkable. The Devonian was as willing as any paid hand, swarmed aloft among the first, pulled his natural weight and firmly upon a rope, and found work for himself when there was none to show him. Alick, on the other hand, was not only a skulker in the grain, but took a humourous and fine gentlemanly view of the transaction. He would speak to me by the hour in ostentatious idleness; and only if the bo's'un or a mate came by. fell-to languidly for just the necessary time till they were out of sight. "I'm not breaking my heart with it," he remarked.

Once there was a hatch to be opened near where he was stationed; he watched the preparations for a second or so suspiciously, and then, "Hullo," said he, "here's some real work coming—I'm off," and he was gone that moment. Again, calculating the six guinea passage-money, and the probable duration of the passage, he remarked pleasantly that he was getting six shillings a day for this job, "and it's pretty dear to the company at that." "They are making nothing by me," was another of his observations; "they're making something by that fellow." And he pointed to the Devonian, who was just then busy to the eyes.

The more you saw of Alick, the more, it must be owned, you learned to despise him. His natural talents were of no use either to himself or others; for his character had degenerated like his face, and become pulpy and pretentious. Even his power of persuasion, which was certainly very surprising, stood in some danger of being lost or neutralised by over-confidence. He lied in an aggressive, brazen manner, like a pert criminal in the dock; and he was so vain of his own cleverness that he could not refrain from boasting, ten minutes after, of the very trick by which he had deceived you. "Why, now I have more money than when I came on board," he said one night, exhibiting a sixpence, "and yet I stood myself a bottle of beer before I went to bed yesterday. And as for tobacco, I have fifteen sticks of it." That was fairly successful indeed; yet a man of his superiority, and with a less obtrusive policy, might, who knows? have got the length of half a crown. A man who prides himself upon persuasion should learn the persuasive faculty of silence, above all as to his own misdeeds. It is only in the farce and for dramatic purposes that Scapin[1] enlarges on his peculiar talents to the world at large.

Scapin is perhaps a good name for this clever, unfortunate Alick; for at the bottom of all his misconduct there was a guiding sense of humour that moved you to forgive him. It was more than half a jest that he conducted his existence. "Oh, man," he said to me once with unusual emotion, like a man thinking of his mistress, "I would give up anything for a lark."

It was in relation to his fellow-stowaway that Alick showed the best, or perhaps I should say the only good, points of his nature. "Mind you," he said suddenly, changing his tone, "mind you that's a good boy. He wouldn't tell you a lie. A lot of them think he is a scamp because his clothes are ragged, but he isn't; he's as good as gold." To hear him, you become aware that Alick himself had a taste for virtue. He thought his own idleness and the other's industry equally becoming. He was no more anxious to insure his own reputation as a liar than to uphold the truthfulness of his companion; and he seemed unaware of what was incongruous in his attitude, and was plainly sincere in both characters.

It was not surprising that he should take an interest in the Devonian, for the lad worshipped and served him in love and wonder. Busy as he was, he would find time to warn Alick of an approaching officer, or even to tell him that the coast was clear, and he might slip off and smoke a pipe in safety. "Tom," he once said to him, for that was the name which Alick ordered him to use, "if you don't like going to the galley, I'll go for you. You ain't used to this kind of thing, you ain't. But I'm a sailor; and I can understand the feelings of any fellow, I can." Again, he was hard up, and casting about for

---

[1] A shrewd, unprincipled servant in Molière's comedy, *Les Fourberies de Scapin.*

some tobacco, for he was not so liberally used in this respect as others perhaps less worthy, when Alick offered him the half of one of his fifteen sticks. I think, for my part, he might have increased the offer to a whole one, or perhaps a pair of them, and not lived to regret his liberality. But the Devonian refused. "No," he said, "you 're a stowaway like me; I won't take it from you, I 'll take it from some one who 's not down on his luck."

It was notable in this generous lad that he was strongly under the influence of sex. If a woman passed near where he was working, his eyes lit up, his hand paused, and his mind wandered instantly to other thoughts. It was natural that he should exercise a fascination proportionally strong upon women. He begged, you will remember, from women only, and was never refused. Without wishing to explain away the charity of those who helped him, I cannot but fancy he may have owed a little to his handsome face, and to that quick, responsive nature, formed for love, which speaks eloquently through all disguises, and can stamp an impression in ten minutes' talk or an exchange of glances. He was the more dangerous in that he was far from bold, but seemed to woo in spite of himself, and with a soft and pleading eye. Ragged as he was, and many a scarecrow is in that respect more comfortably furnished, even on board he was not without some curious admirers.

There was a girl among the passengers, a tall, blonde, handsome, strapping Irishwoman, with a wild, accommodating eye, whom Alick had dubbed Tommy, with that transcendental appropriateness that defies analysis. One day the Devonian was lying for warmth in the upper stoke-hole, which stands open on the deck, when Irish Tommy came past, very neatly attired, as was her custom.

"Poor fellow," she said, stopping, "you haven't a vest."

"No," he said; "I wish I 'ad."

Then she stood and gazed on him in silence, until, in his embarrassment, for he knew not how to look under this scrutiny, he pulled out his pipe and began to fill it with tobacco.

"Do you want a match?" she asked. And before he had time to reply, she ran off and presently returned with more than one.

That was the beginning and the end, as far as our passage is concerned, of what I will make bold to call this love-affair. There are many relations which go on to marriage and last during a lifetime, in which less human feeling is engaged than in this scene of five minutes at the stoke-hole.

Rigidly speaking, this would end the chapter of the stowaways; but in a larger sense of the word I have yet more to add. Jones had discovered and pointed out to me a young woman who was remarkable among her fellows for a pleasing and interesting air. She was poorly clad, to the verge, if not over the line, of disrespectability, with a ragged old jacket and a bit of a sealskin cap no bigger than your fist; but her eyes, her whole expression, and her manner, even in ordinary moments, told of a true womanly nature, capable of love, anger, and devotion. She had a look, too, of refinement, like one who might have been a better lady than most, had she been allowed the opportunity. When alone she seemed preoccupied and sad; but she was not often alone; there was usually by her side a heavy, dull, gross man in rough clothes, chary of speech and gesture—not from caution, but poverty of disposition; a man like a ditcher, unlovely and uninteresting; whom she petted and tended and waited on with her eyes as if he had been Amadis of Gaul.[1] It was strange to see this hulking fellow dog-sick, and this

[1] A legendary hero, appearing in numerous mediæval romances.

delicate, sad woman caring for him. He seemed, from first to last, insensible of her caresses and attentions, and she seemed unconscious of his insensibility. The Irish husband, who sang his wife to sleep, and this Scottish girl serving her Orson,[1] were the two bits of human nature that most appealed to me throughout the voyage.

On the Thursday before we arrived, the tickets were collected; and soon a rumour began to go round the vessel; and this girl, with her bit of sealskin cap, became the centre of whispering and pointed fingers. She also, it was said, was a stowaway of a sort; for she was on board with neither ticket nor money; and the man with whom she travelled was the father of a family, who had left wife and children to be hers. The ship's officers discouraged the story, which may therefore have been a story and no more; but it was believed in the steerage, and the poor girl had to encounter many curious eyes from that day forth.

## PERSONAL EXPERIENCE AND REVIEW

Travel is of two kinds; and this voyage of mine across the ocean combined both. "Out of my country and myself I go," sings the old poet: and I was not only travelling out of my country in latitude and longitude, but out of myself in diet, associates, and consideration. Part of the interest and a great deal of the amusement flowed, at least to me, from this novel situation in the world.

I found that I had what they call fallen in life with absolute success and verisimilitude. I was taken for a steerage passenger; no one seemed surprised that I should be so; and there was nothing but the brass plate

---

[1] Another hero of mediæval romance. According to the story, he was carried off by a bear, and grew up rough and uncouth; hence Stevenson's point.

between decks to remind me that I had once been a gentleman. In a former book, describing a former journey, I expressed some wonder that I could be readily and naturally taken for a pedlar, and explained the accident by the difference of language and manners between England and France. I must now take a humbler view; for here I was among my own countrymen, somewhat roughly clad, to be sure, but with every advantage of speech and manner; and I am bound to confess that I passed for nearly anything you please except an educated gentleman. The sailors called me "mate," the officers addressed me as "my man," my comrades accepted me without hesitation for a person of their own character and experience, but with some curious information. One, a mason himself, believed I was a mason; several, and among these at least one of the seamen, judged me to be a petty officer in the American navy; and I was so often set down for a practical engineer that at last I had not the heart to deny it. From all these guesses I drew one conclusion, which told against the insight of my companions. They might be close observers in their own way, and read the manners in the face; but it was plain that they did not extend their observation to the hands.

To the saloon passengers also I sustained my part without a hitch. It is true I came little in their way; but when we did encounter, there was no recognition in their eye, although I confess I sometimes courted it in silence. All these, my inferiors and equals, took me, like the transformed monarch in the story, for a mere common, human man. They gave me a hard, dead look, with the flesh about the eye kept unrelaxed.

With the women this surprised me less, as I had already experimented on the sex by going abroad through a suburban part of London simply attired in a sleeve-waistcoat. The result was curious. I then learned for the first time, and by the exhaustive process, how much attention ladies are accustomed to bestow on all male creatures of their own station; for, in my humble rig, each one who went by me caused me a certain shock of surprise and a sense of something wanting.  In my normal circumstances, it appeared every young lady must have paid me some tribute of a glance; and though I had often not detected it when it was given, I was well aware of its absence when it was withheld.  My height seemed to decrease with every woman who passed me, for she passed me like a dog.  This is one of my grounds for supposing that what are called the upper classes may sometimes produce a disagreeable impression in what are called the lower; and I wish some one would continue my experiment, and find out exactly at what stage of toilette a man becomes invisible to the well-regulated female eye.

Here on shipboard the matter was put to a more complete test; for, even with the addition of speech and manner, I passed among the ladies for precisely the average man of the steerage.  It was one afternoon that I saw this demonstrated.  A very plainly dressed woman was taken ill on deck.  I think I had the luck to be present at every sudden seizure during all the passage; and on this occasion found myself in the place of importance, supporting the sufferer.  There was not only a large crowd immediately around us, but a considerable knot of saloon passengers leaning over our heads from the hurricane-deck.  One of these, an elderly managing woman, hailed me with counsels.  Of course I had to reply; and as the talk went on, I began to discover that the whole group took me for the husband.  I looked upon my new wife, poor creature, with mingled feelings; and I must own she had not even the appearance of the poorest class of city servant-maids, but looked more like a country wench who should have been employed at a roadside inn. Now was the time for me to go and study the brass plate.

To such of the officers as knew about me—the doctor, the purser, and the stewards—I appeared in the light of a broad joke. The fact that I spent the better part of my day in writing had gone abroad over the ship and tickled them all prodigiously. Whenever they met me they referred to my absurd occupation with familiarity and breadth of humorous intention. Their manner was well calculated to remind me of my fallen fortunes. You may be sincerely amused by the amateur literary efforts of a gentleman, but you scarce publish the feeling to his face. "Well!" they would say: "still writing?" And the smile would widen into a laugh. The purser came one day into the cabin, and, touched to the heart by my misguided industry, offered me some other kind of writing, "for which," he added pointedly, "you will be paid." This was nothing else than to copy out the list of passengers.

Another trick of mine which told against my reputation was my choice of roosting-place in an active draught upon the cabin floor. I was openly jeered and flouted for this eccentricity; and a considerable knot would sometimes gather at the door to see my last dispositions for the night. This was embarrassing, but I learned to support the trial with equanimity.

Indeed I may say that, upon the whole, my new position sat lightly and naturally upon my spirits. I accepted the consequences with readiness, and found them far from difficult to bear. The steerage conquered me; I conformed more and more to the type of the place, not only in manner but at heart, growing hostile to the officers and cabin passengers who looked down upon me, and day by day greedier for small delicacies. Such was the result, as I fancy, of a diet of bread and butter, soup and porridge. We think we have no sweet tooth as long as we are full to the brim of molasses; but a man must have sojourned in the workhouse before he boasts himself indifferent to dainties. Every evening, for instance, I was more and more preoccupied about our doubtful fare at tea. If it was delicate my heart was much lightened; if it was but broken fish I was proportionally downcast. The offer of a little jelly from a fellow-passenger more provident than myself caused a marked elevation in my spirits. And I would have gone to the ship's end and back again for an oyster or a chipped fruit.

In other ways I was content with my position. It seemed no disgrace to be confounded with my company; for I may as well declare at once I found their manners as gentle and becoming as those of any other class. I do not mean that my friends could have sat down without embarrassment and laughable disaster at the table of a duke. That does not imply an inferiority of breeding, but a difference of usage. Thus I flatter myself that I conducted myself well among my fellow-passengers; yet my most ambitious hope is not to have avoided faults, but to have committed as few as possible. I know too well that my tact is not the same as their tact, and that my habit of a different society constituted, not only no qualification, but a positive disability to move easily and becomingly in this. When Jones complimented me— because I "managed to behave very pleasantly" to my fellow-passengers, was how he put it—I could follow the thought in his mind, and knew his compliment to be such as we pay foreigners on their proficiency in English. I dare say this praise was given me immediately on the back of some unpardonable solecism, which had led him to review my conduct as a whole. We are all ready to laugh at the ploughman among lords; we should consider also the case of a lord among the ploughmen. I have seen a lawyer in the house of a Hebridean fisherman; and I know, but nothing will induce me to disclose, which of these two was the better gentleman. Some of our finest behaviour, though it looks well enough from the boxes, may seem even brutal to the gallery. We boast too often manners that are parochial rather than universal; that, like a country wine, will not bear transportation for a hundred miles, nor from the parlour to the kitchen. To be a gentleman is to be one all the world over, and in every relation and grade of society. It is a high calling, to which a man must first be born, and then devote himself for life. And, unhappily, the manners of a certain so-called upper grade have a kind of currency, and meet with a certain external acceptation throughout all the others, and this tends to keep us well satisfied with slight acquirements and the amateurish accomplishments of a clique. But manners, like art, should be human and central.

Some of my fellow-passengers, as I now moved among them in a relation of equality, seemed to me excellent gentlemen. They were not rough, nor hasty, nor disputatious; debated pleasantly, differed kindly; were helpful, gentle, patient, and placid. The type of manners was plain, and even heavy; there was little to please the eye, but nothing to shock; and I thought gentleness lay more nearly at the spring of behaviour than in many more ornate and delicate societies. I say delicate, where I cannot say refined; a thing may be fine, like ironwork, without being delicate, like lace. There was here less delicacy; the skin supported more callously the natural surface of events, the mind received more bravely the crude facts of human existence; but I do not think that there was less effective refinement, less consideration for others, less polite suppression of self. I speak of the best among my fellow-passengers; for in the steerage, as well as in the saloon, there is a mixture. Those, then, with whom I found myself in sympathy, and of whom I may therefore hope to write with a greater measure of truth, were not only as good in their manners, but endowed with very much the same natural capacities, and about as wise in deduction, as the bankers and barristers of what is called society. One and all were too much interested in disconnected facts, and loved information for its own sake with too rash a devotion; but people in all classes display the same appetite as they gorge themselves daily with the miscellaneous gossip of the newspaper. Newspaper reading, as far as I can make out, is often rather a sort of brown study than an act of culture. I have myself palmed off yesterday's issue on a friend, and seen him reperuse it for a continuance of minutes with an air at once refreshed and solemn. Workmen, perhaps, pay more attention; but though they may be eager listeners, they have rarely seemed to me either willing or careful thinkers. Culture is not measured by the greatness of the field which is covered by our knowledge, but by the nicety with which we can perceive relations in that field, whether great or small. Workmen, certainly those who were on board with me, I found wanting in this quality or habit of the mind. They did not perceive relations, but leaped to a so-called cause, and thought the problem settled. Thus the cause of everything in England was the form of government, and the cure for all evils was, by consequence, a revolution. It is surprising how many of them said this, and that none should have had a definite thought in his head as he said it. Some hated the Church because they disagreed with it; some hated Lord Beaconsfield because of war and taxes; all hated the masters, possibly with reason. But these feelings were not at the root of the matter; the true reasoning of their souls ran thus—I have not got on; I ought to have got on; if there was a revolution I should get on. How? They had no idea. Why? Because—because—well, look at America!

To be politically blind is no distinction; we are all so, if you come to that. At bottom, as it seems to me, there is but one question in modern home politics, though it appears in many shapes, and that is the question of money; and but one political remedy, that the people should grow wiser and better. My workmen fellow-passengers were as impatient and dull of hearing on the second of these points as any member of Parliament; but they had some glimmerings of the first. They would not hear of improvement on their part, but wished the world made over again in a crack, so that they might remain improvident and idle and debauched, and yet enjoy the comfort and respect that should accompany the opposite virtues; and it was in this expectation, as far as I could see, that many of them were now on their way to America. But on the point of money they saw clearly enough that inland politics, so far as they were concerned, were reducible to the question of annual income; a question which should long ago have been settled by a revolution, they did not know how, and which they were now about to settle for themselves, once more they knew not how, by crossing the Atlantic in a steamship of considerable tonnage.

And yet it has been amply shown them that the second or income question is in itself nothing, and may as well be left undecided, if there be no wisdom and virtue to profit by the change. It is not by a man's purse, but by his character, that he is rich or poor. Barney will be poor, Alick will be poor, Mackay will be poor; let them go where they will, and wreck all the governments under heaven, they will be poor until they die.

Nothing is perhaps more notable in the average work-man than his surprising idleness, and the candour with which he confesses to the failing. It has to me been always something of a relief to find the poor, as a general rule, so little oppressed with work. I can in consequence enjoy my own more fortunate beginning with a better grace. The other day I was living with a farmer in America, an old frontiersman, who had worked and fought, hunted and farmed, from his childhood up. He excused himself for his defective education on the ground that he had been overworked from first to last. Even now, he said, anxious as he was, he had never the time to take up a book. In consequence of this, I observed him closely; he was occupied for four or, at the extreme outside, for five hours out of the twenty-four, and then principally in walking; and the remainder of the day he passed in born idleness, either eating fruit or standing with his back against a door. I have known men do hard literary work all morning, and then undergo quite as much physical fatigue by way of relief as satisfied this powerful frontiersman for the day. He, at least, like all the educated class, did so much homage to industry as to persuade himself he was industrious. But the average mechanic recognises his idleness with effrontery; he has even, as I am told, organized it.

I give the story as it was told me, and it was told me for a fact. A man fell from a housetop in the city of Aberdeen, and was brought into hospital with broken bones. He was asked what was his trade, and replied that he was a *tapper*. No one had ever heard of such a thing before; the officials were filled with curiosity; they besought an explanation. It appeared that when a party of slaters were engaged upon a roof, they would now and then be taken with a fancy for the public-house. Now a seamstress, for example, might slip away from her work and no one be the wiser; but if these fellows adjourned, the tapping of the mallets would cease, and thus the neighbourhood be advertised of their defection. Hence the career of the tapper. He has to do the tapping and keep up an industrious bustle on the housetop during the absence of the slaters. When he taps for only one or two the thing is child's-play, but when he has to represent a whole troop, it is then that he earns his money in the sweat of his brow. Then must he bound from spot to spot, reduplicate, triplicate, sexduplicate his single personality, and swell and hasten his blows, until he produce a perfect illusion for the ear, and you would swear that a crowd of emulous masons were continuing merrily to roof the house. It must be a strange sight from an upper window.

I heard nothing on board of the tapper; but I was astonished at the stories told by my companions. Skulking, shirking, malingering, were all established tactics, it appeared. They could see no dishonesty where a man who is paid for an hour's work gives half an hour's consistent idling in its place. Thus the tapper would refuse to watch for the police during a burglary, and call himself an honest man. It is not sufficiently recognised that our race detests to work. If I thought that I should have to work every day of my life as hard as I am working now, I should be tempted to give up the struggle. And the workman early begins on his career of toil. He has never had his fill of holidays in the past, and his prospect of holidays in the future is both distant and uncertain. In the circumstances, it would require a high degree of virtue not to snatch alleviations for the moment.

There were many good talkers on the ship; and I believe good talking of a certain sort is a common accomplishment among working-men. Where books are comparatively scarce, a greater amount of information will be given and received by word of mouth; and this tends to produce good taikers, and, what is no less needful for conversation, good listeners. They could all tell a story with effect. I am sometimes tempted to think that the less literary class show always better in narration; they have so much more patience with detail, are so much less hurried to reach the points, and preserve so much juster a proportion among the facts. At the same time their talk is dry; they pursue a topic ploddingly, have not an agile fancy, do not throw sudden lights from unexpected quarters, and when the talk is over they often leave the matter where it was. They mark time instead of marching. They think only to argue, not to reach new conclusions, and use their reason rather as a weapon of offence than as a tool for self-improvement. Hence the talk of some of the cleverest was unprofitable in result, because there was no give and take; they would grant you as little as possible for premise, and begin to dispute under an oath to conquer or to die.

But the talk of a workman is apt to be more interesting than that of a wealthy merchant, because the thoughts, hopes, and fears of which the workman's life is built lie nearer to necessity and nature. They are more immediate to human life. An income calculated by the week is a far more human thing than one calculated by the year, and a small income, simply from its smallness, than a large one. I never wearied listening to the details of a workman's economy, because every item stood for some real pleasure. If he could afford pudding twice a week, you know that twice a week the man ate with genuine gusto and was physically happy; while if you learn that a rich man has seven courses a day, ten to one the half of them remain untasted, and the whole is but misspent money and a weariness to the flesh.

The difference between England and America to a

working-man was thus most humanly put to me by a fellow-passenger: "In America," said he, "you get pies and puddings." I do not hear enough, in economy books, of pies and pudding. A man lives in and for the delicacies, adornments, and accidental attributes of life, such as pudding to eat and pleasant books and theatres to occupy his leisure. The bare terms of existence would be rejected with contempt by all. If a man feeds on bread and butter, soup and porridge, his appetite grows wolfish after dainties. And the workman dwells in a borderland, and is always within sight of those cheerless regions where life is more difficult to sustain than worth sustaining. Every detail of our existence, where it is worth while to cross the ocean after pie and pudding, is made alive and enthralling by the presence of genuine desire; but it is all one to me whether Crœsus has a hundred or a thousand thousands in the bank. There is more adventure in the life of the working-man who descends as a common soldier into the battle of life, than in that of the millionaire who sits apart in an office, like Von Moltke,[1] and only directs the manœuvres by telegraph. Give me to hear about the career of him who is in the thick of the business; to whom one change of market means an empty belly, and another a copious and savoury meal. This is not the philosophical, but the human side of economics; it interests like a story; and the life of all who are thus situated partakes in a small way of the charm of *Robinson Crusoe;* for every step is critical, and human life is presented to you naked and verging to its lowest terms.

[1] Germany's foremost strategist in the Franco-Prussian war (1870–1871).

## NEW YORK

As we drew near to New York I was at first amused, and then somewhat staggered, by the cautious and the grisly tales that went the round. You would have thought we were to land upon a cannibal island. You must speak to no one in the streets, as they would not leave you till you were rooked and beaten. You must enter a hotel with military precautions; for the least you had to apprehend was to awake next morning without money or baggage, or necessary raiment, a lone forked radish in a bed; and if the worst befell, you would instantly and mysteriously disappear from the ranks of mankind.

I have usually found such stories correspond to the least modicum of fact. Thus I was warned, I remember, against the roadside inns of the Cévennes,[1] and that by a learned professor; and when I reached Pradelles the warning was explained—it was but the far-away rumour and reduplication of a single terrifying story already half a century old, and half forgotten in the theatre of the events. So I was tempted to make light of these reports against America. But we had on board with us a man whose evidence it would not do to put aside. He had come near these perils in the body; he had visited a robber inn. The public has an old and well-grounded favour for this class of incident, and shall be gratified to the best of my power.

My fellow-passenger, whom we shall call M'Naughten, had come from New York to Boston with a comrade, seeking work. They were a pair of rattling blades; and, leaving their baggage at the station, passed the day in

---

[1] A mountain range in Southern France through which Stevenson had already taken the trip described in *Travels with a Donkey*.

beer-saloons, and with congenial spirits, until midnight struck. Then they applied themselves to find a lodging, and walked the streets till two, knocking at houses of entertainment and being refused admittance, or themselves declining the terms. By two the inspiration of their liquor had begun to wear off; they were weary and humble, and after a great circuit found themselves in the same street where they had begun their search, and in front of a French hotel where they had already sought accommodation. Seeing the house still open, they returned to the charge. A man in a white cap sat in an office by the door. He seemed to welcome them more warmly than when they had first presented themselves, and the charge for the night had somewhat unaccountably fallen from a dollar to a quarter. They thought him ill-looking, but paid their quarter apiece, and were shown upstairs to the top of the house. There, in a small room, the man in the white cap wished them pleasant slumbers.

It was furnished with a bed, a chair, and some conveniences. The door did not lock on the inside; and the only sign of adornment was a couple of framed pictures, one close above the head of the bed, and the other opposite the foot, and both curtained, as we may sometimes see valuable water-colours, or the portraits of the dead, or works of art more than usually skittish in the subject. It was perhaps in the hope of finding something of this last description that M'Naughten's comrade pulled aside the curtain of the first. He was startlingly disappointed. There was no picture. The frame surrounded, and the curtain was designed to hide, an oblong aperture in the partition, through which they looked forth into the dark corridor. A person standing without could easily take a purse from under the pillow, or even strangle a sleeper as he lay abed. M'Naughten and his comrade stared at each other like Vasco's seamen, "with a wild surmise;"[1] and then the latter, catching up the lamp, ran to the other frame and roughly raised the curtain. There he stood, petrified; and M'Naughten, who had followed, grasped him by the wrist in terror. They could see into another room, larger in size than that which they occupied, where three men sat crouching and silent in the dark. For a second or so these five persons looked each other in the eyes, then the curtain was dropped, and M'Naughten and his friend made but one bolt of it out of the room and downstairs. The man in the white cap said nothing as they passed him; and they were so pleased to be once more in the open night that they gave up all notion of a bed, and walked the streets of Boston till the morning.

No one seemed much cast down by these stories, but all inquired after the address of a respectable hotel; and I, for my part, put myself under the conduct of Mr. Jones. Before noon of the second Sunday we sighted the low shores outside of New York harbour; the steerage passengers must remain on board to pass through Castle Garden[2] on the following morning; but we of the second cabin made our escape along with the lords of the saloon; and by six o'clock Jones and I issued into West Street, sitting on some straw in the bottom of an open baggage-wagon. It rained miraculously; and from that moment till on the following night I left New York, there was scarce a lull, and no cessation of the downpour. The roadways were flooded; a loud strident noise of falling water filled the air; the restaurants smelt heavily of wet people and wet clothing.

It took us but a few minutes, though it cost us a good deal of money, to be rattled along West Street to our

---

[1] An erroneous reference to Keats' *Sonnet on First Looking into Chapman's Homer*, which describes Cortes' (not Vasco's) first view of the Pacific.

[2] Formerly the regular landing place for immigrants.

destination: "Reunion House, No 10 West Street, one minute's walk from Castle Garden; convenient to Castle Garden, the Steamboat Landings, California Steamers and Liverpool Ships; Board and Lodging per day 1 dollar, single meals 25 cents, lodging per night 25 cents; private rooms for families; no charge for storage or baggage; satisfaction guaranteed to all persons; Michael Mitchell, Proprietor." Reunion House was, I may go the length of saying, a humble hostelry. You entered through a long bar-room, thence passed into a little dining-room, and thence into a still smaller kitchen. The furniture was of the plainest; but the bar was hung in the American taste, with encouraging and hospitable mottoes.

Jones was well known; we were received warmly; and two minutes afterwards I had refused a drink from the proprietor, and was going on, in my plain European fashion, to refuse a cigar, when Mr. Mitchell sternly interposed, and explained the situation. He was offering to treat me, it appeared; whenever an American bar-keeper proposes anything, it must be borne in mind that he is offering to treat; and if I did not want a drink, I must at least take the cigar. I took it bashfully, feeling I had begun my American career on the wrong foot. I did not enjoy that cigar; but this may have been from a variety of reasons, even the best cigar often failing to please if you smoke three-quarters of it in a drenching rain.

For many years America was to me a sort of promised land; "westward the march of empire holds its way"; the race is for the moment to the young; what has been and what is we imperfectly and obscurely know; what is to be yet lies beyond the flight of our imaginations. Greece, Rome and Judæa are gone by forever, leaving to generations the legacy of their accomplished work; China still endures, an old-inhabited house in the brand-new city of nations; England has already declined, since she has lost the States; and to these States, therefore, yet undeveloped, full of dark possibilities, and grown, like another Eve, from one rib out of the side of their own old land, the minds of young men in England turn naturally at a certain hopeful period of their age. It will be hard for an American to understand the spirit. But let him imagine a young man, who shall have grown up in an old and rigid circle, following bygone fashions and taught to distrust his own fresh instincts, and who now suddenly hears of a family of cousins, all about his own age, who keep house together by themselves and live far from restraint and tradition; let him imagine this, and he will have some imperfect notion of the sentiment with which spirited English youths turn to the thought of the American Republic. It seems to them as if, out west, the war of life was still conducted in the open air, and on free barbaric terms; as if it had not yet been narrowed into parlours, nor begun to be conducted, like some unjust and dreary arbitration, by compromise, costume, forms of procedure, and sad, senseless self-denial. Which of these two he prefers, a man with any youth still left in him will decide rightly for himself. He would rather be houseless than denied a pass-key; rather go without food than partake of a stalled ox in stiff, respectable society; rather be shot out of hand than direct his life according to the dictates of the world.

He knows or thinks nothing of the Maine Laws, the Puritan sourness, the fierce, sordid appetite for dollars, or the dreary existence of country towns. A few wild story-books which delighted his childhood form the imaginative basis of his picture of America. In course of time, there is added to this a great crowd of stimulating details—vast cities that grow up as by enchantment;

the birds, that have gone south in autumn, returning with the spring to find thousands camped upon their marshes, and the lamps burning far and near along populous streets; forests that disappear like snow; countries larger than Britain that are cleared and settled, one man running forth with his household gods before another, while the bear and the Indian are yet scarce aware of their approach; oil that gushes from the earth; gold that is washed or quarried in the brooks or glens of the Sierras; and all that bustle, courage, action, and constant kaleidoscopic change that Walt Whitman has seized and set forth in his vigorous, cheerful, and loquacious verses.

Here I was at last in America, and was soon out upon New York streets, spying for things foreign. The place had to me an air of Liverpool; but such was the rain that not Paradise itself would have looked inviting. We were a party of four, under two umbrellas; Jones and I and two Scots lads, recent immigrants, and not indisposed to welcome a compatriot. They had been six weeks in New York, and neither of them had yet found a single job or earned a single halfpenny. Up to the present they were exactly out of pocket by the amount of the fare.

The lads soon left us. Now I had sworn by all my gods to have such a dinner as would rouse the dead; there was scarce any expense at which I should have hesitated; the devil was in it but Jones and I should dine like heathen emperors. I set to work, asking after a restaurant; and I chose the wealthiest and most gastronomical-looking passers-by to ask from. Yet, although I had told them I was willing to pay anything in reason, one and all sent me off to cheap, fixed-price houses, where I would not have eaten that night for the cost of twenty dinners. I do not know if this were characteristic of New York, or whether it was only Jones and I who looked un-dinerly and discouraged enterprising suggestions. But at length, by our own sagacity, we found a French restaurant, where there was a French waiter, some fair French cooking, some so-called French wine, and French coffee to conclude the whole. I never entered into the feelings of Jack on land so completely as when I tasted that coffee.

I suppose we had one of the "private rooms for families" at Reunion House. It was very small, furnished with a bed, a chair, and some clothes-pegs; and it derived all that was necessary for the life of the human animal through two borrowed lights; one looking into the passage, and the second opening, without sash, into another apartment, where three men fitfully snored, or in intervals of wakefulness, drearily mumbled to each other all night long. It will be observed that this was almost exactly the disposition of the room in M'Naughten's story. Jones had the bed; I pitched my camp upon the floor; he did not sleep until near morning, and I, for my part, never closed an eye.

At sunrise I heard a cannon fired; and shortly afterwards the men in the next room gave over snoring for good, and began to rustle over their toilettes. The sound of their voices as they talked was low and moaning, like that of people watching by the sick. Jones, who had at last begun to doze, tumbled and murmured, and every now and then opened unconscious eyes upon me where I lay. I found myself growing eerier and eerier, for I daresay I was a little fevered by my restless night, and hurried to dress and get downstairs.

You had to pass through the rain, which still fell thick and resonant, to reach a lavatory on the other side of the court. There were three basin-stands, and a few crumpled towels and pieces of wet soap, white and slippery like fish; nor should I forget a looking-glass and a pair of questionable combs. Another Scots lad was here,

scrubbing his face with a good will.   He had been three
months in New York and had not yet found a single job
nor earned a single halfpenny.   Up to the present, he
also was exactly out of pocket by the amount of the
fare.   I began to grow sick at heart for my fellow-emi-
grants.

Of my nightmare wanderings in New York I spare to
tell.   I had a thousand and one things to do; only the
day to do them in, and a journey across the continent
before me in the evening.   It rained with patient fury;
every now and then I had to get under cover for a while
in order, so to speak, to give my mackintosh a rest; for
under this continued drenching it began to grow damp
on the inside.   I went to banks, post-offices, railway-
offices, restaurants, publishers, book-sellers, money-
changers, and wherever I went a pool would gather about
my feet, and those who were careful of their floors would
look on with an unfriendly eye.   Wherever I went, too,
the same traits struck me; the people were all surprisingly
rude and surprisingly kind.   The money-changer cross-
questioned me like a French commissary, asking my age,
my business, my average income, and my destination,
beating down my attempts at evasion, and receiving my
answers in silence; and yet when all was over, he shook
hands with me up to the elbows, and sent his lad nearly
a quarter of a mile in the rain to get me books at a
reduction.   Again, in a very large publishing and book-
selling establishment, a man, who seemed to be the manager, received me as I had certainly never before been
received in any human shop, indicated squarely that he
put no faith in my honesty, and refused to look up the
names of books or give me the slightest help or information, on the ground, like the steward, that it was none
of his business.   I lost my temper at last, said I was a
stranger in America and not learned in their etiquette;

but I would assure him, if he went to any bookseller in England, of more handsome usage. The boast was perhaps exaggerated; but like many a long shot, it struck the gold. The manager passed at once from one extreme to the other; I may say that from that moment he loaded me with kindness; he gave me all sorts of good advice, wrote me down addresses, and came bare-headed into the rain to point me out a restaurant, where I might lunch, nor even then did he seem to think that he had done enough. These are (it is as well to be bold in statement) the manners of America. It is this same opposition that has most struck me in people of almost all classes and from east to west. By the time a man had about strung me up to be the death of him by his insulting behaviour, he himself would be just upon the point of melting into confidence and serviceable attentions. Yet I suspect, although I have met with the like in so many parts, that this must be the character of some particular state or group of states; for in America, and this again in all classes, you will find some of the softest-mannered gentlemen in the world.

I was so wet when I got back to Mitchell's toward the evening, that I had simply to divest myself of my shoes, socks and trousers, and leave them behind for the benefit of New York city. No fire could have dried them ere I had to start; and to pack them in their present condition was to spread ruin among my other possessions. With a heavy heart I said farewell to them as they lay a pulp in the middle of a pool upon the floor of Mitchell's kitchen. I wonder if they are dry by now. Mitchell hired a man to carry my baggage to the station, which was hard by, accompanied me thither himself, and recommended me to the particular attention of the officials. No one could have been kinder. Those who are out of pocket may go safely to Reunion House, where they will get decent meals and find an honest and obliging land-lord. I owed him this word of thanks, before I enter fairly on the second and far less agreeable chapter of my emigrant experience.

ESSAYS

# ESSAYS

## AN APOLOGY FOR IDLERS[1]

"BOSWELL: We grow weary when idle.

"JOHNSON: That is, sir, because others being busy, we want company; but if we were idle, there would be no growing weary; we should all entertain one another."

JUST now, when every one is bound, under pain of a decree in absence convicting them of *lèse*-respectability,[2] to enter on some lucrative profession, and labour therein with something not far short of enthusiasm, a cry from the opposite party who are content when they have enough, and like to look on and enjoy in the meanwhile, savours a little of bravado and gasconade.[3] And yet this should not be. Idleness so called, which does not consist in doing nothing, but in doing a great deal not recognized in the dogmatic formularies of the ruling class, has as good a right to state its position as industry itself. It is admitted that the presence of people who refuse to enter in the great handicap race for sixpenny pieces, is at once an insult and a disenchantment for those who do. A

[1] Begun before July, 1876; rejected by the *Macmillan Magazine*, afterward accepted for the *Cornhill* by its discriminating editor, Leslie Stephen, and first printed in that magazine July, 1877. It was reprinted in the *Virginibus Puerisque* volume, 1881. "A paper called 'A Defence of Idlers' (which is really a defence of R. L. S.)," Stevenson called it in a letter to Mrs. Sitwell. But Stevenson needed no such defence, for although he knew how to be idle wisely when idle at all, he was usually one of the most industrious of men.

[2] From the French verb *leser*, "to injure." Stevenson's phrase is a humorous take-off on the common expression *lèse-majesté*, "injured majesty," *i.e.*, high treason.

[3] Boasting. Literary tradition has always represented the people of Gascony, France, as boasters, hence the term.

fine fellow (as we see so many) takes his determination, votes for the sixpences, and in the emphatic Americanism. "goes for" them. And while such an one is ploughing distressfully up the road, it is not hard to understand his resentment, when he perceives cool persons in the meadows by the wayside, lying with a handkerchief over their ears and a glass at their elbow. Alexander is touched in a very delicate place by the disregard of Diogenes. Where was the glory of having taken Rome for these tumultuous barbarians, who poured into the Senate house, and found the Fathers sitting silent and unmoved by their success? It is a sore thing to have laboured along and scaled the arduous hilltops, and when all is done, find humanity indifferent to your achievement. Hence physicists condemn the unphysical; financiers have only a superficial toleration for those who know little of stocks; literary persons despise the unlettered; and people of all pursuits combine to disparage those who have none.

But though this is one difficulty of the subject, it is not the greatest. You could not be put in prison for speaking against industry, but you can be sent to Coventry[1] for speaking like a fool. The greatest difficulty with most subjects is to do them well; therefore, please to remember this is an apology. It is certain that much may be judiciously argued in favour of diligence; only there is something to be said against it, and that is what, on the present occasion, I have to say. To state one argument is not necessarily to be deaf to all others, and that a man has written a book of travels in Montenegro, is no reason why he should never have been to Richmond.

It is surely beyond a doubt that people should be a good deal idle in youth. For though here and there a Lord Macaulay may escape from school honours with all

[1] A proverbial expression, meaning to ostracise.

his wits about him, most boys pay so dear for their medals that they never afterwards have a shot in their locker, and begin the world bankrupt. And the same holds true during all the time a lad is educating himself, or suffering others to educate him. It must have been a very foolish old gentleman who addressed Johnson at Oxford in these words: "Young man, ply your book diligently now, and acquire a stock of knowledge; for when years come upon you, you will find that poring upon books will be but an irksome task." The old gentleman seems to have been unaware that many other things besides reading grow irksome, and not a few become impossible, by the time a man has to use spectacles and cannot walk without a stick. Books are good enough in their own way, but they are a mighty bloodless substitute for life. It seems a pity to sit, like the Lady of Shalott, peering into a mirror, with your back turned on all the bustle and glamour of reality. And if a man reads very hard, as the old anecdote reminds us, he will have little time for thoughts.

If you look back on your own education, I am sure it will not be the full, vivid, instructive hours of truantry that you regret; you would rather cancel some lacklustre periods between sleep and waking in the class. For my own part, I have attended a good many lectures in my time. I still remember that the spinning of a top is a case of Kinetic Stability. I still remember that Emphyteusis is not a disease, nor Stillicide a crime. But though I would not willingly part with such scraps of science, I do not set the same store by them, as by certain other odds and ends that I came by in the open street while I was playing truant. This is not the moment to dilate on that mighty place of education, which was the favourite school of Dickens and of Balzac, and turns out yearly many inglorious masters in the Science of the Aspects of Life. Suffice it to say this: if a lad does not learn in the streets, it is because he has no faculty of learning. Nor is the truant always in the streets, for if he prefers, he may go out by the gardened suburbs into the country. He may pitch on some tuft of lilacs over a burn, and smoke innumerable pipes to the tune of the water on the stones. A bird will sing in the thicket. And there he may fall into a vein of kindly thought, and see things in a new perspective. Why, if this be not education, what is? We may conceive Mr. Worldly Wiseman[1] accosting such an one, and the conversation that should thereupon ensue:—

"How now, young fellow, what dost thou here?"

"Truly, sir, I take mine ease."

"Is not this the hour of the class? and should'st thou not be plying thy Book with diligence, to the end thou mayest obtain knowledge?"

"Nay, but thus also I follow after Learning, by your leave."

"Learning, quotha! After what fashion, I pray thee? Is it mathematics?"

"No, to be sure."

"Is it metaphysics?"

"Nor that."

"Is it some language?"

"Nay, it is no language."

"Is it a trade?"

"Nor a trade neither."

"Why, then, what is't?"

"Indeed, sir, as a time may soon come for me to go upon Pilgrimage, I am desirous to note what is commonly done by persons in my case, and where are the ugliest Sloughs and Thickets on the Road; as also, what manner of Staff is of the best service. Moreover, I lie

---

[1] A character in Bunyan's *Pilgrim's Progress*.

here, by this water, to learn by root-of-heart a lesson which my master teaches me to call Peace, or Contentment."

Hereupon Mr. Worldly Wiseman was much commoved with passion, and shaking his cane with a very threatful countenance, broke forth upon this wise: "Learning, quotha!" said he; "I would have all such rogues scourged by the Hangman!"

And so he would go his way, ruffling out his cravat with a crackle of starch, like a turkey when it spread its feathers.

Now this, of Mr. Wiseman's, is the common opinion. A fact is not called a fact, but a piece of gossip, if it does not fall into one of your scholastic categories. An inquiry must be in some acknowledged direction, with a name to go by; or else you are not inquiring at all, only lounging; and the work-house is too good for you. It is supposed that all knowledge is at the bottom of a well. or the far end of a telescope. Sainte-Beuve,[1] as he grew older, came to regard all experience as a single great book, in which to study for a few years ere we go hence; and it seemed all one to him whether you should read in Chapter xx., which is the differential calculus, or in Chapter xxxix., which is hearing the band play in the gardens. As a matter of fact, an intelligent person, looking out of his eyes and hearkening in his ears, with a smile on his face all the time, will get more true education than many another in a life of heroic vigils. There is certainly some chill and arid knowledge to be found upon the summits of formal and laborious science; but it is all round about you, and for the trouble of looking that you will acquire the warm and palpitating facts of life. While others are filling their memory with a lumber of words, one-half of which they will forget be-

[1] A great French writer and critic (1804–1869).

fore the week be out, your truant may learn some really useful art: to play the fiddle, to know a good cigar, or to speak with ease and opportunity to all varieties of men. Many who have "plied their book diligently," and know all about some one branch or another of accepted lore, come out of the study with an ancient and owl-like demeanour, and prove dry, stockish, and dyspeptic in all the better and brighter parts of life. Many make a large fortune, who remain underbred and pathetically stupid to the last. And meantime there goes the idler, who began life along with them—by your leave, a different picture. He has had time to take care of his health and his spirits; he has been a great deal in the open air, which is the most salutary of all things for both body and mind; and if he has never read the great Book in very recondite places, he has dipped into it and skimmed it over to excellent purpose. Might not the student afford some Hebrew roots, and the business man some of his half-crowns, for a share of the idler's knowledge of life at large, and Art of Living? Nay, and the idler has another and more important quality than these. I mean his wisdom. He who has much looked on at the childish satisfaction of other people in their hobbies, will regard his own with only a very ironical indulgence. He will not be heard among the dogmatists. He will have a great and cool allowance for all sorts of people and opinions. If he finds no out-of-the-way truths, he will identify himself with no very burning falsehood. His way takes him along a by-road, not much frequented, but very even and pleasant, which is called Commonplace Lane, and leads to the Belvedere[1] of Commonsense. Thence he shall command an agreeable, if no very noble prospect; and while others behold the East

---

[1] An Italian word, used here in its original meaning, which was a place of observation on top of a house.

and West, the Devil and the Sunrise, he will **be content-**
edly aware of a sort of morning hour upon all sublunary
things, with an army of shadows running speedily and
in many different directions into the great daylight of
Eternity.  The shadows and the generations, the shrill
doctors and the plangent wars, go by into ultimate
silence and emptiness; but underneath all this, a man
may see, out of the Belvedere windows, much green and
peaceful landscape; many firelit parlours; good people
laughing, drinking, and making love as they did before
the Flood or the French Revolution; and the old shepherd telling his tale under the hawthorn.

Extreme *busyness*, whether at school or college, kirk
or market, is a symptom of deficient vitality; and a
faculty for idleness implies a catholic appetite and a
strong sense of personal identity.  There is a sort of
dead-alive, hackneyed people about, who are scarcely
conscious of living except in the exercise of some conventional occupation.  Bring these fellows into the country, or set them aboard ship, and you will see how they
pine for their desk or their study.  They have no curiosity; they cannot give themselves over to random
provocations; they do not take pleasure in the exercise
of their faculties for its own sake; and unless Necessity
lays about them with a stick, they will even stand still.
It is no good speaking to such folk: they *cannot* be idle,
their nature is not generous enough; and they pass those
hours in a sort of coma, which are not dedicated to furious moiling in the gold-mill.  When they do not require
to go to the office, when they are not hungry and have
no mind to drink, the whole breathing world is a blank
to them.  If they have to wait an hour or so for a train,
they fall into a stupid trance with their eyes open.  To
see them, you would suppose there was nothing to look
at and no one to speak with; you would imagine they

were paralysed or alienated; and yet very possibly they
are hard workers in their own way, and have good eyesight for a flaw in a deed or a turn of the market. They
have been to school and college, but all the time they had
their eye on the medal; they have gone about in the world
and mixed with clever people, but all the time they were
thinking of their own affairs. As if a man's soul were not
too small to begin with, they have dwarfed and narrowed
theirs by a life of all work and no play; until here they
are at forty, with a listless attention, a mind vacant of
all material of amusement, and not one thought to rub
against another, while they wait for the train. Before
he was breeched, he might have clambered on the boxes;
when he was twenty, he would have stared at the girls;
but now the pipe is smoked out, the snuff-box empty,
and my gentleman sits bolt upright upon a bench, with
lamentable. eyes. This does not appeal to me as being
Success in Life.

But it is not only the person himself who suffers from
his busy habits, but his wife and children, his friends
and relations, and down to the very people he sits with
in a railway carriage or an omnibus. Perpetual devotion to what a man calls his business, is only to be sustained by perpetual neglect of many other things. And
it is not by any means certain that a man's business is
the most important thing he has to do. To an impar-
tial estimate it will seem clear that many of the wisest,
most virtuous, and most beneficent parts that are to be
played upon the Theatre of Life are filled by gratuitous
performers, and pass, among the world at large, as
phases of idleness. For in that Theatre, not only the
walking gentlemen, singing chambermaids, and diligent
fiddlers in the orchestra, but those who look on and
clap their hands from the benches, do really play a part
and fulfil important offices towards the general result.

You are no doubt very dependent on the care of your lawyer and stockbroker, of the guards and signalmen who convey you rapidly from place to place, and the policemen who walk the streets for your protection; but is there not a thought of gratitude in your heart for certain other benefactors who set you smiling when they fall in your way, or season your dinner with good company? Colonel Newcome[1] helped to lose his friend's money; Fred Bayham had an ugly trick of borrowing shirts; and yet they were better people to fall among than Mr. Barnes. And though Falstaff was neither sober nor very honest, I think I could name one or two long-faced Barabbases whom the world could better have done without. Hazlitt mentions that he was more sensible of obligation to Northcote, who had never done him anything he could call a service, than to his whole circle of ostentatious friends; for he thought a good companion emphatically the greatest benefactor. I know there are people in the world who cannot feel grateful unless the favour has been done them at the cost of pain and difficulty. But this is a churlish disposition. A man may send you six sheets of letter-paper covered with the most entertaining gossip, or you may pass half an hour pleasantly, perhaps profitably, over an article of his; do you think the service would be greater, if he had made the manuscript in his heart's blood, like a compact with the devil? Do you really fancy you should be more beholden to your correspondent, if he had been damning you all the while for your importunity? Pleasures are more beneficial than duties because, like the quality of

[1] Colonel Newcome, Fred Bayham, and Mr. Barnes are characters in Thackeray's novel, *The Newcomes*, the two former impractical but lovable, the third hard-headed and heartless. Falstaff is a most delightful reprobate in Shakespeare's *Henry IV;* Barabbas the Jewish thief who was released instead of Christ. Hazlitt (1778–1830) was a famous English essayist, Northcote (1746–1831) a less well-known artist and writer.

mercy, they are not strained, and they are twice blest.
There must always be two to a kiss, and there may be a
score in a jest; but wherever there is an element of sacrifice, the favour is conferred with pain, and, among
generous people, received with confusion. There is no
duty we so much underrate as the duty of being happy.
By being happy, we sow anonymous benefits upon the
world, which remain unknown even to ourselves, or
when they are disclosed, surprise nobody so much as the
benefactor. The other day, a ragged, barefoot boy ran
down the street after a marble, with so jolly an air that
he set every one he passed into a good humour; one of
these persons, who had been delivered from more than
usually black thoughts, stopped the little fellow and gave
him some money with this remark: "You see what
sometimes comes of looking pleased." If he had looked
pleased before, he had now to look both pleased and
mystified. For my part, I justify this encouragement of
smiling rather than tearful children; I do not wish to pay
for tears anywhere but upon the stage; but I am prepared to deal largely in the opposite commodity. A
happy man or woman is a better thing to find than a
five-pound note. He or she is a radiating focus of good-
will; and their entrance into a room is as though another
candle had been lighted. We need not care whether
they could prove the forty-seventh proposition; they do
a better thing than that, they practically demonstrate
the great Theorem of the Liveableness of Life. Consequently, if a person cannot be happy without remaining
idle, idle he should remain. It is a revolutionary pre-
cept; but thanks to hunger and the workhouse, one not
easily to be abused; and within practical limits, it is one
of the most incontestable truths in the whole Body of
Morality. Look at one of your industrious fellows for
a moment, I beseech you. He sows hurry and reaps

indigestion; he puts a vast deal of activity out to interest, and receives a large measure of nervous derangement in return. Either he absents himself entirely from all fellowship, and lives a recluse in a garret, with carpet slippers and a leaden inkpot; or he comes among people swiftly and bitterly, in a contraction of his whole nervous system, to discharge some temper before he returns to work. I do not care how much or how well he works, this fellow is an evil feature in other people's lives. They would be happier if he were dead. They could easier do without his services in the Circumlocution Office, than they can tolerate his fractious spirits. He poisons life at the well-head. It is better to be beggared out of hand by a scapegrace nephew, than daily hag-ridden by a peevish uncle.

And what, in God's name, is all this pother about? For what cause do they embitter their own and other people's lives? That a man should publish three or thirty articles a year, that he should finish or not finish his great allegorical picture, are questions of little interest to the world. The ranks of life are full; and although a thousand fall, there are always some to go into the breach. When they told Joan of Arc she should be at home minding women's work, she answered there were plenty to spin and wash. And so, even with your own rare gifts! When nature is "so careless of the single life," why should we coddle ourselves into the fancy that our own is of exceptional importance? Suppose Shakespeare had been knocked on the head some dark night in Sir Thomas Lucy's preserves, the world would have wagged on better or worse, the pitcher gone to the well, the scythe to the corn, and the student to his book; and no one been any the wiser of the loss. There are not many works extant, if you look the alternative all over, which are worth the price of a pound of tobacco to

a man of limited means. This is a sobering reflection
for the proudest of our earthly vanities. Even a tobac-
conist may, upon consideration, find no great cause for
personal vainglory in the phrase; for although tobacco
is an admirable sedative, the qualities necessary for re-
tailing it are neither rare nor precious in themselves.
Alas and alas! you may take it how you will, but the
services of no single individual are indispensable. Atlas
was just a gentleman with a protracted nightmare! And
yet you see merchants who go and labour themselves
into a great fortune and thence into the bankruptcy court;
scribblers who keep scribbling at little articles until their
temper is a cross to all who come about them, as though
Pharaoh should set the Israelites to make a pin instead
of a pyramid; and fine young men who work themselves
into a decline, and are driven off in a hearse with white
plumes upon it. Would you not suppose these persons
had been whispered, by the Master of the Ceremonies,
the promise of some momentous destiny? and that this
lukewarm bullet on which they play their farces was the
bull's-eye and centrepoint of all the universe? And yet
it is not so. The ends for which they give away their
priceless youth, for all they know, may be chimerical or
hurtful; the glory and riches they expect may never come,
or may find them indifferent; and they and the world
they inhabit are so inconsiderable that the mind freezes
at the thought.

# ÆS TRIPLEX [1]

The changes wrought by death are in themselves so sharp and final, and so terrible and melancholy in their consequences, that the thing stands alone in man's experience, and has no parallel upon earth. It outdoes all other accidents because it is the last of them. Sometimes it leaps suddenly upon its victims, like a Thug; sometimes it lays a regular siege and creeps upon their citadel during a score of years. And when the business is done, there is sore havoc made in other people's lives, and a pin knocked out by which many subsidiary friendships hung together. There are empty chairs, solitary walks, and single beds at night. Again, in taking away our friends, death does not take them away utterly, but leaves behind a mocking, tragical, and soon intolerable residue, which must be hurriedly concealed. Hence a whole chapter of sights and customs striking to the mind, from the pyramids of Egypt to the gibbets and dule[2] trees of mediæval Europe. The poorest persons have a bit of pageant going towards the tomb; memorial stones are set up over the least memorable; and, in order to preserve some show of respect for what remains of our old loves and friendships, we must accompany it with much

First published in *The Cornhill Magazine* for April, 1878. The time when this essay was written was at once a strenuous and hopeful one for its author, as his first printed book, *An Inland Voyage*, was then being prepared for the press. The title is from a phrase used by Horace, *æs triplex circa pectus*, "breast enclosed by triple brass," *æs* being used by Horace as a symbol of indomitable courage. The essay is generally considered Stevenson's masterpiece; and its noble description of a happy, fearless, painless death seems almost a prophecy of his own end. It was included in *Virginibus Puerisque*, 1881.

[2] A dule or "dool" was a stake used to mark boundaries.

grimly ludicrous ceremonial, and the hired undertaker parades before the door. 'All this, and much more of the same sort, accompanied by the eloquence of poets, has gone a great way to put humanity in error; nay, in many philosophies the error has been embodied and laid down with every circumstance of logic; although in real life the bustle and swiftness, in leaving people little time to think, have not left them time enough to go dangerously wrong in practice.

As a matter of fact, although few things are spoken of with more fearful whisperings than this prospect of death, few have less influence on conduct under healthy circumstances. We have all heard of cities in South America built upon the side of fiery mountains, and how, even in this tremendous neighbourhood, the inhabitants are not a jot more impressed by the solemnity of mortal conditions than if they were delving gardens in the greenest corner of England. There are serenades and suppers and much gallantry among the myrtles overhead; and meanwhile the foundation shudders underfoot, the bowels of the mountain growl, and at any moment living ruin may leap sky-high into the moonlight, and tumble man and his merry-making in the dust. In the eyes of very young people, and very dull old ones, there is something indescribably reckless and desperate in such a picture. It seems not credible that respectable married people, with umbrellas, should find appetite for a bit of supper within quite a long distance of a fiery mountain; ordinary life begins to smell of high-handed debauch when it is carried on so close to a catastrophe; and even cheese and salad, it seems, could hardly be relished in such circumstances without something like a defiance of the Creator. It should be a place for nobody but hermits dwelling in prayer and maceration, or mere born-devils drowning care in a perpetual carouse.

And yet, when one comes to think upon it calmly, the situation of these South American citizens forms only a very pale figure for the state of ordinary mankind. This world itself, travelling blindly and swiftly in over-crowded space, among a million other worlds travelling blindly and swiftly in contrary directions, may very well come by a knock that would set it into explosion like a penny squib. And what, pathologically looked at, is the human body with all its organs, but a mere bagful of petards? The least of these is as dangerous to the whole economy as the ship's powder-magazine to the ship; and with every breath we breathe, and every meal we eat, we are putting one or more of them in peril. If we clung as devotedly as some philosophers pretend we do to the abstract idea of life, or were half as frightened as they make out we are, for the subversive accident that ends it all, the trumpets might sound by the hour and no one would follow them into battle—the blue-peter[1] might fly at the truck, but who would climb into a sea-going ship? Think (if these philosophers were right) with what a preparation of spirit we should affront the daily peril of the dinner-table: a deadlier spot than any battle-field in history, where the far greater proportion of our ancestors have miserably left their bones! What woman would ever be lured into marriage, so much more dangerous than the wildest sea? And what would it be to grow old? For, after a certain distance, every step we take in life we find the ice growing thinner below our feet, and all around us and behind us we see our contemporaries going through. By the time a man gets well into the seventies, his continued existence is a mere miracle; and when he lays his old bones in bed for the night, there is an overwhelming probability that he will never see the day. Do the old men mind it, as a matter of fact?

[1] A flag used as a signal for sailing.

Why, no.   They were never merrier; they have their grog
at night, and tell the raciest stories; they hear of the death
of people about their own age, or even younger, not as if
it was a grisly warning, but with a simple childlike pleasure at having outlived some one else; and when a draught
might puff them out like a guttering candle, or a bit of
a stumble shatter them like so much glass, their old
hearts keep sound and unaffrighted, and they go on,
bubbling with laughter, through years of man's age compared to which the valley at Balaclava[1] was as safe and
peaceful as a village cricket-green on Sunday.   It may
fairly be questioned (if we look to the peril only) whether
it was a much more daring feat for Curtius[2] to plunge
into the gulf, than for any old gentleman of ninety to doff
his clothes and clamber into bed.

Indeed, it is a memorable subject for consideration,
with what unconcern and gaiety mankind pricks on
along the Valley of the Shadow of Death.   The whole
way is one wilderness of snares, and the end of it, for
those who fear the last pinch, is irrevocable ruin.   And
yet we go spinning through it all, like a party for the
Derby.[3]   Perhaps the reader remembers one of the humorous devices of the deified Caligula:[4] how he en-
couraged a vast concourse of holiday-makers on to his
bridge over Baiæ bay; and when they were in the height
of their enjoyment, turned loose the Prætorian guards
among the company, and had them tossed into the sea.
This is no bad miniature of the dealings of nature with
the transitory race of man.   Only, what a chequered
picnic we have of it, even while it lasts! and into what

[1] Scene of the famous charge of the Light Brigade in the Crimean
War.

[2] According to tradition, a Roman who sacrificed his life for his
country, leaping into a gulf to fulfil the requirements of an oracle.

[3] Derby Day, date of the greatest racing event in England.

[4] One of the worst of the Roman tyrants, reigned 37–41 A. D.

great waters, not to be crossed by any swimmer, God's pale Prætorian throws us over in the end!

We live the time that a match flickers; we pop the cork of a ginger-beer bottle, and the earthquake swallows us on the instant. Is it not odd, is it not incongruous, is it not, in the highest sense of human speech, incredible, that we should think so highly of the ginger-beer, and regard so little the devouring earthquake? The love of Life and the fear of Death are two famous phrases that grow harder to understand the more we think about them. It is a well-known fact that an immense proportion of boat accidents would never happen if people held the sheet in their hands instead of making it fast; and yet, unless it be some martinet of a professional mariner or some landsman with shattered nerves, every one of God's creatures makes it fast. A strange instance of man's unconcern and brazen boldness in the face of death!

We confound ourselves with metaphysical phrases, which we import into daily talk with noble inappropriateness. We have no idea of what death is, apart from its circumstances and some of its consequences to others; and although we have some experience of living, there is not a man on earth who has flown so high into abstraction as to have any practical guess at the meaning of the word *life*. All literature, from Job and Omar Khayyam to Thomas Carlyle or Walt Whitman, is but an attempt to look upon the human state with such largeness of view as shall enable us to rise from the consideration of living to the Definition of Life. And our sages give us about the best satisfaction in their power when they say that it is a vapour, or a show, or made out of the same stuff with dreams. Philosophy, in its more rigid sense, has been at the same work for ages; and after a myriad bald heads have wagged over the problem, and piles of words have been heaped one upon another into dry and cloudy volumes without end, philosophy has the honour of laying before us, with modest pride, her contribution towards the subject: that life is a Permanent Possibility of Sensation. Truly a fine result! A man may very well love beef, or hunting, or a woman; but surely, surely, not a Permanent Possibility of Sensation! He may be afraid of a precipice, or a dentist, or a large enemy with a club, or even an undertaker's man; but not certainly of abstract death. We may trick with the word life in its dozen senses until we are weary of tricking; we may argue in terms of all the philosophies on earth, but one fact remains true throughout—that we do not love life, in the sense that we are greatly preoccupied about its conservation; that we do not, properly speaking, love life at all, but living. Into the views of the least careful there will enter some degree of providence: no man's eyes are fixed entirely on the passing hour; but although we have some anticipation of good health, good weather, wine, active employment, love, and self-approval, the sum of these anticipations does not amount to any-thing like a general view of life's possibilities and issues; nor are those who cherish them most vividly at all the most scrupulous of their personal safety. To be deeply interested in the accidents of our existence, to enjoy keenly the mixed texture of human experience, rather leads a man to disregard precautions, and risk his neck against a straw. For surely the love of living is stronger in an Alpine climber roping over a peril, or a hunter rid-ing merrily at a stiff fence, than in a creature who lives upon a diet and walks a measured distance in the interest of his constitution.

There is a great deal of very vile nonsense talked upon both sides of the matter: tearing divines reducing life to the dimensions of a mere funeral procession, so short as to be hardly decent; and melancholy unbelievers yearning for the tomb as if it were a world too far away. Both sides must feel a little ashamed of their performances now and again when they draw in their chairs to dinner. Indeed, a good meal and a bottle of wine is an answer to most standard works upon the question. When a man's heart warms to his viands, he forgets a great deal of sophistry, and soars into a rosy zone of contemplation. Death may be knocking at the door, like the Commander's statue;[1] we have something else in hand, thank God, and let him knock. Passing bells are ringing all the world over. All the world over, and every hour, some one is parting company with all his aches and ecstasies. For us also the trap is laid. But we are so fond of life that we have no leisure to entertain the terror of death. It is a honeymoon with us all through, and none of the longest. Small blame to us if we give our whole hearts to this glowing bride of ours, to the appetites, to honour, to the hungry curiosity of the mind, to the pleasure of the eyes in nature, and the pride of our own nimble bodies.

We all of us appreciate the sensations; but as for caring about the Permanence of the Possibility, a man's head is generally very bald, and his senses very dull, before he comes to that. Whether we regard life as a lane leading to a dead wall—a mere bag's end, as the French say—or whether we think of it as a vestibule or gymnasium, where we wait our turn and prepare our faculties for some more noble destiny; whether we thunder in a pulpit, or pule in little atheistic poetry-books, about its vanity and brevity; whether we look justly for years of health and vigour, or are about to mount into a

[1] In the story of Don Juan (see Molière's play of that name) the hero has an adventure with a statue temporarily endowed with life.

Bath-chair,[1] as a step towards the hearse; in each and all of these views and situations there is but one conclusion possible: that a man should stop his ears against paralysing terror, and run the race that is set before him with a single mind.  No one surely could have recoiled with more heartache and terror from the thought of death than our respected lexicographer;[2] and yet we know how little it affected his conduct, how wisely and boldly he walked, and in what a fresh and lively vein he spoke of life.  Already an old man, he ventured on his Highland tour; and his heart, bound with triple brass, did not recoil before twenty-seven individual cups of tea.  As courage and intelligence are the two qualities best worth a good man's cultivation, so it is the first part of intelligence to recognise our precarious estate in life, and the first part of courage to be not at all abashed before the fact.  A frank and somewhat headlong carriage, not looking too anxiously before, not dallying in maudlin regret over the past, stamps the man who is well armoured for this world.

And not only well armoured for himself, but a good friend and a good citizen to boot.  We do not go to cowards for tender dealing; there is nothing so cruel as panic; the man who has least fear for his own carcass has most time to consider others.  That eminent chemist who took his walks abroad in tin shoes, and subsisted wholly upon tepid milk, had all his work cut out for him in considerate dealings with his own digestion.  So soon as prudence has begun to grow up in the brain, like a dismal fungus, it finds its first expression in a paralysis of generous acts.  The victim begins to shrink spiritually; he develops a fancy for parlours with a regulated tem-

---

[1] An invalid's chair; named from Bath, the well-known health resort.

[2] Dr. Samuel Johnson, author of the famous Dictionary.

perature, and takes his morality on the principle of tin
shoes and tepid milk. The care of one important body
or soul becomes so engrossing, that all the noises of the
outer world begin to come thin and faint into the parlour
with the regulated temperature; and the tin shoes go
equably forward over blood and rain. To be overwise
is to ossify; and the scruple-monger ends by standing
stockstill. Now the man who has his heart on his
sleeve, and a good whirling weathercock of a brain, who
reckons his life as a thing to be dashingly used and
cheerfully hazarded, makes a very different acquaintance
of the world, keeps all his pulses going true and fast, and
gathers impetus as he runs, until, if he be running towards anything better than wildfire, he may shoot up and
become a constellation in the end. Lord look after his
health, Lord have a care of his soul, says he; and he has
at the key of the position, and swashes through incon-
gruity and peril towards his aim. Death is on all sides
of him with pointed batteries, as he is on all sides of
all of us; unfortunate surprises gird him round; mim-
mouthed friends and relations hold up their hands in
quite a little elegiacal synod about his path: and what
cares he for all this? Being a true lover of living, a fellow with something pushing and spontaneous in his inside, he must, like any other soldier, in any other stirring,
deadly warfare, push on at his best pace until he touch
the goal. "A peerage or Westminster Abbey!" cried
Nelson in his bright, boyish, heroic manner. These are
great incentives; not for any of these, but for the plain
satisfaction of living, of being about their business in
some sort or other, do the brave, serviceable men of
every nation tread down the nettle danger, and pass fly-
ingly over all the stumbling-blocks of prudence. Think
of the heroism of Johnson, think of that superb indifference to mortal limitation that set him upon his diction-

ary, and carried him through triumphantly until the end! Who, if he were wisely considerate of things at large, would ever embark upon any work much more considerable than a halfpenny post-card? Who would project a serial novel, after Thackeray and Dickens[1] had each fallen in mid-course? Who would find heart enough to begin to live, if he dallied with the consideration of death?

And, after all, what sorry and pitiful quibbling all this is! To forego all the issues of living in a parlour with a regulated temperature—as if that were not to die a hundred times over, and for ten years at a stretch! As if it were not to die in one's own lifetime, and without even the sad immunities of death! As if it were not to die, and yet be the patient spectators of our own pitiable change! The Permanent Possibility is preserved, but the sensations carefully held at arm's length, as if one kept a photographic plate in a dark chamber. It is better to lose health like a spendthrift than to waste it like a miser. It is better to live and be done with it, than to die daily in the sick-room. By all means begin your folio; even if the doctor does not give you a year, even if he hesitates about a month, make one brave push and see what can be accomplished in a week. It is not only in finished undertakings that we ought to honour useful labour. A spirit goes out of the man who means execution, which outlives the most untimely ending. All who have meant good work with their whole hearts, have done good work, although they may die before they have the time to sign it. Every heart that has beat strong and cheerfully has left a hopeful impulse behind it in the world, and bettered the tradition of mankind. And even if death catch people, like an open pitfall, and in mid-career, laying out vast projects, and planning monstrous

[1] Thackeray and Dickens each left a novel unfinished at his death.

foundations, flushed with hope, and their mouths full of boastful language, they should be at once tripped up and silenced: is there not something brave and spirited in such a termination? and does not life go down with a better grace, foaming in full body over a precipice, than miserably straggling to an end in sandy deltas? When the Greeks made their fine saying that those whom the gods love die young, I cannot help believing they had this sort of death also in their eye. For surely, at whatever age it overtake the man, this is to die young. Death has not been suffered to take so much as an illusion from his heart. In the hot-fit of life, a-tiptoe on the highest point of being, he passes at a bound on to the other side. The noise of the mallet and chisel is scarcely quenched, the trumpets are hardly done blowing, when, trailing with him clouds of glory, this happy-starred, full-blooded spirit shoots into the spiritual land.

# EL DORADO[1]

It seems as if a great deal were attainable in a world where there are so many marriages and decisive battles, and where we all, at certain hours of the day, and with great gusto and despatch, stow a portion of victuals finally and irretrievably into the bag which contains us. And it would seem also, on a hasty view, that the attainment of as much as possible was the one goal of man's contentious life. And yet, as regards the spirit, this is but a semblance. We live in an ascending scale when we live happily, one thing leading to another in an endless series. There is always a new horizon for onward-looking men, and although we dwell on a small planet, immersed in petty business and not enduring beyond a brief period of years, we are so constituted that our hopes are inaccessible, like stars, and the term of hoping is prolonged until the term of life. To be truly happy is a question of how we begin and not of how we end, of what we want and not of what we have. An aspiration is a joy forever, a possession as solid as a landed estate, a fortune which we can never exhaust and which gives us year by year a revenue of pleasurable activity. To have many of these is to be spiritually rich. Life is only a very dull and ill-directed theatre unless we have some interests in the

[1] Published May 11, 1878, in *London*, a newly founded weekly review under the editorship at first of Mr. Glasgow Brown and later of Mr. Henley, both friends of Stevenson. In 1881 the essay was reprinted in *Virginibus Puerisque*. El Dorado was the name of a mythical country of fabulous wealth, long supposed to exist in northern South America. The phrase is Spanish and means "The Golden."

piece; and to those who have neither art nor science, the world is a mere arrangement of colours, or a rough foot-way where they may very well break their shins. It is in virtue of his own desires and curiosities that any man continues to exist with even patience, that he is charmed by the look of things and people, and that he wakens every morning with a renewed appetite for work and pleasure. Desire and curiosity are the two eyes through which he sees the world in the most enchanted colours: it is they that make women beautiful or fossils interesting: and the man may squander his estate and come to beg-gary, but if he keeps these two amulets he is still rich in the possibilities of pleasure. Suppose he could take one meal so compact and comprehensive that he should never hunger any more; suppose him, at a glance, to take in all the features of the world and allay the desire for knowl-edge; suppose him to do the like in any province of ex-perience—would not that man be in a poor way for amusement ever after?

One who goes touring on foot with a single volume in his knapsack reads with circumspection, pausing often to reflect, and often laying the book down to contem-plate the landscape or the prints in the inn parlour; for he fears to come to an end of his entertainment, and be left companionless on the last stages of his journey. A young fellow recently finished the works of Thomas Carlyle, winding up, if we remember aright, with the ten note-books upon Frederick the Great. "What!" cried the young fellow, in consternation, "is there no more Carlyle? Am I left to the daily papers?" A more celebrated instance is that of Alexander, who wept bit-terly because he had no more worlds to subdue. And when Gibbon had finished the *Decline and Fall*,[1] he had

---

[1] *The Decline and Fall of the Roman Empire* occupied the best years of Gibbon's life.

only a few moments of joy; and it was with a "sober melancholy" that he parted from his labours.

Happily we all shoot at the moon with ineffectual arrows; our hopes are set on inaccessible El Dorado; we come to an end of nothing here below. Interests are only plucked up to sow themselves again, like mustard. You would think, when the child was born, there would be an end to trouble; and yet it is only the beginning of fresh anxieties; and when you have seen it through its teething and its education, and at last its marriage, alas! it is only to have new fears, new quivering sensibilities, with every day; and the health of your children's children grows as touching a concern as that of your own. Again, when you have married your wife, you would think you were got upon a hilltop, and might begin to go downward by an easy slope. But you have only ended courting to begin marriage. Falling in love and winning love are often difficult tasks to overbearing and rebellious spirits; but to keep in love is also a business of some importance, to which both man and wife must bring kindness and goodwill. The true love story commences at the altar, when there lies before the married pair a most beautiful contest of wisdom and generosity, and a lifelong struggle towards an unattainable ideal. Unattainable? Ay, surely unattainable, from the very fact that they are two instead of one.

"Of making books there is no end," complained the Preacher;[1] and did not perceive how highly he was praising letters as an occupation. There is no end, indeed, to making books or experiments, or to travel, or to gathering wealth. Problem gives rise to problem. We may study forever, and we are never as learned as we would. We have never made a statue worthy of our dreams. And when we have discovered a continent,

[1] *Ecclesiastes* XII, 12.

or crossed a chain of mountains, it is only to find another ocean or another plain upon the further side. In the infinite universe there is room for our swiftest diligence and to spare. It is not like the works of Carlyle, which can be read to an end. Even in a corner of it, in a private park, or in the neighbourhood of a single hamlet, the weather and the seasons keep so deftly changing that although we walk there for a lifetime there will be always something new to startle and delight us.

There is only one wish realisable on the earth; only one thing that can be perfectly attained: Death. And from a variety of circumstances we have no one to tell us whether it be worth attaining.

A strange picture we make on our way to our chimæras, ceaselessly marching, grudging ourselves the time for rest; indefatigable, adventurous pioneers. It is true that we shall never reach the goal; it is even more than probable that there is no such place; and if we lived for centuries and were endowed with the powers of a god, we should find ourselves not much nearer what we wanted at the end. O toiling hands of mortals! O unwearied feet, travelling ye know not whither! Soon, soon, it seems to you, you must come forth on some conspicuous hilltop, and but a little way further, against the setting sun, descry the spires of El Dorado. Little do ye know your own blessedness; for to travel hopefully is a better thing than to arrive, and the true success is to labour.

# TRUTH OF INTERCOURSE[1]

Among sayings that have a currency in spite of being
wholly false upon the face of them for the sake of a half-
truth upon another subject which is accidentally combined with the error, one of the grossest and broadest
conveys the monstrous proposition that it is easy to tell
the truth and hard to tell a lie. I wish heartily it were.
But the truth is one; it has first to be discovered, then
justly and exactly uttered. Even with instruments specially contrived for such a purpose—with a foot rule, a
level, or a theodolite[2]—it is not easy to be exact; it is
easier, alas! to be inexact. From those who mark the
divisions on a scale to those who measure the boundaries
of empires or the distance of the heavenly stars, it is by
careful method and minute, unwearying attention that
men rise even to material exactness or to sure knowledge
even of external and constant things. But it is easier to
draw the outline of a mountain than the changing appearance of a face; and truth in human relations is of this
more intangible and dubious order: hard to seize, harder
to communicate. Veracity to facts in a loose, colloquial
sense—not to say that I have been in Malabar when as
a matter of fact I was never out of England, not to say
that I have read Cervantes in the original when as a mat-

[1] Written shortly before Stevenson's first voyage to America,
and published in *The Cornhill Magazine*, May, 1879, just a year before the author's marriage. It was later included in the volume
*Virginibus Puerisque* (published 1881) as the fourth of his talks
"to maidens and youths."

[2] A surveying instrument for measuring horizontal angles upon
a graduated circle.

ter of fact I know not one syllable of Spanish—this, indeed, is easy and to the same degree unimportant in itself.
Lies of this sort, according to circumstances, may or may
not be important; in a certain sense even they may or may
not be false.    The habitual liar may be a very honest fellow, and live truly with his wife and friends; while another
man who never told a formal falsehood in his life may
yet be himself one lie—heart and face, from top to bottom.    This is the kind of lie which poisons intimacy.
And, *vice versa*, veracity to sentiment, truth in a relation,
truth to your own heart and your friends, never to feign
or falsify emotion—that is the truth which makes love
possible and mankind happy.

*L'art de bien dire* [1] is but a drawing-room accomplishment unless it be pressed into the service of the truth.
The difficulty of literature is not to write, but to write
what you mean; not to affect your reader, but to affect
him precisely as you wish.    This is commonly understood in the case of books or set orations; even in making your will, or writing an explicit letter, some difficulty
is admitted by the world.    But one thing you can never
make Philistine[2] natures understand; one thing, which
yet lies on the surface, remains as unseizable to their wits
as a high flight of metaphysics—namely, that the business
of life is mainly carried on by means of this difficult art
of literature, and according to a man's proficiency in that
art shall be the freedom and the fulness of his intercourse
with other men.    Anybody, it is supposed, can say what
he means; and, in spite of their notorious experience to
the contrary, people so continue to suppose.    Now, I
simply open the last book I have been reading—Mr. Le-
land's captivating *English Gipsies*.    "It is said," I find

[1] The art of expressing oneself well.
[2] A common term in literature for men who emphasize the sordid
and "practical" side of life at the expense of the spiritual and imaginative.

on p. 7, "that those who can converse with Irish peasants
in their own native tongue form far higher opinions of
their appreciation of the beautiful, and of *the elements of
humour and pathos in their hearts,* than do those who
know their thoughts only through the medium of English.
I know from my own observations that this is quite the
case with the Indians of North America, and it is unquestionably so with the gipsy." In short, where a man
has not a full possession of the language, the most important, because the most amiable, qualities of his nature have
to lie buried and fallow; for the pleasure of comradeship,
and the intellectual part of love, rest upon these very
"elements of humour and pathos." Here is a man
opulent in both, and for lack of a medium he can put none
of it out to interest in the market of affection! But what
is thus made plain to our apprehensions in the case of a
foreign language is partially true even with the tongue
we learned in childhood. Indeed, we all speak different
dialects; one shall be copious and exact, another loose and
meagre; but the speech of the ideal talker shall correspond and fit upon the truth of fact—not clumsily, obscur-
ing lineaments, like a mantle, but cleanly adhering, like
an athlete's skin. And what is the result? That the one
can open himself more clearly to his friends, and can enjoy more of what makes life truly valuable—intimacy
with those he loves. An orator makes a false step; he em-
ploys some trivial, some absurd, some vulgar phrase;
in the turn of a sentence he insults, by a side wind, those
whom he is labouring to charm; in speaking to one sentiment he unconsciously ruffles another in parenthesis; and
you are not surprised, for you know his task to be delicate
and filled with perils. "O frivolous mind of man, light
ignorance!" As if yourself, when you seek to explain
some misunderstanding or excuse some apparent fault,
speaking swiftly and addressing a mind still recently in-

censed, were not harnessing for a more perilous adventure; as if yourself required less tact and eloquence; as if an angry friend or a suspicious lover were not more easy to offend than a meeting of indifferent politicians! Nay, and the orator treads in a beaten round; the matters he discusses have been discussed a thousand times before; language is ready-shaped to his purpose; he speaks out of a cut and dry vocabulary. But you—may it not be that your defence reposes on some subtlety of feeling, not so much as touched upon in Shakespeare, to express which, like a pioneer, you must venture forth into zones of thought still unsurveyed, and become yourself a literary innovator? For even in love there are unlovely humours; ambiguous acts, unpardonable words, may yet have sprung from a kind sentiment. If the injured one could read your heart, you may be sure that he would understand and pardon; but, alas! the heart cannot be shown —it has to be demonstrated in words. Do you think it is a hard thing to write poetry? Why, that is to write poetry, and of a high, if not the highest, order.

I should even more admire "the lifelong and heroic literary labours" of my fellow-men, patiently clearing up in words their loves and their contentions, and speaking their autobiography daily to their wives, were it not for a circumstance which lessens their difficulty and my admiration by equal parts. For life, though largely, is not entirely carried on by literature. We are subject to physical passions and contortions; the voice breaks and changes, and speaks by unconscious and winning inflections; we have legible countenances, like an open book; things that cannot be said look eloquently through the eyes; and the soul, not locked into the body as a dungeon, dwells ever on the threshold with appealing signals. Groans and tears, looks and gestures, a flush or a paleness, are often the most clear reporters of the heart, and speak more directly to the hearts of others. The message flies by these interpreters in the least space of time, and the misunderstanding is averted in the moment of its birth. To explain in words takes time and a just and patient hearing; and in the critical epochs of a close relation, patience and justice are not qualities on which we can rely. But the look or the gesture explains things in a breath; they tell their message without ambiguity; unlike speech, they cannot stumble, by the way, on a reproach or an allusion that should steel your friend against the truth; and then they have a higher authority, for they are the direct expression of the heart, not yet transmitted through the unfaithful and sophisticating brain. Not long ago I wrote a letter to a friend which came near involving us in quarrel; but we met, and in personal talk I repeated the worst of what I had written, and added worse to that; and with the commentary of the body it seemed not unfriendly either to hear or say. Indeed, letters are in vain for the purposes of intimacy; an absence is a dead break in the relation; yet two who know each other fully and are bent on perpetuity in love, may so preserve the attitude of their affections that they may meet on the same terms as they had parted.

Pitiful is the case of the blind, who cannot read the face; pitiful that of the deaf, who cannot follow the changes of the voice. And there are others also to be pitied; for there are some of an inert, uneloquent nature, who have been denied all the symbols of communication, who have neither a lively play of facial expression, nor speaking gestures, nor a responsive voice, nor yet the gift of frank, explanatory speech: people truly made of clay, people tied for life into a bag which no one can undo. They are poorer than the gypsy, for their heart can speak no language under heaven. Such people we must learn slowly by the tenor of their acts, or through yea and nay communications; or we take them on trust on the strength of a general air, and now and again, when we see the spirit breaking through in a flash, correct or change our estimate. But these will be uphill intimacies, without charm or freedom, to the end; and freedom is the chief ingredient in confidence. Some minds, romantically dull, despise physical endowments. That is a doctrine for a misanthrope; to those who like their fellow-creatures it must always be meaningless; and, for my part, I can see few things more desirable, after the possession of such radical qualities as honour and humour and pathos, than to have a lively and not a stolid countenance; to have looks to correspond with every feeling; to be elegant and delightful in person, so that we shall please even in the intervals of active pleasing, and may never discredit speech with uncouth manners or become unconsciously our own burlesques. But of all unfortunates there is one creature (for I will not call him man) conspicuous in misfortune. This is he who has forfeited his birthright of expression, who has cultivated artful intonations, who has taught his face tricks, like a pet monkey, and on every side perverted or cut off his means of communication with his fellow-men. The body is a house of many windows: there we all sit, showing ourselves and crying on the passers-by to come and love us. But this fellow has filled his windows with opaque glass, elegantly coloured. His house may be admired for its design, the crowd may pause before the stained windows, but meanwhile the poor proprietor must lie languishing within, uncomforted, unchangeably alone.

Truth of intercourse is something more difficult than to refrain from open lies. It is possible to avoid falsehood and yet not tell the truth. It is not enough to answer formal questions. To reach the truth by yea and nay communications implies a questioner with a share of inspiration, such as is often found in mutual love. *Yea* and *nay* mean nothing; the meaning must have been related in the question. Many words are often necessary to convey a very simple statement; for in this sort of exercise we never hit the gold; the most that we can hope is by many arrows, more or less far off on different sides, to indicate, in the course of time, for what target we are aiming, and after an hour's talk, back and forward, to convey the purport of a single principle or a single thought. And yet while the curt, pithy speaker misses the point entirely, a wordy, prolegomenous[1] babbler will often add three new offences in the process of excusing one. It is really a most delicate affair. The world was made before the English language, and seemingly upon a different design. Suppose we held our converse not in words, but in music, those who have a bad ear would find themselves cut off from all near commerce, and no better than foreigners in this big world. But we do not consider how many have "a bad ear" for words, nor how often the most eloquent find nothing to reply. I hate questioners and questions; there are so few that can be spoken to without a lie. "*Do you forgive me?*" Madam and sweetheart, so far as I have gone in life I have never yet been able to discover what forgiveness means. "*Is it still the same between us?*" Why, how can it be? It is eternally different; and yet you are still the friend of my heart. "*Do you understand me?*" God knows; I should think it highly improbable.

The cruellest lies are often told in silence. A man may have sat in a room for hours and not opened his teeth, and yet come out of that room a disloyal friend or a vile calumniator. And how many loves have perished because, from pride, or spite, or diffidence, or that unmanly shame which withholds a man from daring to be-

[1] Given to long prefatory remarks.

tray emotion, a lover, at the critical point of the relation, has but hung his head and held his tongue? And, again, a lie may be told by a truth, or a truth conveyed through a lie. Truth to facts is not always truth to sentiment; and part of the truth, as often happens in answer to a question, may be the foulest calumny. A fact may be an exception; but the feeling is the law, and it is that which you must neither garble nor belie. The whole tenor of a conversation is a part of the meaning of each separate statement; the beginning and the end define and travesty the intermediate conversation. You never speak to God; you address a fellow-man, full of his own tempers; and to tell truth, rightly understood, is not to state the true facts, but to convey a true impression; truth in spirit, not truth to letter, is the true veracity. To reconcile averted friends a Jesuitical discretion is often needful, not so much to gain a kind hearing as to communicate sober truth. Women have an ill name in this connection; yet they live in as true relations; the lie of a good woman is the true index of her heart.

"It takes," says Thoreau, in the noblest and most useful passage I remember to have read in any modern author,[1] "two to speak truth—one to speak and another to hear." He must be very little experienced, or have no great zeal for truth, who does not recognise the fact. A grain of anger or a grain of suspicion produces strange acoustical effects, and makes the ear greedy to remark offence. Hence we find those who have once quarrelled carry themselves distantly, and are ever ready to break the truce. To speak truth there must be moral equality or else no respect; and hence between parent and child intercourse is apt to degenerate into a verbal fencing bout, and misapprehensions to become ingrained. And

[1] *A Week on the Concord and Merrimack Rivers*, Wednesday, p. 283.

there is another side to this, for the parent begins with an imperfect notion of the child's character, formed in early years or during the equinoctial gales of youth; to this he adheres, noting only the facts which suit with his pre-conception; and wherever a person fancies himself un-justly judged, he at once and finally gives up the effort to speak truth. With our chosen friends, on the other hand, and still more between lovers (for mutual under-standing is love's essence), the truth is easily indicated by the one and aptly comprehended by the other. A hint taken, a look understood, conveys the gist of long and delicate explanations; and where the life is known even *yea* and *nay* become luminous. In the closest of all relations—that of a love well founded and equally shared —speech is half discarded, like a roundabout, infantile process or a ceremony of formal etiquette; and the two communicate directly by their presences, and with few looks and fewer words contrive to share their good and evil and uphold each other's hearts in joy. For love rests upon a physical basis; it is a familiarity of nature's making and apart from voluntary choice. Understand-ing has in some sort outrun knowledge, for the affection perhaps began with the acquaintance; and as it was not made like other relations, so it is not, like them, to be perturbed or clouded. Each knows more than can be uttered; each lives by faith, and believes by a natural compulsion; and between man and wife the language of the body is largely developed and grown strangely elo-quent The thought that prompted and was conveyed in a caress would only lose to be set down in words—ay, although Shakespeare himself should be the scribe.

Yet it is in these dear intimacies, beyond all others, that we must strive and do battle for the truth. Let but a doubt arise, and alas! all the previous intimacy and confidence is but another charge against the person doubted. *"What a monstrous dishonesty is this if 1 have been deceived so long and so completely!"* Let but that thought gain entrance, and you plead before a deaf tribunal. Appeal to the past; why, that is your crime! Make all clear, convince the reason; alas! speciousness is but a proof against you. *"If you can abuse me now, the more likely that you have abused me from the first."*

For a strong affection such moments are worth supporting, and they will end well; for your advocate is in your lover's heart, and speaks her own language; it is not you but she herself who can defend and clear you of the charge. But in slighter intimacies, and for a less stringent union? Indeed, is it worth while? We are *all incompris,*[1] only more or less concerned for the mischance; all trying wrongly to do right; all fawning at each other's feet like dumb, neglected lap-dogs. Sometimes we catch an eye—this is our opportunity in the ages—and we wag our tail with a poor smile. *"Is that all?"* All? If you only knew! But how can they know? They do not love us; the more fools we to squander life on the indifferent.

But the morality of the thing, you will be glad to hear, is excellent; for it is only by trying to understand others that we can get our own hearts understood; and in matters of human feeling the clement judge is the most successful pleader.

[1] Not understood.

# TALK AND TALKERS [1]

"Sir, we had a good talk."—JOHNSON.

"As we must account for every idle word, so we must for every idle silence."—FRANKLIN.

There can be no fairer ambition than to excel in talk; to be affable, gay, ready, clear and welcome; to have a fact, a thought, or an illustration, pat to every subject; and not only to cheer the flight of time among our intimates, but bear our part in that great international congress, always sitting, where public wrongs are first declared, public errors first corrected, and the course of public opinion shaped, day by day, a little nearer to the right. No measure comes before Parliament but it has been long ago prepared by the grand jury of the talkers; no book is written that has not been largely composed by their assistance. Literature in many of its branches is no other than the shadow of good talk; but the imitation falls far short of the original in life, freedom and effect. There are always two to a talk, giving and taking, comparing experience and according conclusions. Talk is fluid, tentative, continually, "in further search and progress;" while written words remain fixed, become idols even to the writer, found wooden dogmatisms, and preserve flies

[1] Composed at Davos in the Alps during the winter of 1881–1882, and printed in *The Cornhill Magazine* the following April. The end of the essay describes with admirable skill the conversational abilities of Stevenson's various friends; but a full appreciation of these word-portraits requires so much familiarity with Stevenson's life that they have here been omitted. In August of the same year the *Cornhill* published *Talk and Talkers*. (*A Sequel.*) Both papers were reprinted in *Memories and Portraits*, 1887.

of obvious error in the amber of the truth. Last and chief, while literature, gagged with linsey-woolsey, can only deal with a fraction of the life of man, talk goes fancy free and may call a spade a spade. Talk has none of the freezing immunities of the pulpit. It cannot, even if it would, become merely æsthetic or merely classical like literature. A jest intervenes, the solemn humbug is dissolved in laughter, and speech runs forth out of the contemporary groove into the open fields of nature, cheery and cheering, like schoolboys out of school. And it is in talk alone that we can learn our period and ourselves. In short, the first duty of a man is to speak; that is his chief business in this world; and talk, which is the harmonious speech of two or more, is by far the most accessible of pleasures. It costs nothing in money; it is all profit; it completes our education, founds and fosters our friendships, and can be enjoyed at any age and in almost any state of health.

The spice of life is battle; the friendliest relations are still a kind of contest; and if we would not forego all that is valuable in our lot, we must continually face some other person, eye to eye, and wrestle a fall whether in love or enmity. It is still by force of body, or power of character or intellect, that we attain to worthy pleasures. Men and women contend for each other in the lists of love, like rival mesmerists; the active and adroit decide their challenges in the sports of the body; and the sedentary sit down to chess or conversation. All sluggish and pacific pleasures are, to the same degree, solitary and selfish; and every durable bond between human beings is founded in or heightened by some element of competition. Now, the relation that has the least root in matter is undoubtedly that airy one of friendship; and hence, I suppose, it is that good talk most commonly arises among friends. Talk is, indeed, both the scene and instrument of friendship. It is in talk alone that the friends can measure strength, and enjoy that amicable counter-assertion of personality which is the gauge of relations and the sport of life.

A good talk is not to be had for the asking. Humours must first be accorded in a kind of overture or prologue; hour, company and circumstance be suited; and then, at a fit juncture, the subject, the quarry of two heated minds, spring up like a deer out of the wood. Not that the talker has any of the hunter's pride, though he has all and more than all his ardour. The genuine artist follows the stream of conversation as an angler follows the windings of a brook, not dallying where he fails to "kill." He trusts implicitly to hazard; and he is rewarded by continual variety, continual pleasure, and those changing prospects of the truth that are the best of education. There is nothing in a subject, so called, that we should regard it as an idol, or follow it beyond the promptings of desire. Indeed, there are few subjects; and so far as they are truly talkable, more than the half of them may be reduced to three: that I am I, that you are you, and that there are other people dimly understood to be not quite the same as either. Wherever talk may range, it still runs half the time on these eternal lines. The theme being set, each plays on himself as on an instrument; asserts and justifies himself; ransacks his brain for instances and opinions, and brings them forth new-minted, to his own surprise and the admiration of his adversary. All natural talk is a festival of ostentation; and by the laws of the game each accepts and fans the vanity of the other. It is from that reason that we venture to lay ourselves so open, that we dare to be so warmly eloquent, and that we swell in each other's eyes to such a vast proportion. For talkers, once launched, begin to overflow the limits of their ordinary selves, tower up to the height of their

secret pretensions, and give themselves out for the
heroes, brave, pious, musical and wise, that in their most
shining moments they aspire to be. So they weave for
themselves with words and for a while inhabit a palace of
delights, temple at once and theatre, where they fill the
round of the world's dignities, and feast with the gods,
exulting in Kudos.[1] And when the talk is over, each
goes his way, still flushed with vanity and admiration,
still trailing clouds of glory; each declines from the height
of his ideal orgie, not in a moment, but by slow declension.
I remember, in the *entr'acte* of an afternoon performance,
coming forth into the sunshine, in a beautiful green, gardened corner of a romantic city; and as I sat and smoked,
the music moving in my blood, I seemed to sit there and
evaporate *The Flying Dutchman*[2] (for it was that I had
been hearing) with a wonderful sense of life, warmth, well-
being and pride; and the noises of the city, voices, bells
and marching feet, fell together in my ears like a sympho-
nious orchestra. In the same way, the excitement of a
good talk lives for a long while after in the blood, the
heart still hot within you, the brain still simmering, and
the physical earth swimming around you with the colours of the sunset.

Natural talk, like ploughing, should turn up a large
surface of life, rather than dig mines into geological
strata. Masses of experience, anecdote, incident, cross-
lights, quotation, historical instances, the whole flotsam
and jetsam of two minds forced in and in upon the matter
in hand from every point of the compass, and from every
degree of mental elevation and abasement—these are the
material with which talk is fortified, the food on which
the talkers thrive. Such argument as is proper to the
exercise should still be brief and seizing. Talk should

[1] The Greek word for glory, renown.
[2] Wagner's opera, *Der Fliegende Holländer*.

proceed by instances; by the apposite, not the expository. It should keep close along the lines of humanity, near the bosoms and businesses of men, at the level where history, fiction and experience intersect and illuminate each other. I am I, and You are You, with all my heart; but conceive how these lean propositions change and brighten when, instead of words, the actual you and I sit cheek by jowl, the spirit housed in the live body, and the very clothes uttering voices to corroborate the story in the face. Not less surprising is the change when we leave off to speak of generalities—the bad, the good, the miser, and all the characters of Theophrastus[1]—and call up other men, by anecdote or instance, in their very trick and feature; or trading on a common knowledge, toss each other famous names, still glowing with the hues of life. Communication is no longer by words, but by the instancing of whole biographies, epics, systems of philosophy, and epochs of history, in bulk. That which is understood excels that which is spoken in quantity and quality alike; ideas thus figured and personified, change hands, as we may say, like coin; and the speakers imply without effort the most obscure and intricate thoughts. Strangers who have a large common ground of reading will, for this reason, come the sooner to the grapple of genuine converse. If they know Othello and Napoleon, Consuelo and Clarissa Harlowe, Vautrin and Steenie Steenson,[2] they can leave generalities and begin at once to speak by figures.

Conduct and art are the two subjects that arise most frequently and that embrace the widest range of facts. A few pleasures bear discussion for their own sake, but

[1] A Greek philosopher who died 288 B. C. His *Ethical Characters* delineates various moral types of humanity.

[2] Characters in various novels, Consuelo in George Sand's *Consuelo*, Clarissa Harlowe in Richardson's *Clarissa Harlowe*, Vautrin in several novels of Balzac, and Steenie Steenson in Scott's *Redgauntlet*.

only those which are most social or most radically human; and even these can only be discussed among their devotees. A technicality is always welcome to the expert, whether in athletics, art or law; I have heard the best kind of talk on technicalities from such rare and happy persons as both know and love their business. No human being ever spoke of scenery for above two minutes at a time, which makes me suspect we hear too much of it in literature. The weather is regarded as the very nadir and scoff of conversational topics. And yet the weather, the dramatic element in scenery, is far more tractable in language, and far more human both in import and suggestion than the stable features of the landscape. Sailors and shepherds, and the people generally of coast and mountain, talk well of it; and it is often excitingly presented in literature. But the tendency of all living talk draws it back and back into the common focus of humanity. Talk is a creature of the street and market-place, feeding on gossip; and its last resort is still in a discussion on morals. That is the heroic form of gossip; heroic in virtue of its high pretensions; but still gossip, because it turns on personalities. You can keep no men long, nor Scotchmen at all, off moral or theological discussion. These are to all the world what law is to lawyers; they are everybody's technicalities; the medium through which all consider life, and the dialect in which they express their judgments. I knew three young men who walked together daily for some two months in a solemn and beautiful forest and in cloudless summer weather; daily they talked with unabated zest, and yet scarce wandered that whole time beyond two subjects—theology and love. And perhaps neither a court of love nor an assembly of divines would nave granted their premises or welcomed their conclusions.

Conclusions, indeed, are not often reached by talk any more than by private thinking. That is not the profit. The profit is in the exercise, and above all in the experience; for when we reason at large on any subject, we review our state and history in life. From time to time, however, and specially, I think, in talking art, talk becomes effective, conquering like war, widening the boundaries of knowledge like an exploration. A point arises; the question takes a problematical, a baffling, yet a likely air; the talkers begin to feel lively presentiments of some conclusion near at hand; towards this they strive with emulous ardour, each by his own path, and struggling for first utterance; and then one leaps upon the summit of that matter with a shout, and almost at the same moment the other is beside him; and behold they are agreed. Like enough, the progress is illusory, a mere cat's cradle having been wound and unwound out of words. But the sense of joint discovery is none the less giddy and inspiriting. And in the life of the talker such triumphs, though imaginary, are neither few nor far apart; they are attained with speed and pleasure, in the hour of mirth; and by the nature of the process, they are always worthily shared.

There is a certain attitude, combative at once and deferential, eager to fight yet most averse to quarrel, which marks out at once the talkable man. It is not eloquence, not fairness, not obstinacy, but a certain proportion of all of these that I love to encounter in my amicable adversaries. They must not be pontiffs holding doctrine, but huntsmen questing after elements of truth. Neither must they be boys to be instructed, but fellow-teachers with whom I may wrangle and agree on equal terms. We must reach some solution, some shadow of consent; for without that, eager talk becomes a torture. But we do not wish to reach it cheaply, or quickly, or without the tussle and effort wherein pleasure lies. . . .

One last remark occurs: It is the mark of genuine conversation that the sayings can scarce be quoted with their full effect beyond the circle of common friends. To have their proper weight they should appear in a biography, and with the portrait of the speaker. Good talk is dramatic; it is like an impromptu piece of acting where each should represent himself to the greatest advantage; and that is the best kind of talk where each speaker is most fully and candidly himself, and where, if you were to shift the speeches round from one to another, there would be the greatest loss in significance and perspicuity. It is for this reason that talk depends so wholly on our company. We should like to introduce Falstaff and Mercutio, or Falstaff and Sir Toby; but Falstaff in talk with Cordelia seems even painful.[1] Most of us, by the Protean[2] quality of man, can talk to some degree with all; but the true talk, that strikes out all the slumbering best of us, comes only with the peculiar brethren of our spirits, is founded as deep as love in the constitution of our being, and is a thing to relish with all our energy, while yet we have it, and to be grateful for for ever.

[1] Falstaff in *Henry IV*, Mercutio in *Romeo and Juliet*, Sir Toby Belch in *Twelfth Night* are comic or witty figures; but Cordelia, in *Lear*, is tragic.
[2] In Greek mythology Proteus was a sea-god especially noted for his power of changing rapidly from one form to another.

# BEGGARS[1]

## I

In a pleasant, airy, up-hill country, it was my fortune when I was young to make the acquaintance of a certain beggar. I call him beggar, though he usually allowed his coat and his shoes (which were open-mouthed, indeed) to beg for him. He was the wreck of an athletic man, tall, gaunt, and bronzed; far gone in consumption, with that disquieting smile of the mortally stricken on his face; but still active afoot, still with the brisk military carriage, the ready military salute. Three ways led through this piece of country; and as I was inconstant in my choice, I believe he must often have awaited me in vain. But often enough, he caught me; often enough, from some place of ambush by the roadside, he would spring suddenly forth in the regulation attitude, and launching at once into his inconsequential talk, fall into step with me upon my farther course. "A fine morning, sir, though perhaps a trifle inclining to rain. I hope I see you well, sir. Why, no, sir, I don't feel as hearty myself as I could wish, but I am keeping about my ordinary. I am pleased to meet you on the road, sir. I assure you I quite look

[1] Written in the latter part of 1887 while Stevenson was preparing for his winter at Saranac. This was one of twelve articles which the author, by agreement, contributed to *Scribner's Magazine* during the year 1888, *Beggars* appearing in the March number. The essay contains five sections, only the first two of which are here given. These two are, in Stevenson's opinion, better than the remainder, and are included by him more than once in the list of his own best works. *Beggars* was republished in the volume, *Across the Plains*, 1892.

forward to one of our little conversations." He loved the sound of his own voice inordinately, and though (with something too off-hand to call servility) he would always hasten to agree with anything you said, yet he could never suffer you to say it to an end. By what transition he slid to his favourite subject I have no memory; but we had never been long together on the way before he was dealing, in a very military manner, with the English poets. "Shelley was a fine poet, sir, though a trifle atheistical in his opinions. His Queen Mab, sir, is quite an atheistical work. Scott, sir, is not so poetical a writer. With the works of Shakespeare I am not so well acquainted, but he was a fine poet. Keats—John Keats, sir—he was a very fine poet." With such references, such trivial criticism, such loving parade of his own knowledge, he would beguile the road, striding forward up-hill, his staff now clapped to the ribs of his deep, resonant chest, now swinging in the air with the remembered jauntiness of the private soldier; and all the while his toes looking out of his boots, and his shirt looking out of his elbows, and death looking out of his smile, and his big, crazy frame shaken by accesses of cough.

He would often go the whole way home with me: often to borrow a book, and that book always a poet. Off he would march, to continue his mendicant rounds, with the volume slipped into the pocket of his ragged coat; and although he would sometimes keep it quite a while, yet it came always back again at last, not much the worse for its travels into beggardom. And in this way, doubtless, his knowledge grew and his glib, random criticism took a wider range. But my library was not the first he had drawn upon: at our first encounter, he was already brimful of Shelley and the atheistical Queen Mab, and "Keats—John Keats, sir." And I have often

wondered how he came by these acquirements; just as I
often wondered how he fell to be a beggar.  He had
served through the Mutiny[1]—of which (like so many people) he could tell practically nothing beyond the names
of places, and that it was "difficult work, sir," and very
hot, or that so-and-so was "a very fine commander, sir."
He was far too smart a man to have remained a private;
in the nature of things, he must have won his stripes.
And yet here he was without a pension.  When I touched
on this problem, he would content himself with diffidently
offering me advice.  "A man should be very careful when
he is young, sir.  If you 'll excuse me saying so, a spirited
young gentleman like yourself, sir, should be very careful.
I was perhaps a trifle inclined to atheistical opinions
myself."  For (perhaps with a deeper wisdom than we
are inclined in these days to admit) he plainly bracketed
agnosticism with beer and skittles.

Keats—John Keats, sir—and Shelley were his favourite bards.  I cannot remember if I tried him with Ros-
setti; but I know his taste to a hair, and if ever I did, he
must have doted on that author.  What took him was
a richness in the speech; he loved the exotic, the unexpected word; the moving cadence of a phrase; a vague
sense of emotion (about nothing) in the very letters of the
alphabet: the romance of language.  His honest head
was very nearly empty, his intellect like a child's; and
when he read his favourite authors, he can almost never
have understood what he was reading.  Yet the taste
was not only genuine, it was exclusive; I tried in vain to
offer him novels; he would none of them; he cared for
nothing but romantic language that he could not understand.  The case may be commoner than we suppose.  I
am reminded of a lad who was laid in the next cot to

[1] The great uprising of the Hindoos against their English rulers,
1857-1859.

a friend of mine in a public hospital, and who was no
sooner installed than he sent out (perhaps with his last
pence) for a cheap Shakespeare. My friend pricked up
his ears; fell at once in talk with his new neighbour, and
was ready, when the book arrived, to make a singular discovery. For this lover of great literature understood not
one sentence out of twelve, and his favourite part was
that of which he understood the least—the inimitable,
mouth-filling rodomontade of the ghost in *Hamlet*. It
was a bright day in hospital when my friend expounded
the sense of this beloved jargon: a task for which I am
willing to believe my friend was very fit, though I can
never regard it as an easy one. I know indeed a point or
two, on which I would gladly question Mr. Shakespeare,
that lover of big words, could he revisit the glimpses of the
moon, or could I myself climb backward to the spacious
days of Elizabeth. But in the second case, I should most
likely pretermit these questionings, and take my place
instead in the pit at the Blackfriars,[1] to hear the actor in
his favourite part, playing up to Mr. Burbage,[2] and rolling
out—as I seem to hear him—with a ponderous gusto—

"Unhousel'd, disappointed, unanel'd."

What a pleasant chance, if we could go there in a party!
and what a surprise for Mr. Burbage, when the ghost
received the honours of the evening!

As for my old soldier, like Mr. Burbage and Mr.
Shakespeare, he is long since dead; and now lies buried,
I suppose, and nameless and quite forgotten, in some
poor city graveyard.—But not for me, you brave heart,
have you been buried! For me, you are still afoot, tasting the sun and air, and striding southward. By the

[1] One of the theatres with which Shakespeare was connected.
[2] Richard Burbage, the foremost tragic actor of Shakespeare's
time

groves of Comiston and beside the Hermitage of Braid,
by the Hunters' Tryst, and where the curlews and
plovers cry around Fairmilehead, I see and hear you,
stalwartly carrying your deadly sickness, cheerfully
discoursing of uncomprehended poets.

## II

The thought of the old soldier recalls that of another
tramp, his counterpart. This was a little, lean, and fiery
man, with the eyes of a dog and the face of a gipsy; whom
I found one morning encamped with his wife and children
and his grinder's wheel, beside the burn of Kinnaird.
To this beloved dell I went, at that time, daily; and daily
the knife-grinder and I (for as long as his tent continued
pleasantly to interrupt my little wilderness) sat on two
stones, and smoked, and plucked grass, and talked to the
tune of the brown water. His children were mere whelps,
they fought and bit among the fern like vermin. His
wife was a mere squaw; I saw her gather brush and tend
the kettle, but she never ventured to address her lord while
I was present. The tent was a mere gipsy hovel, like a
sty for pigs. But the grinder himself had the fine self-
sufficiency and grave politeness of the hunter and the
savage; he did me the honours of this dell, which had
been mine but the day before, took me far into the secrets
of his life, and used me (I am proud to remember) as a
friend.

Like my old soldier, he was far gone in the national
complaint. Unlike him, he had a vulgar taste in letters;
scarce flying higher than the story papers; probably
finding no difference, certainly seeking none, between
Tannahill and Burns;[1] his noblest thoughts, whether of

[1] Robert Tannahill (1774–1810), a minor Scotch poet. Robert
Burns (1759–1796), the greatest lyric poet of Scotland.

poetry or music, adequately embodied in that somewhat
obvious ditty,

> "Will ye gang, lassie, gang
>   To the braes o' Balquidder:"

—which is indeed apt to echo in the ears of Scottish
children, and to him, in view of his experience, must have
found a special directness of address.    But if he had no
fine sense of poetry in letters, he felt with a deep joy the
poetry of life.    You should have heard him speak of what
he loved; of the tent pitched beside the talking water;
of the stars overhead at night; of the blest return of morning, the peep of day over the moors, the awaking birds
among the birches; how he abhorred the long winter shut
in cities; and with what delight, at the return of the
spring, he once more pitched his camp in the living out-
of-doors.    But we were a pair of tramps; and to you, who
are doubtless sedentary and a consistent first-class passenger in life, he would scarce have laid himself so open;—
to you, he might have been content to tell his story of a
ghost—that of a buccaneer with his pistols as he lived—
whom he had once encountered in a seaside cave near
Buckie; and that would have been enough, for that would
have shown you the mettle of the man.    Here was a piece
of experience solidly and livingly built up in words,
here was a story created, *teres atque rotundus.*[1]

And to think of the old soldier, that lover of the literary bards!    He had visited stranger spots than any
seaside cave; encountered men more terrible than any
spirit; done and dared and suffered in that incredible,
unsung epic of the Mutiny War; played his part with the
field force of Delhi, beleaguering and beleaguered; shared
in that enduring, savage anger and contempt of death
and decency that, for long months together, bedevil'd and

---

[1] Smooth-polished and rounded, a quotation from Horace.

inspired the army; was hurled to and fro in the battle-smoke of the assault; was there, perhaps, where Nicholson[1] fell; was there when the attacking column, with hell upon every side, found the soldier's enemy—strong drink, and the lives of tens of thousands trembled in the scale, and the fate of the flag of England staggered. And of all this he had no more to say than "hot work, sir," or "the army suffered a great deal, sir," or "I believe General Wilson, sir, was not very highly thought of in the papers." His life was naught to him, the vivid pages of experience quite blank: in words his pleasure lay—melodious, agitated words—printed words, about that which he had never seen and was connatally incapable of comprehending. We have here two temperaments face to face; both untrained, unsophisticated, surprised (we may say) in the egg; both boldly charactered:—that of the artist, the lover and artificer of words; that of the maker, the seeër, the lover and forger of experience. If the one had a daughter and the other had a son, and these married, might not some illustrious writer count descent from the beggar-soldier and the needy knife-grinder?

[1] John Nicholson, a British general, died of his wounds received at Delhi, September, 1857.

# PULVIS ET UMBRA [1]

We look for some reward of our endeavours and are disappointed; not success, not happiness, not even peace of conscience, crowns our ineffectual efforts to do well. Our frailties are invincible, are virtues barren; the battle goes sore against us to the going down of the sun. The canting moralist tells us of right and wrong; and we look abroad, even on the face of our small earth, and find them change with every climate, and no country where some action is not honoured for a virtue and none where it is not branded for a vice; and we look in our experience, and find no vital congruity in the wisest rules, but at the best a municipal fitness. It is not strange if we are tempted to despair of good. We ask too much. Our religions and moralities have been trimmed to flatter us, till they are all emasculate and sentimentalised, and only please and weaken. Truth is of a rougher strain. In the harsh face of life, faith can read a bracing gospel. The human race is a thing more ancient than the ten

[1] This, like *Beggars*, was one of the twelve articles contributed to *Scribner's Magazine* during 1888; and with *Beggars* it was included in *Across the Plains*, 1892. "I think there is some fine writing in it," wrote Stevenson to Colvin, "some very apt and pregnant phrases. *Pulvis et Umbra*, I call it; I might have called it a *Darwinian Sermon*." To Miss Adelaide Boodle he says, "I wrote it with great feeling and conviction; to me it seemed bracing and healthful. . . . But I find that to some people this vision of mine is a nightmare, and extinguishes all ground of faith in God or pleasure in man. . . . If my view be everything but the nonsense that it may be—to me it seems self-evident and blinding truth—surely of all things it makes this world holier." The title is from Horace, *Pulvis et umbra sumus*, "we are dust and shadow," or "dust and ashes."

commandments; and the bones and revolutions of the Kosmos,[1] in whose joints we are but moss and fungus, more ancient still.

I

Of the Kosmos in the last resort, science reports many doubtful things and all of them appalling. There seems no substance to this solid globe on which we stamp: nothing but symbols and ratios. Symbols and ratios carry us and bring us forth and beat us down; gravity that swings the incommensurable suns and worlds through space, is but a figment varying inversely as the squares of distances; and the suns and worlds themselves, imponderable figures of abstraction, $NH_3$ and $H_2O$.[2] Consideration dares not dwell upon this view; that way madness lies; science carries us into zones of speculation, where there is no habitable city for the mind of man.

But take the Kosmos with a grosser faith, as our senses give it us. We behold space sown with rotatory islands, suns and worlds and the shards and wrecks of systems: some, like the sun, still blazing; some rotting, like the earth; others, like the moon, stable in desolation. All of these we take to be made of something we call matter: a thing which no analysis can help us to conceive; to whose incredible properties no familiarity can reconcile our minds. This stuff, when not purified by the lustration of fire, rots uncleanly into something we call life; seized through all its atoms with a pediculous[3] malady; swelling in tumours that become independent, sometimes even (by an abhorrent prodigy) locomotory; one splitting into millions, millions cohering into one,

[1] The orderly system of the universe.
[2] Chemical formulas for ammonia and water respectively.
[3] Infested with lice.

as the malady proceeds through varying stages. This vital putrescence of the dust, used as we are to it, yet strikes us with occasional disgust, and the profusion of worms in a piece of ancient turf, or the air of a marsh darkened with insects, will sometimes check our breathing so that we aspire for cleaner places. But none is clean: the moving sand is infected with lice; the pure spring, where it bursts out of the mountain, is a mere issue of worms; even in the hard rock the crystal is forming.

In two main shapes this eruption covers the countenance of the earth: the animal and the vegetable: one in some degree the inversion of the other: the second rooted to the spot; the first coming detached out of its natal mud, and scurrying abroad with the myriad feet of insects or towering into the heavens on the wings of birds: a thing so inconceivable that, if it be well considered, the heart stops. To what passes with the anchored vermin, we have little clue: doubtless they have their joys and sorrows, their delights and killing agonies: it appears not how. But of the locomotory, to which we ourselves belong, we can tell more. These share with us a thousand miracles: the miracles of sight, of hearing, of the projection of sound, things that bridge space; the miracles of memory and reason, by which the present is conceived, and when it is gone, its image kept living in the brains of man and brute; the miracle of reproduction, with its imperious desires and staggering consequences. And to put the last touch upon this mountain mass of the revolting and the inconceivable, all these prey upon each other, lives tearing other lives in pieces, cramming them inside themselves, and by that summary process, growing fat: the vegetarian, the whale, perhaps the tree, not less than the lion of the desert; for the vegetarian is only the eater of the dumb.

Meanwhile our rotatory island loaded with predatory life, and more drenched with blood, both animal and vegetable, than ever mutinied ship, scuds through space with unimaginable speed, and turns alternate cheeks to the reverberation of a blazing world, ninety million miles away.

II

What a monstrous spectre is this man, the disease of the agglutinated dust, lifting alternate feet or lying drugged with slumber; killing, feeding, growing, bringing forth small copies of himself; grown upon with hair like grass, fitted with eyes that move and glitter in his face; a thing to set children screaming;—and yet looked at nearlier, known as his fellows know him, how surprising are his attributes! Poor soul, here for so little, cast among so many hardships, filled with desires so incommensurate and so inconsistent, savagely surrounded, savagely descended, irremediably condemned to prey upon his fellow lives: who should have blamed him had he been of a piece with his destiny and a being merely barbarous? And we look and behold him instead filled with imperfect virtues: infinitely childish, often admirably valiant, often touchingly kind; sitting down, amidst his momentary life, to debate of right and wrong and the attributes of the deity; rising up to do battle for an egg or die for an idea; singling out his friends and his mate with cordial affection; bringing forth in pain, rearing with long-suffering solicitude, his young. To touch the heart of his mystery, we find in him one thought, strange to the point of lunacy: the thought of duty; the thought of something owing to himself, to his neighbour, to his God: an ideal of decency, to which he would rise if it were possible; a limit of shame, below which, if it be possible, he

will not stoop.  The design in most men is one of con-
formity; here and there, in picked natures, it transcends
itself and soars on the other side, arming martyrs with
independence; but in all, in their degrees, it is a bosom
thought:—Not in man alone, for we trace it in dogs and
cats whom we know fairly well, and doubtless some similar point of honour sways the elephant, the oyster, and
the louse, of whom we know so little:—But in man, at
least, it sways with so complete an empire that merely
selfish things come second, even with the selfish: that appetites are starved, fears are conquered, pains supported;
that almost the dullest shrinks from the reproof of a
glance, although it were a child's; and all but the most
cowardly stand amid the risks of war; and the more
noble, having strongly conceived an act as due to their
ideal, affront and embrace death.  Strange enough if,
with their singular origin and perverted practice, they
think they are to be rewarded in some future life:
stranger still, if they are persuaded of the contrary, and
think this blow, which they solicit, will strike them
senseless for eternity.  I shall be reminded what a
tragedy of misconception and misconduct man at large
presents: of organised injustice, cowardly violence and
treacherous crime; and of the damning imperfections of
the best.  They cannot be too darkly drawn.  Man is
indeed marked for failure in his efforts to do right.  But
where the best consistently miscarry, how tenfold more
remarkable that all should continue to strive; and surely
we should find it both touching and inspiriting, that in a
field from which success is banished, our race should not
cease to labour.

If the first view of this creature, stalking in his rotatory isle, be a thing to shake the courage of the stoutest,
on this nearer sight, he startles us with an admiring wonder.  It matters not where we look, under what climate

we observe him, in what stage of society, in what depth
of ignorance, burthened with what erroneous morality;
by camp-fires in Assiniboia,[1] the snow powdering his
shoulders, the wind plucking his blanket, as he sits, passing the ceremonial calumet[2] and uttering his grave
opinions like a Roman senator; in ships at sea, a man
inured to hardship and vile pleasures, his brightest hope
a fiddle in a tavern and a bedizened trull who sells herself
to rob him, and he for all that simple, innocent, cheerful,
kindly like a child, constant to toil, brave to drown, for
others; in the slums of cities, moving among indifferent
millions to mechanical employments, without hope of
change in the future, with scarce a pleasure in the present,
and yet true to his virtues, honest up to his lights, kind to
his neighbours, tempted perhaps in vain by the bright
gin-palace, perhaps long-suffering with the drunken wife
that ruins him; in India (a woman this time) kneeling
with broken cries and streaming tears, as she drowns her
child in the sacred river; in the brothel, the discard of
society, living mainly on strong drink, fed with affronts,
a fool, a thief, the comrade of thieves, and even here keeping the point of honour and the touch of pity, often repay-
ing the world's scorn with service, often standing firm
upon a scruple, and at a certain cost, rejecting riches:—
everywhere some virtue cherished or affected, everywhere some decency of thought and carriage, everywhere
the ensign of man's ineffectual goodness:—ah! if I could
show you this! if I could show you these men and
women, all the world over, in every stage of history, under
every abuse of error, under every circumstance of failure, without hope, without help, without thanks, still obscurely fighting the lost fight of virtue, still clinging, in
the brothel or on the scaffold, to some rag of honour, the

---

[1] A district in central Canada.
[2] The Indian pipe of peace.

poor jewel of their souls! They may seek to escape, and yet they cannot; it is not alone their privilege and glory, but their doom; they are condemned to some nobility; all their lives long, the desire of good is at their heels, the implacable hunter.

Of all earth's meteors, here at least is the most strange and consoling: that this ennobled lemur,[1] this hair-crowned bubble of the dust, this inheritor of a few years and sorrows, should yet deny himself his rare delights, and add to his frequent pains, and live for an ideal, however misconceived. Nor can we stop with man. A new doctrine,[2] received with screams a little while ago by cant-ing moralists, and still not properly worked into the body of our thoughts, lights us a step farther into the heart of this rough but noble universe. For nowadays the pride of man denies in vain his kinship with the original dust. He stands no longer like a thing apart. Close at his heels we see the dog, prince of another genus: and in him too, we see dumbly testified the same cultus of an unattainable ideal, the same constancy in failure. Does it stop with the dog? We look at our feet where the ground is blackened with the swarming ant: a creature so small, so far from us in the hierarchy of brutes, that we can scarce trace and scarce comprehend his doings; and here also, in his ordered polities and rigorous jus-tice, we see confessed the law of duty and the fact of in-dividual sin. Does it stop, then, with the ant? Rather this desire of well-doing and this doom of frailty run through all the grades of life: rather is this earth, from the frosty top of Everest to the next margin of the inter-nal fire, one stage of ineffectual virtues and one temple of pious tears and perseverance. The whole creation groaneth and travaileth together. It is the common and

---

[1] A small animal allied to the monkey.
[2] The theory of evolution.

the god-like law of life. The browsers, the biters, the barkers, the hairy coats of field and forest, the squirrel in the oak, the thousand-footed creeper in the dust, as they share with us the gift of life, share with us the love of an ideal: strive like us—like us are tempted to grow weary of the struggle—to do well; like us receive at times unmerited refreshment, visitings of support, returns of courage; and are condemned like us to be crucified between that double law of the members and the will. Are they like us, I wonder, in the timid hope of some reward, some sugar with the drug? do they, too, stand aghast at unrewarded virtues, at the sufferings of those whom, in our partiality, we take to be just, and the prosperity of such as, in our blindness, we call wicked? It may be, and yet God knows what they should look for. Even while they look, even while they repent, the foot of man treads them by thousands in the dust, the yelping hounds burst upon their trail, the bullet speeds, the knives are heating in the den of the vivisectionist; or the dew falls, and the generation of a day is blotted out. For these are creatures, compared with whom our weakness is strength, our ignorance wisdom, our brief span eternity.

And as we dwell, we living things, in our isle of terror and under the imminent hand of death, God forbid it should be man the erected, the reasoner, the wise in his own eyes—God forbid it should be man that wearies in well-doing, that despairs of unrewarded effort, or utters the language of complaint. Let it be enough for faith, that the whole creation groans in mortal frailty, strives with inconquerable constancy: Surely not all in vain.

# FATHER DAMIEN

# FATHER DAMIEN [1]

## AN OPEN LETTER TO THE REVEREND DR. HYDE OF HONOLULU

SYDNEY, *February* 25, 1890.

SIR,—It may probably occur to you that we have met, and visited, and conversed; on my side, with interest. You may remember that you have done me several courtesies, for which I was prepared to be grateful. But there are duties which come before gratitude, and offences which justly divide friends, far more acquaintances. Your letter to the Reverend H. B. Gage is a document which, in my sight, if you had filled me with bread when I was starving, if you had sat up to nurse my father when he lay a-dying, would yet absolve me from the bonds of gratitude. You know enough, doubtless, of the process of canonisation to be aware that, a hundred years after the death of Damien, there will appear a man

[1] Father Damien died April 15, 1889. Stevenson visited Molokai, the island of the lepers, in May of the same year. While he was in Sydney, Australia, in February of 1890, he read Dr. Hyde's letter and heard at the same time a report that a proposed memorial to Damien in London had been abandoned on account of it, or of charges similar to those which it contained. The fiery invective printed above was the result. It was first published on March 27th of this year in pamphlet form at Sydney; afterwards reprinted in *The Scots Observer* at Edinburgh, and in the collected works. Stevenson's letters describing his visit to Molokai (printed on pp. 30–36 of these selections) should be read in connection with *Father Damien*. In justice to Dr. Hyde, it should be noted that he was possessed of an independent fortune, and so did not grow rich in the course of his "evangelical calling"; furthermore, that his letter to the Rev. H. B. Gage seems not to have been intended for publication.

charged with the painful office of the *devil's advocate.*
After that noble brother of mine, and of all frail clay, shall
have lain a century at rest, one shall accuse, one defend
him.   The circumstance is unusual that the devil's advocate should be a volunteer, should be a member of a sect
immediately rival, and should make haste to take upon
himself his ugly office ere the bones are cold; unusual, and
of a taste which I shall leave my readers free to qualify:
unusual, and to me inspiring.   If I have at all learned the
trade of using words to convey truth and to arouse emotion, you have at last furnished me with a subject.   For
it is in the interest of all mankind and the cause of public decency in every quarter of the world, not only that
Damien should be righted, but that you and your letter
should be displayed at length, in their true colours, to
the public eye.

To do this properly, I must begin by quoting you at
large: I shall then proceed to criticise your utterance
from several points of view, divine and human, in the
course of which I shall attempt to draw again and with
more specification the character of the dead saint whom
it has pleased you to vilify: so much being done, I shall
say farewell to you forever.

"Honolulu, *August* 2, 1889.
"Rev. H. B. Gage.

"Dear Brother,—In answer to your inquiries about
Father Damien, I can only reply that we who knew the
man are surprised at the extravagant newspaper lauda-
tions, as if he was a most saintly philanthropist.   The
simple truth is, he was a coarse, dirty man, headstrong
and bigoted.   He was not sent to Molokai, but went there
without orders; did not stay at the leper settlement (before he became one himself), but circulated freely over
the whole island (less than half the island is devoted to

the lepers), and he came often to Honolulu.  He had no hand in the reforms and improvements inaugurated, which were the work of our Board of Health, as occasion required and means were provided.  He was not a pure man in his relations with women, and the leprosy of which he died should be attributed to his vices and carelessness. Others have done much for the lepers, our own ministers, the government physicians, and so forth, but never with the Catholic idea of meriting eternal life.—Yours, etc.,

"C. M. HYDE." [1]

To deal fitly with a letter so extraordinary, I must draw at the outset on my private knowledge of the signatory and his sect.  It may offend others; scarcely you, who have been so busy to collect, so bold to publish, gossip on your rivals.  And this is perhaps the moment when I may best explain to you the character of what you are to read: I conceive you as a man quite beyond and below the reticences of civility: with what measure you mete, with that shall it be measured you again; with you, at last, I rejoice to feel the button off the foil and to plunge home. And if in aught that I shall say I should offend others, your colleagues, whom I respect and remember with affection, I can but offer them my regret; I am not free, I am inspired by the consideration of interests far more large; and such pain as can be inflicted by anything from me must be indeed trifling when compared with the pain with which they read your letter.  It is not the hangman, but the criminal, that brings dishonour on the house.

You belong, sir, to a sect—I believe my sect, and that in which my ancestors laboured—which has enjoyed, and partly failed to utilise, an exceptional advantage in the islands of Hawaii.  The first missionaries came; they found the land already self-purged of its old and bloody

[1] From the Sydney *Presbyterian*, October 26, 1889.

faith; they were embraced, almost on their arrival, with enthusiasm; what troubles they supported came far more from whites than from 'Hawaiians; and to these last they stood (in a rough figure) in the shoes of God. This is not the place to enter into the degree or causes of their failure, such as it is. One element alone is pertinent, and must here be plainly dealt with. In the course of their evangelical calling, they—or too many of them— grew rich. It may be news to you that the houses of missionaries are a cause of mocking on the streets of Honolulu. It will at least be news to you, that when I returned your civil visit, the driver of my cab commented on the size, the taste, and the comfort of your home. It would have been news certainly to myself, had any one told me that afternoon that I should live to drag such matter into print. But you see, sir, how you degrade better men to your own level; and it is needful that those who are to judge betwixt you and me, betwixt Damien and the devil's advocate, should understand your letter to have been penned in a house which could raise, and that very justly, the envy and the comments of the passers-by. I think (to employ a phrase of yours which I admire) it "should be attributed" to you that you have never visited the scene of Damien's life and death. If you had, and had recalled it, and looked about your pleasant rooms, even your pen perhaps would have been stayed.

Your sect (and remember, as far as any sect avows me, it is mine) has not done ill in a worldly sense in the Hawaiian Kingdom. When calamity befell their inno- cent parishioners, when leprosy descended and took root in the Eight Islands, a *quid pro quo* was to be looked for. To that prosperous mission, and to you, as one of its adornments, God had sent at last an opportunity. I know I am touching here upon a nerve acutely sensitive. I know that others of your colleagues look back on the inertia of your Church, and the intrusive and decisive heroism of Damien, with something almost to be called remorse. I am sure it is so with yourself; I am persuaded your letter was inspired by a certain envy, not essentially ignoble, and the one human trait to be espied in that performance. You were thinking of the lost chance, the past day; of that which should have been conceived and was not; of the service due and not rendered. *Time was*, said the voice in your ear, in your pleasant room, as you sat raging and writing; and if the words written were base beyond parallel, the rage, I am happy to repeat—it is the only compliment I shall pay you—the rage was almost virtuous. But, sir, when we have failed, and another has succeeded; when we have stood by, and another has stepped in; when we sit and grow bulky in our charming mansions, and a plain, uncouth peasant steps into the battle, under the eyes of God, and succours the afflicted, and consoles the dying, and is himself afflicted in his turn, and dies upon the field of honour—the battle cannot be retrieved as your unhappy irritation has suggested. It is a lost battle, and lost forever. One thing remained to you in your defeat —some rags of common honour; and these you have made haste to cast away.

Common honour; not the honour of having done anything right, but the honour of not having done aught conspicuously foul; the honour of the inert: that was what remained to you. We are not all expected to be Damiens; a man may conceive his duty more narrowly, he may love his comforts better; and none will cast a stone at him for that. But will a gentleman of your reverend profession allow me an example from the fields of gallantry? When two gentlemen compete for the favour of a lady, and the one succeeds and the other is rejected, and (as will sometimes happen) matter damaging tc the successful rival's credit reaches the ear of the defeated, it is held by plain men of no pretensions that his mouth is, in the circumstance, almost necessarily closed. Your Church and Damien's were in Hawaii upon a rivalry to do well: to help, to edify, to set divine examples. You having (in one huge instance) failed, and Damien succeeded, I marvel it should not have occurred to you that you were doomed to silence; that when you had been outstripped in that high rivalry, and sat inglorious in the midst of your well-being, in your pleasant room—and Damien, crowned with glories and horrors, toiled and rotted in that pigstye of his under the cliffs of Kalawao—you, the elect who would not, were the last man on earth to collect and propagate gossip on the volunteer who would and did.

I think I see you—for I try to see you in the flesh as I write these sentences—I think I see you leap at the word pigstye, a hyperbolical expression at the best. "He had no hand in the reforms," he was "a coarse, dirty man"; these were your own words; and you may think it possible that I am come to support you with fresh evidence. In a sense, it is even so. Damien has been too much depicted with a conventional halo and conventional features; so drawn by men who perhaps had not the eye to remark or the pen to express the individual; or who perhaps were only blinded and silenced by generous admiration, such as I partly envy for myself—such as you, if your soul were enlightened, would envy on your bended knees. It is the least defect of such a method of portraiture that it makes the path easy for the devil's advocate, and leaves for the misuse of the slanderer a considerable field of truth. For the truth that is suppressed by friends is the readiest weapon of the enemy. The world, in your despite, may perhaps owe you something, if your letter be the means of substituting once for all a credible likeness for a wax abstraction. For, if that world at all re-

member you, on the day when Damien of Molokai shall
be named Saint, it will be in virtue of one work: your
letter to the Reverend H. B. Gage.

You may ask on what authority I speak. It was my
inclement destiny to become acquainted, not with Damien, but with Dr. Hyde. When I visited the lazaretto
Damien was already in his resting grave. But such information as I have, I gathered on the spot in conversation with those who knew him well and long: some indeed who revered his memory; but others who had
sparred and wrangled with him, who beheld him with
no halo, who perhaps regarded him with small respect,
and through whose unprepared and scarcely partial communications the plain, human features of the man shone
on me convincingly. These gave me what knowledge
I possess; and I learnt it in that scene where it could
be most completely and sensitively understood—Kalawao, which you have never visited, about which you
have never so much as endeavoured to inform yourself:
for, brief as your letter is, you have found the means to
stumble into that confession. "*Less than one-half* of the
island," you say, "is devoted to the lepers." Molokai—
"*Molokai ahina*," the "grey," lofty, and most desolate
island—along all its northern side plunges a front of precipice into a sea of unusual profundity. This range of cliff
is, from east to west, the true end and frontier of the
island. Only in one spot there projects into the ocean
a certain triangular and rugged down, grassy, stony,
windy, and rising in the midst into a hill with a dead
crater: the whole bearing to the cliff that overhangs it
somewhat the same relation as a bracket to a wall. With
this hint you will now be able to pick out the leper station
on a map; you will be able to judge how much of Molokai
is thus cut off between the surf and precipice, whether
less than a half, or less than a quarter, or a fifth, or a

tenth—or say, a twentieth; and the next time you burst into print you will be in a position to share with us the issue of your calculations.

I imagine you to be one of those persons who talk with cheerfulness of that place which oxen and wainropes could not drag you to behold. You, who do not even know its situation on the map, probably denounce sensational descriptions, stretching your limbs the while in your pleasant parlour on Beretania Street. When I was pulled ashore there one early morning, there sat with me in the boat two sisters, bidding farewell (in humble imitation of Damien) to the lights and joys of human life. One of these wept silently; I could not withhold myself from joining her. Had you been there, it is my belief that nature would have triumphed even in you; and as the boat drew but a little nearer, and you beheld the stairs crowded with abominable deformations of our common manhood, and saw yourself landing in the midst of such a population as only now and then surrounds us in the horror of a nightmare—what a haggard eye you would have rolled over your reluctant shoulder towards the house on Beretania Street! Had you gone on; had you found every fourth face a blot upon the landscape; had you visited the hospital and seen the butt-ends of human beings lying there almost unrecognisable, but still breathing, still thinking, still remembering; you would have understood that life in the lazaretto is an ordeal from which the nerves of a man's spirit shrink, even as his eye quails under the brightness of the sun; you would have felt it was (even to-day) a pitiful place to visit and a hell to dwell in. It is not the fear of possible infection. That seems a little thing when compared with the pain, the pity, and the disgust of the visitor's surroundings, and the atmosphere of affliction, disease, and physical disgrace in which he breathes. I do not think I am a man

more than u ually timid; but I never recall the days and
nights I spent upon that island promontory (eight days
and seven nights), without heartfelt thankfulness that I
am somewhere else. I find in my diary that I speak of
my stay as a "grinding experience": I have once jotted
in the margin, "*Harrowing* is the word"; and when
the *Mokolii* bore me at last towards the outer world, I
kept repeating to myself, with a new conception of their
pregnancy, those simple words of the song—

"'T is the most distressful country that ever yet was seen."

And observe: that which I saw and suffered from was
a settlement purged, bettered, beautified; the new village
built, the hospital and the Bishop-Home excellently arranged; the sisters, the doctor, and the missionaries, all
indefatigable in their noble tasks. It was a different
place when Damien came there, and made his great renunciation, and slept that first night under a tree amidst
his rotting brethren: alone with pestilence; and looking
forward (with what courage, with what pitiful sinkings
of dread, God only knows) to a lifetime of dressing sores
and stumps.

You will say, perhaps, I am too sensitive, that sights
as painful abound in cancer hospitals and are confronted
daily by doctors and nurses. I have long learned to admire and envy the doctors and the nurses. But there is
no cancer hospital so large and populous as Kalawao and
Kalaupapa; and in such a matter every fresh case, like
every inch of length in the pipe of an organ, deepens the
note of the impression; for what daunts the onlooker is
that monstrous sum of human suffering by which he
stands surrounded. Lastly, no doctor or nurse is called
upon to enter once for all the doors of that gehenna; they
do not say farewell, they need not abandon hope, on its
sad threshold; they but go for a time to their high calling,

and can look forward as they go to relief, to recreation, and to rest.     But Damien shut to with his own hand the doors of his own sepulchre.

I shall now extract three passages from my diary at Kalawao.

*A*.   "Damien is dead and already somewhat ungratefully remembered in the field of his labours and sufferings.   'He was a good man, but very officious,' says one.   Another tells me he had fallen (as other priests so easily do) into something of the ways and habits of thought of a Kanaka; but he had the wit to recognise the fact, and the good sense to laugh at" [over] "it.   A plain man it seems he was; I cannot find he was a popular."

*B*.   "After Ragsdale's death" [Ragsdale was a famous Luna, or overseer, of the unruly settlement] "there followed a brief term of office by Father Damien which served only to publish the weakness of that noble man.   He was rough in his ways, and he had no control.   Authority was relaxed; Damien's life was threatened, and he was soon eager to resign."

*C*.   "Of Damien I begin to have an idea.   He seems to have been a man of the peasant class, certainly of the peasant type: shrewd; ignorant and bigoted, yet with an open mind, and capable of receiving and digesting a reproof if it were bluntly administered; superbly generous in the least thing as well as in the greatest, and as ready to give his last shirt (although not without human grumbling) as he had been to sacrifice his life; essentially indiscreet and officious, which made him a troublesome colleague; domineering in all his ways, which made him incurably unpopular with the Kanakas, but yet destitute of real authority, so that his boys laughed at him and he must carry out his wishes by the means of bribes.   He learned to have a mania for doctoring; and set up the Kanakas against the remedies of his regular rivals: perhaps (if anything matter at all in the treatment of such a disease) the worst thing that he did, and certainly the easiest. The best and worst of the man appear very plainly in his dealings with Mr. Chapman's money; he had originally laid it out" [intended to lay it out] "entirely for the benefit of Catholics, and even so not wisely; but after a long, plain talk, he admitted his error fully and revised the list. The sad state of the boys' home is in part the result of his lack of control; in part, of his own slovenly ways and false ideas of hygiene. Brother officials used to call it 'Damien's Chinatown.' 'Well,' they would say, 'your Chinatown keeps growing.' And he would laugh with perfect good-nature, and adhere to his errors with perfect obstinacy. So much I have gathered of truth about this plain, noble human brother and father of ours; his imperfections are the traits of his face, by which we know him for our fellow; his martyrdom and his example nothing can lessen or annul; and only a person here on the spot can properly appreciate their greatness."

I have set down these private passages, as you perceive, without correction; thanks to you, the public has them in their bluntness. They are almost a list of the man's faults, for it is rather these that I was seeking: with his virtues, with the heroic profile of his life, I and the world were already sufficiently acquainted. I was besides a little suspicious of Catholic testimony; in no ill sense, but merely because Damien's admirers and disciples were the least likely to be critical. I know you will be more suspicious still; and the facts set down above were one and all collected from the lips of Protestants who had opposed the father in his life. Yet I am strangely deceived, or they build up the image of a man, with all his weaknesses, essentially heroic, and alive with rugged honesty, generosity, and mirth.

Take it for what it is, rough private jottings of the worst sides of Damien's character, collected from the lips of those who had laboured with and (in your own phrase) "knew the man";—though I question whether Damien would have said that he knew you. Take it, and observe with wonder how well you were served by your gossips, how ill by your intelligence and sympathy; in how many points of fact we are at one, and how widely our appreciations vary. There is something wrong here; either with you or me. It is possible, for instance, that you, who seem to have so many ears in Kalawao, had heard of the affair of Mr. Chapman's money, and were singly struck by Damien's intended wrong-doing. I was struck with that also, and set it fairly down; but I was struck much more by the fact that he had the honesty of mind to be convinced. I may here tell you that it was a long business; that one of his colleagues sat with him late into the night, multiplying arguments and accusations; that the father listened as usual with "perfect good-nature and perfect obstinacy"; but at the last, when he was persuaded—"Yes," said he, "I am very much obliged to you; you have done me a service; it would have been a theft." There are many (not Catholics merely) who require their heroes and saints to be infallible; to these the story will be painful; not to the true lovers, patrons, and servants of mankind.

And I take it, this is a type of our division; that you are one of those who have an eye for faults and failures; that you take a pleasure to find and publish them; and that, having found them, you make haste to forget the overvailing virtues and the real success which had alone introduced them to your knowledge. It is a dangerous frame of mind. That you may understand how dangerous, and into what a situation it has already brought you, we will (if you please) go hand-in-hand through the different phrases of your letter, and candidly examine each from the point of view of its truth, its appositeness, and its charity.

Damien was *coarse*.

It is very possible. You make us sorry for the lepers who had only a coarse old peasant for their friend and father. But you, who were so refined, why were you not there, to cheer them with the lights of culture? Or may I remind you that we have some reason to doubt if John the Baptist were genteel; and in the case of Peter, on whose career you doubtless dwell approvingly in the pulpit, no doubt at all he was a "coarse, headstrong" fisherman! Yet even in our Protestant Bibles Peter is called Saint.

Damien was *dirty*.

He was. Think of the poor lepers annoyed with this dirty comrade! But the clean Dr. Hyde was at his food in a fine house.

Damien was *headstrong*.

I believe you are right again; and I thank God for his strong head and heart.

Damien was *bigoted*.

I am not fond of bigots myself, because they are not fond of me. But what is meant by bigotry, that we should regard it as a blemish in a priest? Damien believed his own religion with the simplicity of a peasant or a child; as I would I could suppose that you do. For this, I wonder at him some way off; and had that been his only character, should have avoided him in life. But the point of interest in Damien, which has caused him to be so much talked about and made him at last the subject of your pen and mine, was that, in him, his bigotry, his intense and narrow faith, wrought potently for good, and strengthened him to be one of the world's heroes and exemplars.

Damien *was not sent to Molokai, but went there without orders.*

Is this a misreading? or do you really mean the words for blame? I have heard Christ, in the pulpits of our Church, held up for imitation on the ground that His sacrifice was voluntary. Does Dr. Hyde think otherwise?

Damien *did not stay at the settlement, etc.*

It is true he was allowed many indulgences. Am I to understand that you blame the father for profiting by these, or the officers for granting them? In either case, it is a mighty Spartan standard to issue from the house on Beretania Street; and I am convinced you will find yourself with few supporters.

Damien *had no hand in the reforms, etc.*

I think even you will admit that I have already been frank in my description of the man I am defending; but before I take you up upon this head, I will be franker still, and tell you that perhaps nowhere in the world can a man taste a more pleasurable sense of contrast than when he passes from Damien's "Chinatown" at Kalawao to the beautiful Bishop-Home at Kalaupapa. At this point, in my desire to make all fair for you, I will break my rule and adduce Catholic testimony. Here is a passage from my diary about my visit to the Chinatown, from which you will see how it is (even now) regarded by its own officials: "We went round all the dormitories, refectories, etc.—dark and dingy enough, with a superficial cleanliness, which he" [Mr. Dutton, the lay brother] "did not seek to defend. 'It is almost decent,' said he; 'the sisters will make that all right when we get them here.'" And yet I gathered it was already better since Damien was dead, and far better than when he was there alone and had his own (not always excellent) way. I have now come far enough to meet you on a common ground of fact; and I tell you that, to a mind not prejudiced by jealousy, all the reforms of the lazaretto, and even those which he most vigorously opposed, are properly the work of Damien. They are the evidence of his success; they are what his heroism provoked from the reluctant and the careless. Many were before him in the field; Mr. Meyer, for instance, of whose faithful work we hear too little: there have been many since; and some had more worldly wisdom, though none had more devotion, than our saint. Before his day, even you will confess, they had effected little. It was his part, by one striking act of martyrdom, to direct all men's eyes on that distressful country. At a blow, and with the price of his life, he made the place illustrious and public. And that, if you will consider largely, was the one reform needful; pregnant of all that should succeed. It brought money; it brought (best individual addition of them all) the sisters; it brought supervision, for public opinion and public interest landed with the man at Kalawao. If ever any man brought reforms, and died to bring them, it was he. There is not a clean cup or towel in the Bishop-Home, but dirty Damien washed it.

*Damien was not a pure man in his relations with women, etc.*

How do you know that? Is this the nature of the conversation in that house on Beretania Street which the cabman envied, driving past?—racy details of the misconduct of the poor peasant priest, toiling under the cliffs of Molokai?

Many have visited the station before me; they seem not to have heard the rumour. When I was there I heard many shocking tales, for my informants were men speaking with the plainness of the laity; and I heard plenty of complaints of Damien. Why was this never mentioned? and how came it to you in the retirement of your clerical parlour?

But I must not even seem to deceive you. This scandal, when I read it in your letter, was not new to me. I had heard it once before; and I must tell you how. There came to Samoa a man from Honolulu; he, in a public-house on the beach, volunteered the statement that Damien had "contracted the disease from having connection with the female lepers"; and I find a joy in telling you how the report was welcomed in a public-house. A man sprang to his feet; I am not at liberty to give his name, but from what I heard I doubt if you would care to have him to dinner in Beretania Street. "You miserable little —— " (here is a word I dare not print, it would so shock your ears). "You miserable little ——," he cried, "if the story were a thousand times true, can't you see you are a million times a lower —— for daring to repeat it?" I wish it could be told of you that when the report reached you in your house, perhaps after family worship, you had found in your soul enough holy anger to receive it with the same expressions: ay, even with that one which I dare not print; it would not need to have been blotted away, like Uncle Toby's oath, by the tears of the recording angel; it would have been counted to you for your brightest righteousness. But you have deliberately chosen the part of the man from Honolulu, and you have played it with improvements of your own. The man from Honolulu — miserable, leering creature — communicated the tale to a rude knot of beach-combing drinkers in a public-house, where (I will so far agree with your temperance opinions) man is not always at his noblest; and the man from Honolulu had himself been drinking—drinking, we may charitably fancy, to excess. It was to your "Dear Brother, the Reverend H. B. Gage," that you chose to communicate the sickening story; and the blue ribbon which adorns your portly bosom forbids me to allow you the extenuating plea that you were drunk when it was done. Your "dear brother"—a brother indeed—made haste to deliver up your letter (as a means of grace, perhaps) to the religious papers; where, after many months, I found and read and wondered at it; and whence I have now reproduced it for the wonder of others. And you and your dear brother have, by this cycle of operations, built up a contrast very edifying to examine in detail. The man whom you would not care to have to dinner, on the one side; on the other, the Reverend Dr. Hyde and the Reverend H. B. Gage: the Apia bar-room, the Honolulu manse.

But I fear you scarce appreciate how you appear to your fellow-men; and to bring it home to you, I will suppose your story to be true. I will suppose—and God forgive me for supposing it—that Damien faltered and stumbled in his narrow path of duty; I will suppose that, in the horror of his isolation, perhaps in the fever of incipient disease, he, who was doing so much more than he had sworn, failed in the letter of his priestly oath—he, who was so much a better man than either you or me, who did what we have never dreamed of daring—he too tasted of our common frailty. "O, Iago, the pity of it!" The least tender should be moved to tears; the most incredulous to prayer. And all that you could do was to pen your letter to the Reverend H. B. Gage!

Is it growing at all clear to you what a picture you have drawn of your own heart? I will try yet once again to make it clearer. You had a father: suppose this tale were about him, and some informant brought it to you, proof in hand: I am not making too high an estimate of your emotional nature when I suppose you would regret the circumstance? that you would feel the tale of frailty the more keenly since it shamed the author of your days? and that the last thing you would do would be to publish it in the religious press? Well, the man who tried to do what Damien did, is my father, and the father of the man in the Apia bar, and the father of all who love goodness; and he was your father too, if God had given you grace to see it.

# STORIES

# STORIES

## A LODGING FOR THE NIGHT[1]

It was late in November, 1456. The snow fell over
Paris with rigorous, relentless persistence; sometimes the
wind made a sally and scattered it in flying vortices; sometimes there was a lull, and flake after flake descended
out of the black night air, silent, circuitous, intermi-
nable. To poor people, looking up under moist eyebrows, it seemed a wonder where it all came from.
Master Francis Villon had propounded an alternative
that afternoon, at a tavern window: was it only Pagan
Jupiter plucking geese upon Olympus? or were the holy
angels moulting? He was only a poor Master of Arts,

---

[1] Published in *Temple Bar* in October, 1877, this story was the
first of Stevenson's to be printed. It was inspired by a study of
the life of François Villon (1431–? 1484), an early French poet, one
of the great masters of gay scurrility in verse, and the author of the
most famous of *ballades*, "Where are the snows of yesteryear?"
Stevenson's study of this reprobate and genius had already borne
fruit in an essay, *François Villon, Student, Poet, and Housebreaker*,
which had been published in *The Cornhill Magazine* for August of
this year, and is reprinted in the volume entitled *Familiar Studies of
Men and Books*. In that essay, which is chiefly biographical, Dom
Nicholas, Tabary, and Montigny appear as historical figures, companion pickpockets with Villon, and gripped at last, as he was, by
the law. The chaplain of St. Benoît-le-Bétourné, who adopted
Villon, and the poet's mother also find a place in this historical study,
but the Seigneur de Brisetout is probably fictitious. Stevenson re-
fers to a record of the murder of Thevenin in a house by the cemetery of St. John. Its possibilities seem to have caught his eye, for
in the above-mentioned essay he says, "If time had only spared us
some particulars, might not this last [the murder] have furnished us
with the matter of a grisly writer's tale?" Time did not spare the
particulars, but in *A Lodging for the Night* Stevenson has invented
them. This story was reprinted in the volume entitled *New Arabian
Nights*, 1882.

he went on; and as the question somewhat touched upon divinity, he durst not venture to conclude. A silly old priest from Montargis, who was among the company, treated the young rascal to a bottle of wine in honour of the jest and grimaces with which it was accompanied, and swore on his own white beard that he had been just such another irreverent dog when he was Villon's age.

The air was raw and pointed, but not far below freezing; and the flakes were large, damp, and adhesive. The whole city was sheeted up. An army might have marched from end to end and not a footfall given the alarm. If there were any belated birds in heaven, they saw the island like a large white patch, and the bridges like slim white spars, on the black ground of the river. High up overhead the snow settled among the tracery of the cathedral towers. Many a niche was drifted full; many a statue wore a long white bonnet on its grotesque or sainted head. The gargoyles had been transformed into great false noses, drooping towards the point. The crockets were like upright pillows swollen on one side. In the intervals of the wind, there was a dull sound of dripping about the precincts of the church.

The cemetery of St. John had taken its own share of the snow. All the graves were decently covered; tall white housetops stood around in grave array; worthy burghers were long ago in bed, be-nightcapped like their domiciles; there was no light in all the neighbourhood but a little peep from a lamp that hung swinging in the church choir, and tossed the shadows to and fro in time to its oscillations. The clock was hard on ten when the patrol went by with halberds and a lantern, beating their hands; and they saw nothing suspicious about the cemetery of St. John.

Yet there was a small house, backed up against the cemetery wall, which was still awake, and awake to evil

purpose, in that snoring district. There was not much
to betray it from without; only a stream of warm vapour
from the chimney-top, a patch where the snow melted
on the roof, and a few half-obliterated footprints at the
door. But within, behind the shuttered windows, Master Francis Villon the poet, and some of the thievish crew
with whom he consorted, were keeping the night alive
and passing round the bottle.

A great pile of living embers diffused a strong and
ruddy glow from the arched chimney. Before this straddled Dom Nicolas, the Picardy monk, with his skirts
picked up and his fat legs bared to the comfortable
warmth. His dilated shadow cut the room in half; and
the firelight only escaped on either side of his broad person, and in a little pool between his outspread feet. His
face had the beery, bruised appearance of the continual
drinker's; it was covered with a network of congested
veins; purple in ordinary circumstances, but now pale
violet, for even with his back to the fire the cold pinched
him on the other side. His cowl had half fallen back, and
made a strange excrescence on either side of his bull neck.
So he straddled, grumbling, and cut the room in half with
the shadow of his portly frame.

On the right, Villon and Guy Tabary were huddled
together over a scrap of parchment; Villon making a ballade which he was to call the "Ballade of Roast Fish,"
and Tabary spluttering admiration at his shoulder. The
poet was a rag of a man, dark, little, and lean, with hollow cheeks and thin black locks. He carried his four-
and-twenty years with feverish animation. Greed had
made folds about his eyes, evil smiles had puckered his
mouth. The wolf and pig struggled together in his face.
It was an eloquent, sharp, ugly, earthly countenance.
His hands were small and prehensile, with fingers knot-
ted like a cord; and they were continually flickering in

front of him in violent and expressive pantomime. As for Tabary, a broad, complacent, admiring imbecility breathed from his squash nose and slobbering lips: he had become a thief, just as he might have become the most decent of burgesses, by the imperious chance that rules the lives of human geese and human donkeys.

At the monk's other hand, Montigny and Thevenin Pensete played a game of chance. About the first there clung some flavour of good birth and training, as about a fallen angel; something long, lithe, and courtly in the person; something aquiline and darkling in the face. Thevenin, poor soul, was in great feather: he had done a good stroke of knavery that afternoon in the Faubourg St. Jacques, and all night he had been gaining from Montigny. A flat smile illuminated his face; his bald head shone rosily in a garland of red curls; his little protuberant stomach shook with silent chucklings as he swept in his gains.

"Doubles or quits?" said Thevenin.

Montigny nodded grimly.

"*Some may prefer to dine in state*," wrote Villon, "*On bread and cheese on silver plate*. Or, or—help me out, Guido!"

Tabary giggled.

"*Or parsley on a golden dish*," scribbled the poet.

The wind was freshening without; it drove the snow before it, and sometimes raised its voice in a victorious whoop, and made sepulchral grumblings in the chimney. The cold was growing sharper as the night went on. Villon, protruding his lips, imitated the gust with something between a whistle and a groan. It was an eerie, uncomfortable talent of the poet's, much detested by the Picardy monk.

"Can't you hear it rattle in the gibbet?" said Villon. "They are all dancing the devil's jig on nothing, up there. You may dance, my gallants, you'll be none the warmer! Whew! what a gust! Down went somebody just now! A medlar the fewer on the three-legged medlar-tree!—I say, Dom Nicolas, it'll be cold to-night on the St. Denis Road?" he asked.

Dom Nicolas winked both his big eyes, and seemed to choke upon his Adam's apple. Montfaucon, the great grisly Paris gibbet, stood hard by the St. Denis Road, and the pleasantry touched him on the raw. As for Tabary, he laughed immoderately over the medlars; he had never heard anything more light-hearted; and he held his sides and crowed. Villon fetched him a fillip on the nose, which turned his mirth into an attack of coughing.

"Oh, stop that row," said Villon, "and think of rhymes to 'fish.'"

"Doubles or quits," said Montigny doggedly.

"With all my heart," quoth Thevenin.

"Is there any more in that bottle?" asked the monk.

"Open another," said Villon. "How do you ever hope to fill that big hogshead, your body, with little things like bottles? And how do you expect to get to heaven? How many angels, do you fancy, can be spared to carry up a single monk from Picardy? Or do you think yourself another Elias—and they'll send the coach for you?"

"*Hominibus impossibile*,"[1] replied the monk as he filled his glass.

Tabary was in ecstasies.

Villon filliped his nose again.

"Laugh at my jokes, if you like," he said.

"It was very good," objected Tabary.

Villon made a face at him. "Think of rhymes to 'fish,'" he said. "What have you to do with Latin? You'll wish you knew none of it at the great assizes,

[1] Impossible to man.

when the devil calls for Guido Tabary, clericus—the devil with the hump-back and red-hot finger-nails. Talking of the devil," he added in a whisper, "look at Montigny!"

All three peered covertly at the gamester. He did not seem to be enjoying his luck. His mouth was a little to a side; one nostril nearly shut, and the other much inflated. The black dog was on his back, as people say, in terrifying nursery metaphor; and he breathed hard under the gruesome burden.

"He looks as if he could knife him," whispered Tabary, with round eyes.

The monk shuddered, and turned his face and spread his open hands to the red embers. It was the cold that thus affected Dom Nicolas, and not any excess of moral sensibility.

"Come now," said Villon—"about this ballade. How does it run so far?" And beating time with his hand, he read it aloud to Tabary.

They were interrupted at the fourth rhyme by a brief and fatal movement among the gamesters. The round was completed, and Thevenin was just opening his mouth to claim another victory, when Montigny leaped up, swift as an adder, and stabbed him to the heart. The blow took effect before he had time to utter a cry, before he had time to move. A tremor or two convulsed his frame; his hands opened and shut, his heels rattled on the floor; then his head rolled backward over one shoulder with the eyes wide open; and Thevenin Pensete's spirit had returned to Him who made it.

Every one sprang to his feet; but the business was over in two twos. The four living fellows looked at each other in rather a ghastly fashion; the dead man contemplating a corner of the roof with a singular and ugly leer.

"My God!" said Tabary; and he began to pray in Latin.

Villon broke out into hysterical laughter. He came a step forward and ducked a ridiculous bow at Thevenin, and laughed still louder. Then he sat down suddenly, all of a heap, upon a stool, and continued laughing bitterly, as though he would shake himself to pieces.

Montigny recovered his composure first.

"Let's see what he has about him," he remarked, and he picked the dead man's pockets with a practised hand, and divided the money into four equal portions on the table. "There's for you," he said.

The monk received his share with a deep sigh, and a single stealthy glance at the dead Thevenin, who was beginning to sink into himself and topple sideways off the chair.

"We're all in for it," cried Villon, swallowing his mirth. "It's a hanging job for every man jack of us that's here—not to speak of those who aren't." He made a shocking gesture in the air with his raised right hand, and put out his tongue and threw his head on one side, so as to counterfeit the appearance of one who has been hanged. Then he pocketed his share of the spoil, and executed a shuffle with his feet as if to restore the circulation.

Tabary was the last to help himself; he made a dash at the money, and retired to the other end of the apartment.

Montigny stuck Thevenin upright in the chair, and drew out the dagger, which was followed by a jet of blood.

"You fellows had better be moving," he said, as he wiped the blade on his victim's doublet.

"I think we had," returned Villon, with a gulp. "Damn his fat head!" he broke out. "It sticks in my throat like phlegm. What right has a man to have red hair when he is dead?" And he fell all of a heap again upon the stool, and fairly covered his face with his hands.

Montigny and Dom Nicolas laughed aloud, even Tabary feebly chiming in.

"Cry baby," said the monk.

"I always said he was a woman," added Montigny, with a sneer. "Sit up, can't you?" he went on, giving another shake to the murdered body. "Tread out that fire, Nick!"

But Nick was better employed; he was quietly taking Villon's purse, as the poet sat, limp and trembling, on the stool where he had been making a ballade not three minutes before. Montigny and Tabary dumbly demanded a share of the booty, which the monk silently promised as he passed the little bag into the bosom of his gown. In many ways an artistic nature unfits a man for practical existence.

No sooner had the theft been accomplished than Villon shook himself, jumped to his feet, and began helping to scatter and extinguish the embers. Meanwhile Montigny opened the door and cautiously peered into the street. The coast was clear; there was no meddlesome patrol in sight. Still it was judged wiser to slip out severally; and as Villon was himself in a hurry to escape from the neighbourhood of the dead Thevenin, and the rest were in a still greater hurry to get rid of him before he should discover the loss of his money, he was the first by general consent to issue forth into the street.

The wind had triumphed and swept all the clouds from heaven. Only a few vapours, as thin as moonlight, fleeted rapidly across the stars. It was bitter cold; and by a common optical effect, things seemed almost more definite than in the broadest daylight. The sleeping city was absolutely still; a company of white hoods, a field full of little alps, below the twinkling stars. Villon cursed his fortune. Would it were still snowing! Now, wherever he went, he left an indelible trail behind him on the glittering streets; wherever he went he was still tethered to the house by the cemetery of St. John; wherever he went he must weave, with his own plodding feet, the rope that bound him to the crime and would bind him to the gallows. The leer of the dead man came back to him with a new significance. He snapped his fingers as if to pluck up his own spirits, and choosing a street at random, stepped boldly forward in the snow.

Two things preoccupied him as he went; the aspect of the gallows at Montfaucon in this bright, windy phase of the night's existence, for one; and for another, the look of the dead man with his bald head and garland of red curls. Both struck cold upon his heart, and he kept quickening his pace as if he could escape from unpleasant thoughts by mere fleetness of foot. Sometimes he looked back over his shoulder with a sudden nervous jerk; but he was the only moving thing in the white streets, except when the wind swooped round a corner and threw up the snow, which was beginning to freeze, in spouts of glittering dust.

Suddenly he saw, a long way before him, a black clump and a couple of lanterns. The clump was in motion, and the lanterns swung as though carried by men walking. It was a patrol. And though it was merely crossing his line of march he judged it wiser to get out of eyeshot as speedily as he could. He was not in the humour to be challenged, and he was conscious of making a very conspicuous mark upon the snow. Just on his left hand there stood a great hotel, with some turrets and a large porch before the door; it was half-ruinous, he remembered, and had long stood empty; and so he made three steps of it, and jumped into the shelter of the porch. It was pretty dark inside, after the glimmer of the snowy streets, and he was groping forward with outspread hands, when he stumbled over some substance which offered an indescribable mixture of resistances, hard and soft, firm and loose. His heart gave a leap, and he sprang two steps back and stared dreadfully at the obstacle. Then he gave a little laugh of relief. It was only a woman, and she dead. He knelt beside her to make sure upon this latter point. She was freezing cold, and rigid like a stick. A little ragged finery fluttered in the wind about her hair, and her cheeks had been heavily rouged that same afternoon. Her pockets were quite empty; but in her stocking, underneath the garter, Villon found two of the small coins that went by the name of whites. It was little enough; but it was always something; and the poet was moved with a deep sense of pathos that she should have died before she had spent her money. That seemed to him a dark and pitiable mystery; and he looked from the coins in his hand to the dead woman, and back again to the coins, shaking his head over the riddle of man's life. Henry V. of England, dying at Vincennes just after he had conquered France, and this poor jade cut off by a cold draught in a great man's doorway, before she had time to spend her couple of whites—it seemed a cruel way to carry on the world. Two whites would have taken such a little while to squander; and yet it would have been one more good taste in the mouth, one more smack of the lips, before the devil got the soul, and the body was left to birds and vermin. He would like to use all his tallow before the light was blown out and the lantern broken.

While these thoughts were passing through his mind, he was feeling, half mechanically, for his purse. Suddenly his heart stopped beating; a feeling of cold scales passed up the back of his legs, and a cold blow seemed to fall upon his scalp. He stood petrified for a moment; then he felt again with one feverish movement; and then his loss burst upon him, and he was covered at once with

perspiration.  To spendthrifts money is so living and
actual—it is such a thin veil between them and their
pleasures!  There is only one limit to their fortune—that
of time; and a spendthrift with only a few crowns is the
Emperor of Rome until they are spent.  For such a person to lose his money is to suffer the most shocking reverse, and fall from heaven to hell, from all to nothing,
in a breath.  And all the more if he has put his head in
the halter for it; if he may be hanged to-morrow for that
same purse, so dearly earned, so foolishly departed!  Villon stood and cursed; he threw the two whites into the
street; he shook his fist at heaven; he stamped, and was
not horrified to find himself trampling the poor corpse.
Then he began rapidly to retrace his steps towards the
house beside the cemetery.  He had forgotten all fear
of the patrol, which was long gone by at any rate, and had
no idea but that of his lost purse.  It was in vain that he
looked right and left upon the snow: nothing was to be
seen.  He had not dropped it in the streets.  Had it fallen
in the house?  He would have liked dearly to go in and
see; but the idea of the grisly occupant unmanned him.
And he saw besides, as he drew near, that their efforts to
put out the fire had been unsuccessful; on the contrary, it
had broken into a blaze, and a changeful light played in
the chinks of door and window, and revived his terror
for the authorities and Paris gibbet.

He returned to the hotel with the porch, and groped
about upon the snow for the money he had thrown away
in his childish passion.  But he could only find one
white; the other had probably struck sideways and sunk
deeply in.  With a single white in his pocket, all his
projects for a rousing night in some wild tavern vanished
utterly away.  And it was not only pleasure that fled
laughing from his grasp; positive discomfort, positive
pain, attacked him as he stood ruefully before the porch.

His perspiration had dried upon him; and although the wind had now fallen, a binding frost was setting in stronger with every hour, and he felt benumbed and sick at heart. What was to be done? Late as was the hour, improbable as was success, he would try the house of his adopted father, the chaplain of St. Benoît.

He ran there all the way, and knocked timidly. There was no answer. He knocked again and again, taking heart with every stroke; and at last steps were heard approaching from within. A barred wicket fell open in the iron-studded door, and emitted a gush of yellow light.

"Hold up your face to the wicket," said the chaplain from within.

"It 's only me," whimpered Villon.

"Oh, it 's only you, is it?" returned the chaplain; and he cursed him with foul unpriestly oaths for disturbing him at such an hour, and bade him be off to hell, where he came from.

"My hands are blue to the wrist," pleaded Villon; "my feet are dead and full of twinges; my nose aches with the sharp air; the cold lies at my heart. I may be dead before morning. Only this once, father, and before God, I will never ask again!"

"You should have come earlier," said the ecclesiastic coolly. "Young men require a lesson now and then." He shut the wicket and retired deliberately into the interior of the house.

Villon was beside himself; he beat upon the door with his hands and feet, and shouted hoarsely after the chaplain.

"Wormy old fox!" he cried. "If I had my hand under your twist,[1] I would send you flying headlong into the bottomless pit."

---

[1] Between your legs.

A door shut in the interior, faintly audible to the poet down long passages. He passed his hand over his mouth with an oath. And then the humour of the situation struck him, and he laughed and looked lightly up to heaven, where the stars seemed to be winking over his discomfiture.

What was to be done? It looked very like a night in the frosty streets. The idea of the dead woman popped into his imagination, and gave him a hearty fright; what had happened to her in the early night might very well happen to him before morning. And he so young! and with such immense possibilities of disorderly amusement before him! He felt quite pathetic over the notion of his own fate, as if it had been some one else's, and made a little imaginative vignette of the scene in the morning when they should find his body.

He passed all his chances under review, turning the white between his thumb and forefinger. Unfortunately he was on bad terms with some old friends who would once have taken pity on him in such a plight. He had lampooned them in verses; he had beaten and cheated them; and yet now, when he was in so close a pinch, he thought there was at least one who might perhaps relent. It was a chance. It was worth trying at least, and he would go and see.

On the way, two little accidents happened to him which coloured his musings in a very different manner. For, first, he fell in with the track of a patrol, and walked in it for some hundred yards, although it lay out of his direction. And this spirited him up; at least he had confused his trail; for he was still possessed with the idea of people tracking him all about Paris over the snow, and collaring him next morning before he was awake. The other matter affected him quite differently. He passed a street corner, where, not so long before, a

woman and her child had been devoured by wolves
This was just the kind of weather, he reflected, when
wolves might take it into their heads to enter Paris again;
and a lone man in these deserted streets would run the
chance of something worse than a mere scare. He
stopped and looked upon the place with an unpleasant
interest—it was a centre where several lanes intersected
each other; and he looked down them all, one after another, and held his breath to listen, lest he should detect
some galloping black things on the snow or hear the sound
of howling between him and the river. He remembered
his mother telling him the story and pointing out the spot,
while he was yet a child. His mother! if he only knew
where she lived, he might make sure at least of shelter.
He determined he would inquire upon the morrow; nay,
he would go and see her too, poor old girl! So thinking,
he arrived at his destination—his last hope for the night.

The house was quite dark, like its neighbours; and
yet after a few taps, he heard a movement overhead, a
door opening, and a cautious voice asking who was
there. The poet named himself in a loud whisper, and
waited, not without some trepidation, the result. Nor
had he to wait long. A window was suddenly opened,
and a pailful of slops splashed down upon the doorstep.
Villon had not been unprepared for something of the
sort, and had put himself as much in shelter as the nature
of the porch admitted; but for all that, he was deplorably
drenched below the waist. His hose began to freeze almost at once. Death from cold and exposure stared him
in the face; he remembered he was of phthisical tendency,
and began coughing tentatively. But the gravity of the
danger steadied his nerves. He stopped a few hundred
yards from the door where he had been so rudely used,
and reflected with his finger to his nose. He could only
see one way of getting a lodging, and that was to take it.

He had noticed a house not far away, which looked as if it might be easily broken into, and thither he betook himself promptly, entertaining himself on the way with the idea of a room still hot, with a table still loaded with the remains of supper, where he might pass the rest of the black hours and whence he should issue, on the morrow, with an armful of valuable plate. He even considered on what viands and what wines he should prefer; and as he was calling the roll of his favourite dainties, roast fish presented itself to his mind with an odd mixture of amusement and horror.

"I shall never finish that ballade," he thought to himself; and then, with another shudder at the recollection, "Oh, damn his fat head!" he repeated fervently, and spat upon the snow.

The house in question looked dark at first sight; but as Villon made a preliminary inspection in search of the handiest point of attack, a little twinkle of light caught his eye from behind a curtained window.

"The devil!" he thought. "People awake! Some student or some saint, confound the crew! Can't they get drunk and lie in bed snoring like their neighbours! What's the good of curfew, and poor devils of bell-ringers jumping at a rope's end in bell-towers? What's the use of day, if people sit up all night? The gripes to them!" He grinned as he saw where his logic was leading him. "Every man to his business, after all," added he, "and if they're awake, by the Lord, I may come by a supper honestly for once, and cheat the devil."

He went boldly to the door and knocked with an assured hand. On both previous occasions, he had knocked timidly and with some dread of attracting notice; but now when he had just discarded the thought of a burglarious entry, knocking at a door seemed a mighty simple and innocent proceeding. The sound of his blows echoed through the house with thin, phantasmal reverberations, as though it were quite empty; but these had scarcely died away before a measured tread drew near, a couple of bolts were withdrawn, and one wing was opened broadly, as though no guile or fear of guile were known to those within. A tall figure of a man, muscular and spare, but a little bent confronted Villon. The head was massive in bulk, but finely sculptured; the nose blunt at the bottom, but refining upward to where it joined a pair of strong and honest eyebrows; the mouth and eyes surrounded with delicate markings, and the whole face based upon a thick white beard, boldly and squarely trimmed. Seen as it was by the light of a flickering hand-lamp, it looked perhaps nobler than it had a right to do; but it was a fine face, honourable rather than intelligent, strong, simple, and righteous.

"You knock late, sir," said the old man in resonant, courteous tones.

Villon cringed and brought up many servile words of apology; at a crisis of this sort the beggar was uppermost in him, and the man of genius hid his head with confusion.

"You are cold," repeated the old man, "and hungry? Well, step in." And he ordered him into the house with a noble enough gesture.

"Some great seigneur," thought Villon, as his host, setting down the lamp on the flagged pavement of the entry, shot the bolts once more into their places.

"You will pardon me if I go in front," he said, when this was done; and he preceded the poet upstairs into a large apartment, warmed with a pan of charcoal and lit by a great lamp hanging from the roof. It was very bare of furniture: only some gold plate on a sideboard; some folios; and a stand of armour between the windows. Some smart tapestry hung upon the walls, representing the crucifixion of our Lord in one piece, and in another a scene of shepherds and shepherdesses by a running stream.  Over the chimney was a shield of arms.

"Will you seat yourself," said the old man, "and forgive me if I leave you?   I am alone in my house to-night, and if you are to eat I must forage for you myself."

No sooner was his host gone than Villon leaped from the chair on which he had just seated himself, and began examining the room, with the stealth and passion of a cat. He weighed the gold flagons in his hand, opened all the folios, and investigated the arms upon the shield, and the stuff with which the seats were lined.  He raised the window curtains, and saw that the windows were set with rich stained glass in figures, so far as he could see, of martial import.  Then he stood in the middle of the room, drew a long breath, and retaining it with puffed cheeks, looked round and round him, turning on his heels, as if to impress every feature of the apartment on his memory.

"Seven pieces of plate," he said.   "If there had been ten, I would have risked it.  A fine house, and a fine old master, so help me all the saints!"

And just then, hearing the old man's tread returning along the corridor, he stole back to his chair, and began humbly toasting his wet legs before the charcoal pan.

His entertainer had a plate of meat in one hand and a jug of wine in the other.   He set down the plate upon the table, motioning Villon to draw in his chair, and going to the sideboard, brought back two goblets which he filled.

"I drink your better fortune," he said, gravely touching Villon's cup with his own.

"To our better acquaintance," said the poet, growing bold.  A mere man of the people would have been awed by the courtesy of the old seigneur, but Villon was hardened in that matter; he had made mirth for great lords before now, and found them as black rascals as himself.

And so he devoted himself to the viands with a ravenous gusto, while the old man, leaning backward, watched him with steady, curious eyes.

"You have blood on your shoulder, my man," he said.

Montigny must have laid his wet right hand upon him as he left the house. He cursed Montigny in his heart.

"It was none of my shedding," he stammered.

"I had not supposed so," returned his host quietly. "A brawl?"

"Well, something of that sort," Villon admitted with a quaver.

"Perhaps a fellow murdered?"

"Oh, no, not murdered," said the poet, more and more confused. "It was all fair play—murdered by accident. I had no hand in it, God strike me dead!" he added fervently.

"One rogue the fewer, I dare say," observed the master of the house.

"You may dare to say that," agreed Villon, infinitely relieved. "As big a rogue as there is between here and Jerusalem. He turned up his toes like a lamb. But it was a nasty thing to look at. I dare say you 've seen dead men in your time, my lord?" he added, glancing at the armour.

"Many," said the old man. "I have followed the wars, as you imagine."

Villon laid down his knife and fork, which he had just taken up again.

"Were any of them bald?" he asked.

"Oh yes, and with hair as white as mine."

"I don't think I should mind the white so much," said Villon. "His was red." And he had a return of his shuddering and tendency to laughter, which he drowned with a great draught of wine. "I 'm a little put out when I think of it," he went on. "I knew him—damn him!

And then the cold gives a man fancies—or the fancies give a man cold, I don't know which."

"Have you any money?" asked the old man.

"I have one white," returned the poet, laughing. "I got it out of a dead jade's stocking in a porch. She was as dead as Cæsar, poor wench, and as cold as a church, with bits of ribbon sticking in her hair. This is a hard world in winter for wolves and wenches and poor rogues like me."

"I," said the old man, "am Enguerrand de la Feuil-lèe, seigneur de Brisetout, bailly du Patatrac. Who and what may you be?"

Villon rose and made a suitable reverence. "I am called Francis Villon," he said, "a poor Master of Arts of this university. I know some Latin, and a deal of vice. I can make chansons, ballades, lais, virelais, and roundels,[1] and I am very fond of wine. I was born in a garret, and I shall not improbably die upon the gallows. I may add, my lord, that from this night forward I am your lordship's very obsequious servant to command."

"No servant of mine," said the knight; "my guest for this evening, and no more."

"A very grateful guest," said Villon politely, and he drank in dumb show to his entertainer.

"You are shrewd," began the old man, tapping his forehead, "very shrewd; you have learning; you are a clerk; and yet you take a small piece of money off a dead woman in the street. Is it not a kind of theft?"

"It is a kind of theft much practised in the wars, my lord."

"The wars are the field of honour," returned the old man proudly. "There a man plays his life upon the cast; he fights in the name of his lord the king, his Lord God, and all their lordships the holy saints and angels."

---

[1] Various forms of French verse.

"Put it," said Villon, "that I were really a thief, should I not play my life also, and against heavier odds?"

"For gain but not for honour."

"Gain?" repeated Villon with a shrug. "Gain! The poor fellow wants supper, and takes it. So does the soldier in a campaign. Why, what are all these requisitions we hear so much about? If they are not gain to those who take them, they are loss enough to the others. The men-at-arms drink by a good fire, while the burgher bites his nails to buy them wine and wood. I have seen a good many ploughmen swinging on trees about the country; ay, I have seen thirty on one elm, and a very poor figure they made; and when I asked some one how all these came to be hanged, I was told it was because they could not scrape together enough crowns to satisfy the men-at-arms."

"These things are a necessity of war, which the low-born must endure with constancy. It is true that some captains drive overhard; there are spirits in every rank not easily moved by pity; and indeed many follow arms who are no better than brigands."

"You see," said the poet, "you cannot separate the soldier from the brigand; and what is a thief but an isolated brigand with circumspect manners? I steal a couple of mutton chops, without so much as disturbing people's sleep; the farmer grumbles a bit, but sups none the less wholesomely on what remains. You come up blowing gloriously on a trumpet, take away the whole sheep, and beat the farmer pitifully into the bargain. I have no trumpet; I am only Tom, Dick, or Harry; I am a rogue and a dog, and hanging 's too good for me—with all my heart; but just ask the farmer which of us he prefers, just find out which of us he lies awake to curse on cold nights."

"Look at us two," said his lordship. "I am old, strong, and honoured. If I were turned from my house to-morrow, hundreds would be proud to shelter me. Poor people would go out and pass the night in the streets with their children, if I merely hinted that I wished to be alone. And I find you up, wandering homeless, and picking farthings off dead women by the wayside! I fear no man and nothing; I have seen you tremble and lose countenance at a word. I wait God's summons contentedly in my own house, or, if it please the king to call me out again, upon the field of battle. You look for the gallows; a rough, swift death, without hope or honour. Is there no difference between these two?"

"As far as to the moon," Villon acquiesced. "But if I had been born lord of Brisetout, and you had been the poor scholar Francis, would the difference have been any the less? Should not I have been warming my knees at this charcoal pan, and would not you have been groping for farthings in the snow? Should not I have been the soldier, and you the thief?"

"A thief?" cried the old man. "I a thief! If you understood your words, you would repent them."

Villon turned out his hands with a gesture of inimitable impudence. "If your lordship had done me the honour to follow my argument!" he said.

"I do you too much honour in submitting to your presence," said the knight. "Learn to curb your tongue when you speak with old and honourable men, or some one hastier than I may reprove you in a sharper fashion." And he rose and paced the lower end of the apartment, struggling with anger and antipathy. Villon surreptitiously refilled his cup, and settled himself more comfortably in the chair, crossing his knees and leaning his head upon one hand and the elbow against the back of the chair. He was now replete and warm; and he was in nowise frightened for his host, having gauged him as justly as was possible between two such different characters. The night was far spent, and in a very comfortable fashion after all; and he felt morally certain of a safe departure on the morrow.

"Tell me one thing," said the old man, pausing in his walk. "Are you really a thief?"

"I claim the sacred rights of hospitality," returned the poet. "My lord, I am."

"You are very young," the knight continued.

"I should never have been so old," replied Villon, showing his fingers, "if I had not helped myself with these ten talents. They have been my nursing mothers and my nursing fathers."

"You may still repent and change."

"I repent daily," said the poet. "There are few people more given to repentance than poor Francis. As for change, let somebody change my circumstances. A man must continue to eat, if it were only that he may continue to repent."

"The change must begin in the heart," returned the old man solemnly.

"My dear lord," answered Villon, "do you really fancy that I steal for pleasure? I hate stealing, like any other piece of work or of danger. My teeth chatter when I see a gallows. But I must eat, I must drink, I must mix in society of some sort. What the devil! Man is not a solitary animal—*Cui Deus fœminam tradit*.[1] Make me king's pantler—make me abbot of St. Denis; make me bailly of the Patatrac; and then I shall be changed indeed. But as long as you leave me the poor scholar Francis Villon, without a farthing, why, of course, I remain the same."

"The grace of God is all-powerful."

[1] To whom God gave woman.

"I should be a heretic to question it," said Francis. "It has made you lord of Brisetout and bailly of the Patatrac; it has given me nothing but the quick wits under my hat and these ten toes upon my hands. May I help myself to wine? I thank you respectfully. By God's grace, you have a very superior vintage."

The lord of Brisetout walked to and fro with his hands behind his back. Perhaps he was not yet quite settled in his mind about the parallel between thieves and soldiers; perhaps Villon had interested him by some cross-thread of sympathy; perhaps his wits were simply muddled by so much unfamiliar reasoning; but whatever the cause, he somehow yearned to convert the young man to a better way of thinking, and could not make up his mind to drive him forth again into the street.

"There is something more than I can understand in this," he said at length. "Your mouth is full of subtleties, and the devil has led you very far astray; but the devil is only a very weak spirit before God's truth, and all his subtleties vanish at a word of true honour, like darkness at morning. Listen to me once more. I learned long ago that a gentleman should live chivalrously and lovingly to God, and the king, and his lady; and though I have seen many strange things done, I have still striven to command my ways upon that rule. It is not only written in all noble histories, but in every man's heart, if he will take care to read. You speak of food and wine, and I know very well that hunger is a difficult trial to endure; but you do not speak of other wants; you say nothing of honour, of faith to God and other men, of courtesy, of love without reproach. It may be that I am not very wise—and yet I think I am—but you seem to me like one who has lost his way and made a great error in life. You are attending to the little wants, and you have totally forgotten the great and only real ones, like a man who should be doctoring toothache on the Judgment Day. For such things as honour and love and faith are not only nobler than food and drink, but indeed I think we desire them more, and suffer more sharply for their absence. I speak to you as I think you will most easily understand me. Are you not, while careful to fill your belly, disregarding another appetite in your heart, which spoils the pleasure of your life and keeps you continually wretched?"

Villon was sensibly nettled under all this sermonizing. "You think I have no sense of honour!" he cried. "I'm poor enough, God knows! It's hard to see rich people with their gloves, and you blowing in your hands. An empty belly is a bitter thing, although you speak so lightly of it. If you had had as many as I, perhaps you would change your tune. Any way I'm a thief—make the most of that—but I'm not a devil from hell, God strike me dead. I would have you to know I've an honour of my own, as good as yours, though I don't prate about it all day long, as if it was a God's miracle to have any. It seems quite natural to me; I keep it in its box till it's wanted. Why now, look you here, how long have I been in this room with you? Did you not tell me you were alone in the house? Look at your gold plate! You're strong, if you like, but you're old and unarmed, and I have my knife. What did I want but a jerk of the elbow and here would have been you with the cold steel in your bowels, and there would have been me, linking in the streets, with an armful of golden cups! Did you suppose I hadn't wit enough to see that? And I scorned the action. There are your damned goblets, as safe as in a church; there are you, with your heart ticking as good as new; and here am I, ready to go out again as poor as I came in, with my one white that you threw in my teeth! And you think I have no sense of honour—God strike me dead!"

The old man stretched out his right arm. "I will tell ʻou what you are," he said. "You are a rogue, my man, an impudent and black-hearted rogue and vagabond. I have passed an hour with you. Oh! believe me, I feel myself disgraced! And you have eaten and drunk at my table. But now I am sick at your presence; the day has come, and the night-bird should be off to his roost. Will you go before, or after?"

"Which you please," returned the poet, rising. "I believe you to be strictly honourable." He thoughtfully emptied his cup. "I wish I could add you were intelligent," he went on, knocking on his head with his knuckles. "Age! age! the brains stiff and rheumatic."

The old man preceded him from a point of self-respect. Villon followed, whistling, with his thumbs in his girdle.

"God pity you," said the lord of Brisetout at the door.

"Good-bye, papa," returned Villon with a yawn. "Many thanks for the cold mutton."

The door closed behind him. The dawn was breaking over the white roofs. A chill, uncomfortable morning ushered in the day. Villon stood and heartily stretched himself in the middle of the road.

"A very dull old gentleman," he thought. "I wonder what his goblets may be worth."

# WILL O' THE MILL [2]

## THE PLAIN AND THE STARS

THE Mill where Will lived with his adopted parents stood in a falling valley between pinewoods and great mountains. Above, hill after hill soared upwards until they soared out of the depth of the hardiest timber, and stood naked against the sky. Some way up, a long grey village lay like a seam or a rag of vapour on a wooded hillside; and when the wind was favourable, the sound of the church bells would drop down, thin and silvery, to Will. Below, the valley grew ever steeper and steeper, and at the same time widened out on either hand; and from an eminence beside the mill it was possible to see its whole length and away beyond it over a wide plain, where the river turned and shone, and moved on from city to city on its voyage towards the sea. It chanced that over this valley there lay a pass into a neighbouring kingdom, so that, quiet and rural as it was, the road that ran along beside the river was a high thoroughfare between two splendid and powerful societies. All through the summer

[1] Written in 1877, probably in Edinburgh after a return from France, at the time of a sudden burst of activity in story-telling. The mountain scenery is a reminiscence of the Brenner Pass over which Stevenson journeyed on his return from Italy in 1863 when he was only thirteen years old, combined with some memories of the valleys of Baden. He told Graham Balfour, afterwards his biographer, that it was an experiment in what could be said for a theory of life opposite to his own. His own theory is expressed in one of his favourite maxims, "Acts may be forgiven; not even God can forgive the hanger-back." Published in *The Cornhill Magazine*, January, 1878, and afterwards in the volume entitled *The Merry Men, and Other Tales*, 1887.

travelling-carriages came crawling up, or went plunging briskly downwards past the mill; and as it happened that the other side was very much easier of ascent, the path was not much frequented, except by people going in one direction; and of all the carriages that Will saw go by, five-sixths were plunging briskly downwards and only one-sixth crawling up. Much more was this the case with foot-passengers. All the light-footed tourists, all the pedlars laden with strange wares, were tending downward like the river that accompanied their path. Nor was this all; for when Will was yet a child a disastrous war arose over a great part of the world. The newspapers were full of defeats and victories, the earth rang with cavalry hoofs, and often for days together and for miles around the coil of battle terrified good people from their labours in the field. Of all this, nothing was heard for a long time in the valley; but at last one of the commanders pushed an army over the pass by forced marches, and for three days horse and foot, cannon and tumbril,[1] drum and standard, kept pouring downward past the mill. All day the child stood and watched them on their passage— the rhythmical stride, the pale, unshaven faces tanned about the eyes, the discoloured regimentals and the tattered flags, filled him with a sense of weariness, pity, and wonder; and all night long, after he was in bed, he could hear the cannon pounding and the feet trampling, and the great armament sweeping onward and downward past the mill. No one in the valley ever heard the fate of the expedition, for they lay out of the way of gossip in those troublous times; but Will saw one thing plainly, that not a man returned. Whither had they all gone? Whither went all the tourists and pedlars with strange wares? whither all the brisk barouches with servants in the dicky? whither the water of the stream, ever cours-

---

[1] The two-wheeled cart for carrying tools, etc., which acts as tender for a battery.

ing downward and ever renewed from above? Even the wind blew oftener down the valley, and carried the dead leaves along with it in the fall. It seemed like a great conspiracy of things animate and inanimate; they all went downward, fleetly and gaily downward, and only he, it seemed, remained behind, like a stock upon the wayside. It sometimes made him glad when he noticed how the fishes kept their heads up stream. They, at least, stood faithfully by him, while all else were posting downward to the unknown world.

One evening he asked the miller where the river went.

"It goes down the valley," answered he, "and turns a power of mills—six score mills, they say, from here to Unterdeck—and it none the wearier after all. And then it goes out into the lowlands, and waters the great corn country, and runs through a sight of fine cities (so they say) where kings live all alone in great palaces, with a sentry walking up and down before the door. And it goes under bridges with stone men upon them, looking down and smiling so curious at the water, and living folks leaning their elbows on the wall and looking over too. And then it goes on and on, and down through marshes and sands, until at last it falls into the sea, where the ships are that bring parrots and tobacco from the Indies. Ay, it has a long trot before it as it goes singing over our weir, bless its heart!"

"And what is the sea?" asked Will.

"The sea!" cried the miller. "Lord help us all, it is the greatest thing God made! That is where all the water in the world runs down into a great salt lake. There it lies, as flat as my hand and as innocent-like as a child; but they do say when the wind blows it gets up into water-mountains bigger than any of ours, and swallows down great ships bigger than our mill, and makes such a roaring that you can hear it miles away upon the land. There

are great fish in it five times bigger than a bull, and one
old serpent as long as our river and as old as all the world,
with whiskers like a man, and a crown of silver on her
head."

Will thought he had never heard anything like this,
and he kept on asking question after question about the
world that lay away down the river, with all its perils and
marvels, until the old miller became quite interested himself, and at last took him by the hand and led him to the
hill-top that overlooks the valley and the plain. The sun
was near setting, and hung low down in a cloudless sky.
Everything was defined and glorified in golden light.
Will had never seen so great an expanse of country in his
life; he stood and gazed with all his eyes. He could see
the cities, and the woods and fields, and the bright
curves of the river, and far away to where the rim of
the plain trenched along the shining heavens. An over-
mastering emotion seized upon the boy, soul and body;
his heart beat so thickly that he could not breathe; the
scene swam before his eyes; the sun seemed to wheel
round and round, and throw off, as it turned, strange
shapes which disappeared with the rapidity of thought,
and were succeeded by others. Will covered his face
with his hands, and burst into a violent fit of tears; and
the poor miller, sadly disappointed and perplexed, saw
nothing better for it than to take him up in his arms and
carry him home in silence.

From that day forward Will was full of new hopes and
longings. Something kept tugging at his heart-strings;
the running water carried his desires along with it as
he dreamed over its fleeting surface; the wind, as it ran
over innumerable tree-tops, hailed him with encouraging
words; branches beckoned downward; the open road, as
it shouldered round the angles and went turning and vanishing faster and faster down the valley, tortured him

with its solicitations.   He spent long whiles on the eminence, looking down the river-shed and abroad on the flat lowlands, and watched the clouds that travelled forth upon the sluggish wind and trailed their purple shadows on the plain; or he would linger by the wayside, and follow the carriages with his eyes as they rattled downward by the river.   It did not matter what it was; everything that went that way, were it cloud or carriage, bird or brown water in the stream, he felt his heart flow out after it in an ecstasy of longing.

We are told by men of science that all the ventures of mariners on the sea, all that counter-marching of tribes and races that confounds old history with its dust and rumour, sprang from nothing more abstruse than the laws of supply and demand, and a certain natural instinct for cheap rations.   To any one thinking deeply, this will seem a dull and pitiful explanation.   The tribes that came swarming out of the North and East, if they were indeed pressed onward from behind by others, were drawn at the same time by the magnetic influence of the South and West.   The fame of other lands had reached them; the name of the eternal city rang in their ears; they were not colonists, but pilgrims; they travelled towards wine and gold and sunshine, but their hearts were set on something higher.   That divine unrest, that old stinging trouble of humanity that makes all high achievements and all miserable failure, the same that spread wings with Icarus, the same that sent Columbus into the desolate Atlantic, inspired and supported these barbarians on their perilous march.   There is one legend which profoundly represents their spirit, of how a flying party of these wanderers encountered a very old man shod with iron.   The old man asked them whither they were going; and they answered with one voice: "To the Eternal City!"   He looked upon them gravely.   "I have sought it," he said, "over the most part of the world. Three such pairs as I now carry on my feet have I worn out upon this pilgrimage, and now the fourth is growing slender underneath my steps. And all this while I have not found the city." And he turned and went his own way alone, leaving them astonished.

And yet this would scarcely parallel the intensity of Will's feeling for the plain. If he could only go far enough out there, he felt as if his eyesight would be purged and clarified, as if his hearing would grow more delicate, and his very breath would come and go with luxury. He was transplanted and withering where he was; he lay in a strange country and was sick for home. Bit by bit, he pieced together broken notions of the world below: of the river, ever moving and growing until it sailed forth into the majestic ocean; of the cities, full of brisk and beautiful people, playing fountains, bands of music and marble palaces, and lighted up at night from end to end with artificial stars of gold; of the great churches, wise universities, brave armies, and untold money lying stored in vaults; of the high-flying vice that moved in the sunshine, and the stealth and swiftness of midnight murder. I have said he was sick as if for home: the figure halts. He was like some one lying in twilit, formless pre-existence, and stretching out his hands lovingly towards many-coloured, many-sounding life. It was no wonder he was unhappy, he would go and tell the fish: they were made for their life, wished for no more than worms and running water, and a hole below a falling bank; but he was differently designed, full of desires and aspirations, itching at the fingers, lusting with the eyes, whom the whole variegated world could not satisfy with aspects. The true life, the true bright sunshine, lay far out upon the plain. And O! to see this sunlight once before he died! to move with a jocund spirit in a golden land! to hear the trained singers and sweet church bells, and see the holiday gardens! "And O fish!" he would cry, "if you would only turn your noses down stream, you could swim so easily into the fabled waters and see the vast ships passing over your head like clouds, and hear the great water-hills making music over you all day long!" But the fish kept looking patiently in their own direction, until Will hardly knew whether to laugh or cry.

Hitherto the traffic on the road had passed by Will, like something seen in a picture: he had perhaps exchanged salutations with a tourist, or caught sight of an old gentleman in a travelling-cap at a carriage window; but for the most part it had been a mere symbol, which he contemplated from apart and with something of a superstitious feeling. A time came at last when this was to be changed. The miller, who was a greedy man in his way, and never forewent an opportunity of honest profit, turned the mill-house into a little wayside inn, and, several pieces of good fortune falling in opportunely, built stables and got the position of post-master on the road. It now became Will's duty to wait upon people, as they sat to break their fasts in the little arbour at the top of the mill garden; and you may be sure that he kept his ears open, and learned many new things about the outside world as he brought the omelette or the wine. Nay, he would often get into conversation with single guests, and by adroit questions and polite attention, not only gratify his own curiosity, but win the good-will of the travellers. Many complimented the old couple on their serving-boy; and a professor was eager to take him away with him, and have him properly educated in the plain. The miller and his wife were mightily astonished and even more pleased. They thought it a very good thing that they should have opened their inn. "You see," the old man would remark, "he has a kind of talent for a publican; he never would have

made anything else!" And so life wagged on in the valley, with high satisfaction to all concerned but Will.
Every carriage that left the inn-door seemed to take a
part of him away with it; and when people jestingly offered him a lift, he could with difficulty command his
emotion. Night after night he would dream that he
was awakened by flustered servants, and that a splendid
equipage waited at the door to carry him down into
the plain; night after night; until the dream, which had
seemed all jollity to him at first, began to take on a colour of gravity, and the nocturnal summons and waiting
equipage occupied a place in his mind as something to
be both feared and hoped for.

One day, when Will was about sixteen, a fat young
man arrived at sunset to pass the night. He was a con-
tented-looking fellow, with a jolly eye, and carried a knapsack. While dinner was preparing, he sat in the arbour
to read a book; but as soon as he had begun to observe
Will, the book was laid aside; he was plainly one of those
who prefer living people to people made of ink and paper.
Will, on his part, although he had not been much interested in the stranger at first sight, soon began to take a
great deal of pleasure in his talk, which was full of good
nature and good sense, and at last conceived a great respect for his character and wisdom. They sat far into the
night; and about two in the morning Will opened his
heart to the young man, and told him how he longed to
leave the valley and what bright hopes he had connected
with the cities of the plain. The young man whistled,
and then broke into a smile.

"My young friend," he remarked, "you are a very
curious little fellow to be sure, and wish a great many
things which you will never get. Why, you would feel
quite ashamed if you knew how the little fellows in these
fairy cities of yours are all after the same sort of nonsense,

and keep breaking their hearts to get up into the mountains. And let me tell you, those who go down into the plains are a very short while there before they wish themselves heartily back again. The air is not so light nor so pure; nor is the sun any brighter. As for the beautiful men and women, you would see many of them in rags and many of them deformed with horrible disorders; and a city is so hard a place for people who are poor and sensitive that many choose to die by their own hand."

"You must think me very simple," answered Will. "Although I have never been out of this valley, believe me, I have used my eyes. I know how one thing lives on another; for instance, how the fish hangs in the eddy to catch his fellows; and the shepherd, who makes so pretty a picture carrying home the lamb, is only carrying it home for dinner. I do not expect to find all things right in your cities. That is not what troubles me; it might have been that once upon a time; but although I live here always, I have asked many questions and learned a great deal in these last years, and certainly enough to cure me of my old fancies. But you would not have me die like a dog and not see all that is to be seen, and do all that a man can do, let it be good or evil? you would not have me spend all my days between this road here and the river, and not so much as make a motion to be up and live my life?—I would rather die out of hand," he cried, "than linger on as I am doing."

"Thousands of people," said the young man, "live and die like you, and are none the less happy."

"Ah!" said Will, "if there are thousands who would like, why should not one of them have my place?"

It was quite dark; there was a hanging lamp in the arbour which lit up the table and the faces of the speakers; and along the arch, the leaves upon the trellis stood out illuminated against the night sky, a pattern of trans-

parent green upon a dusky purple. The fat young man
rose, and, taking Will by the arm, led him out under the
open heavens.

"Did you ever look at the stars?" he asked, pointing
upwards.

"Often and often," answered Will.

"And do you know what they are?"

"I have fancied many things."

"They are worlds like ours," said the young man.
"Some of them less; many of them a million times greater;
and some of the least sparkles that you see are not only
worlds, but whole clusters of worlds turning about each
other in the midst of space. We do not know what there
may be in any of them; perhaps the answer to all our difficulties or the cure of all our sufferings: and yet we can
never reach them; not all the skill of the craftiest of men
can fit out a ship for the nearest of these our neighbours,
nor would the life of the most aged suffice for such a journey. When a great battle has been lost or a dear friend
is dead, when we are hipped or in high spirits, there they
are unweariedly shining overhead. We may stand down
here, a whole army of us together, and shout until we
break our hearts, and not a whisper reaches them. We
may climb the highest mountain, and we are no nearer
them. All we can do is to stand down here in the garden
and take off our hats; the starshine lights upon our heads,
and where mine is a little bald, I dare say you can see it
glisten in the darkness. The mountain and the mouse.
That is like to be all we shall ever have to do with
Arcturus or Aldebaran. Can you apply a parable?" he
added, laying his hand upon Will's shoulder. "It is not
the same thing as a reason, but usually vastly more con-
vincing."

Will hung his head a little, and then raised it once more
to heaven. The stars seemed to expand and emit a

sharper brilliancy; and as he kept turning his eyes higher and higher, they seemed to increase in multitude under his gaze.

"I see," he said, turning to the young man. "We are in a rat-trap."

"Something of that size. Did you ever see a squirrel turning in a cage? and another squirrel sitting philosophically over his nuts? I needn't ask you which of them looked more of a fool."

### THE PARSON'S MARJORY

After some years the old people died, both in one winter, very carefully tended by their adopted son, and very quietly mourned when they were gone. People who had heard of his roving fancies supposed he would hasten to sell the property, and go down the river to push his fortunes. But there was never any sign of such an intention on the part of Will. On the contrary, he had the inn set on a better footing, and hired a couple of servants to assist him in carrying it on; and there he settled down, a kind, talkative, inscrutable young man, six feet three in his stockings, with an iron constitution and a friendly voice. He soon began to take rank in the district as a bit of an oddity: it was not much to be wondered at from the first, for he was always full of notions, and kept calling the plainest common-sense in question; but what most raised the report upon him was the odd circumstance of his courtship with the parson's Marjory.

The parson's Marjory was a lass about nineteen, when Will would be about thirty; well enough looking, and much better educated than any other girl in that part of the country, as became her parentage. She held her head very high, and had already refused several offers of marriage with a grand air, which had got her hard names among the neighbours. For all that she was a good girl, and one that would have made any man well contented.

Will had never seen much of her; for although the church and parsonage were only two miles from his own door, he was never known to go there but on Sundays. It chanced, however, that the parsonage fell into disrepair, and had to be dismantled; and the parson and his daughter took lodgings for a month or so, on very much reduced terms, at Will's inn. Now, what with the inn, and the mill, and the old miller's savings, our friend was a man of substance; and besides that, he had a name for good temper and shrewdness, which make a capital portion in marriage; and so it was currently gossiped, among their ill-wishers, that the parson and his daughter had not chosen their temporary lodging with their eyes shut. Will was about the last man in the world to be cajoled or frightened into marriage. You had only to look into his eyes, limpid and still like pools of water, and yet with a sort of clear light that seemed to come from within, and you would understand at once that here was one who knew his own mind, and would stand to it immovably. Marjory herself was no weakling by her looks, with strong steady eyes and a resolute and quiet bearing. It might be a question whether she was not Will's match in steadfastness, after all, or which of them would rule the roast in marriage. But Marjory had never given it a thought, and accompanied her father with the most unshaken innocence and unconcern.

The season was still so early that Will's customers were few and far between; but the lilacs were already flowering, and the weather was so mild that the party took dinner under the trellis, with the noise of the river in their ears and the woods ringing about them with the songs of birds. Will soon began to take a particular pleasure in these dinners. The parson was rather a dull companion, with a habit of dozing at table; but nothing rude or cruel ever fell from his lips. And as for the parson's daughter, she suited her surroundings with the best grace imaginable; and whatever she said seemed so pat and pretty that Will conceived a great idea of her talents. He could see her face, as she leaned forward, against a background of rising pine woods; her eyes shone peaceably; the light lay around her hair like a kerchief; something that was hardly a smile rippled her pale cheeks, and Will could not contain himself from gazing on her in an agreeable dismay. She looked, even in her quietest moments, so complete in herself, and so quick with life down to her finger tips and the very skirts of her dress, that the remainder of created things became no more than a blot by comparison; and if Will glanced away from her to her surroundings, the trees looked inanimate and senseless, the clouds hung in heaven like dead things, and even the mountain tops were disenchanted. The whole valley could not compare in looks with this one girl.

Will was always observant in the society of his fellow-creatures; but his observation became almost painfully eager in the case of Marjory. He listened to all she uttered, and read her eyes, at the same time, for the unspoken commentary. Many kind, simple, and sincere speeches found an echo in his heart. He became conscious of a soul beautifully poised upon itself, nothing doubting, nothing desiring, clothed in peace. It was not possible to separate her thoughts from her appearance. The turn of her wrist, the still sound of her voice, the light in her eyes, the lines of her body, fell in tune with her grave and gentle words, like the accompaniment that sustains and harmonises the voice of the singer. Her influence was one thing, not to be divided or discussed, only to be felt with gratitude and joy. To Will, her presence recalled something of his childhood, and the thought of her took its place in his mind beside that of dawn, of running water, and of the earliest violets and lilacs. It is the property of things seen for the first time, or for the first time after long, like the flowers in spring, to reawaken in us the sharp edge of sense and that impression of mystic strangeness which otherwise passes out of life with the coming of years; but the sight of a loved face is what renews a man's character from the fountain upwards.

One day after dinner Will took a stroll among the firs; a grave beatitude possessed him from top to toe, and he kept smiling to himself and the landscape as he went. The river ran between the stepping-stones with a pretty wimple; a bird sang loudly in the wood; the hill-tops looked immeasurably high, and as he glanced at them from time to time seemed to contemplate his movements with a beneficent but awful curiosity. His way took him to the eminence which overlooked the plain; and there he sat down upon a stone, and fell into deep and pleasant thought. The plain lay abroad with its cities and silver river; everything was asleep, except a great eddy of birds which kept rising and falling and going round and round in the blue air. He repeated Marjory's name aloud, and the sound of it gratified his ear. He shut his eyes, and her image sprang up before him, quietly luminous and attended with good thoughts. The river might run for ever; the birds fly higher and higher till they touched the stars. He saw it was empty bustle after all; for here, without stirring a foot, waiting patiently in his own narrow valley, he also had attained the better sunlight.

The next day Will made a sort of declaration across the dinner-table, while the parson was filling his pipe.

"Miss Marjory," he said, "I never knew any one I liked so well as you. I am mostly a cold, unkindly sort of man; not from want of heart, but out of strangeness in my way of thinking; and people seem far away from me.

'Tis as if there were a circle round me, which kept every one out but you; I can hear the others talking and laughing; but you come quite close. Maybe this is disagreeable to you?" he asked.

Marjory made no answer.

"Speak up, girl," said the parson.

"Nay, now," returned Will, "I wouldn't press her, parson. I feel tongue-tied myself, who am not used to it; and she's a woman, and little more than a child, when all is said. But for my part, as far as I can understand what people mean by it, I fancy I must be what they call in love. I do not wish to be held as committing myself; for I may be wrong; but that is how I believe things are with me. And if Miss Marjory should feel any otherwise on her part, mayhap she would be so kind as shake her head."

Marjory was silent, and gave no sign that she had heard.

"How is that, parson?" asked Will.

"The girl must speak," replied the parson, laying down his pipe. "Here's our neighbour who says he loves you, Madge. Do you love him, ay or no?"

"I think I do," said Marjory faintly.

"Well, then, that's all that could be wished!" cried Will heartily. And he took her hand across the table, and held it a moment in both of his with great satisfaction.

"You must marry," observed the parson, replacing his pipe in his mouth.

"Is that the right thing to do, think you?" demanded Will.

"It is indispensable," said the parson.

"Very well," replied the wooer.

Two or three days passed away with great delight to Will, although a bystander might scarce have found it out. He continued to take his meals opposite Marjory, and to talk with her and gaze upon her in her father's presence; but he made no attempt to see her alone, nor in any other way changed his conduct towards her from what it had been since the beginning. Perhaps the girl was a little disappointed, and perhaps not unjustly; and yet if it had been enough to be always in the thoughts of another person, and so pervade and alter his whole life, she might have been thoroughly contented. For she was never out of Will's mind for an instant. He sat over the stream, and watched the dust of the eddy, and the poised fish, and straining weeds; he wandered out alone into the purple even, with all the blackbirds piping round him in the wood; he rose early in the morning, and saw the sky turn from grey to gold, and the light leap upon the hill-tops; and all the while he kept wondering if he had never seen such things before, or how it was that they should look so different now. The sound of his own mill-wheel, or of the wind among the trees, confounded and charmed his heart. The most enchanting thoughts presented themselves unbidden in his mind. He was so happy that he could not sleep at night, and so restless that he could hardly sit still out of her company. And yet it seemed as if he avoided her rather than sought her out.

One day, as he was coming home from a ramble, Will found Marjory in the garden picking flowers, and as he came up with her, slackened his pace and continued walking by her side.

"You like flowers?" he said.

"Indeed I love them dearly," she replied. "Do you?"

"Why, no," said he, "not so much. They are a very small affair, when all is done. I can fancy people caring for them greatly, but not doing as you are just now."

"How?" she asked, pausing and looking up at him.

"Plucking them," said he. "They are a deal better off where they are, and look a deal prettier, if you go to that."

"I wish to have them for my own," she answered, "to carry them near my heart, and keep them in my room. They tempt me when they grow here; they seem to say, 'Come and do something with us'; but once I have cut them and put them by, the charm is laid, and I can look at them with quite an easy heart."

"You wish to possess them," replied Will, "in order to think no more about them. It's a bit like killing the goose with the golden eggs. It's a bit like what I wished to do when I was a boy. Because I had a fancy for looking out over the plain, I wished to go down there—where I couldn't look out over it any longer. Was not that fine reasoning? Dear, dear, if they only thought of it, all the world would do like me; and you would let your flowers alone, just as I stay up here in the mountains." Suddenly he broke off sharp. "By the Lord!" he cried. And when she asked him what was wrong, he turned the question off, and walked away into the house with rather a humorous expression of face.

He was silent at table; and after the night had fallen and the stars had come out overhead, he walked up and down for hours in the court-yard and garden with an uneven pace. There was still a light in the window of Marjory's room: one little oblong patch of orange in a world of dark blue hills and silver starlight. Will's mind ran a great deal on the window; but his thoughts were not very lover-like. "There she is in her room," he thought, "and there are the stars overhead:—a blessing upon both!" Both were good influences in his life; both soothed and braced him in his profound contentment with the world. And what more should he desire with either? The fat young man and his councils were so present to his mind that he threw back his head, and, putting his hands before his mouth, shouted aloud to the populous heavens. Whether from the position of his head or the sudden strain of the exertion, he seemed to see a momentary shock among the stars, and a diffusion of frosty light pass from one to another along the sky. At the same instant, a corner of the blind was lifted up and lowered again at once. He laughed a loud ho-ho! "One and another!" thought Will. "The stars tremble, and the blind goes up. Why, before Heaven, what a great magician I must be! Now, if I were only a fool, should not I be in a pretty way?" And he went off to bed, chuckling to himself: "If I were only a fool!"

The next morning, pretty early, he saw her once more in the garden, and sought her out.

"I have been thinking about getting married," he began abruptly; "and after having turned it all over, I have made up my mind it's not worth while."

She turned upon him for a single moment; but his radiant, kindly appearance would, under the circumstances, have disconcerted an angel, and she looked down again upon the ground in silence. He could see her tremble.

"I hope you don't mind," he went on, a little taken aback. "You ought not. I have turned it all over, and upon my soul there's nothing in it. We should never be one whit nearer than we are just now, and, if I am a wise man, nothing like so happy."

"It is unnecessary to go round about with me," she said. "I very well remember that you refused to commit yourself; and now that I see you were mistaken, and in reality have never cared for me, I can only feel sad that I have been so far misled."

"I ask your pardon," said Will stoutly; "you do not understand my meaning. As to whether I have ever loved you or not, I must leave that to others. But for one thing, my feeling is not changed; and for another, you may make it your boast that you have made my whole life and character something different from what they were. I mean what I say; no less. I do not think getting married is worth while. I would rather you went on living with your father, so that I could walk over and see you once, or maybe twice a week, as people go to church, and then we should both be all the happier between whiles. That's my notion. But I'll marry you if you will," he added.

"Do you know that you are insulting me?" she broke out.

"Not I, Marjory," said he; "if there is anything in a clear conscience, not I. I offer all my heart's best affections; you can take it or want it, though I suspect it's beyond either your power or mine to change what has once been done, and set me fancy-free. I'll marry you, if you like; but I tell you again and again, it's not worth while, and we had best stay friends. Though I am a quiet man I have noticed a heap of things in my life. Trust in me, and take things as I propose; or, if you don't like that, say the word, and I'll marry you out of hand."

There was a considerable pause, and Will, who began to feel uneasy, began to grow angry in consequence.

"It seems you are too proud to say your mind," he said. "Believe me, that's a pity. A clean shrift makes simple living. Can a man be more downright or honourable to a woman than I have been? I have said my say, and given you your choice. Do you want me to marry you? or will you take my friendship, as I think best? or have you had enough of me for good? Speak out for the dear God's sake! You know your father told you a girl should speak her mind in these affairs."

She seemed to recover herself at that, turned without a word, walked rapidly through the garden, and disappeared into the house, leaving Will in some confusion as to the result. He walked up and down the garden, whistling softly to himself. Sometimes he stopped and contemplated the sky and hill-tops; sometimes he went down to the tail of the weir and sat there, looking foolishly in the water. All this dubiety and perturbation was so foreign to his nature and the life which he had resolutely chosen for himself, that he began to regret Marjory's arrival. "After all," he thought, "I was as happy as a man need be. I could come down here and watch my fishes all day long if I wanted: I was as settled and contented as my old mill."

Marjory came down to dinner, looking very trim and quiet; and no sooner were all three at table than she made her father a speech, with her eyes fixed upon her plate, but showing no other sign of embarrassment or distress.

"Father," she began, "Mr. Will and I have been talking things over. We see that we have each made a mistake about our feelings, and he has agreed, at my request, to give up all idea of marriage, and be no more than my very good friend, as in the past. You see, there is no shadow of a quarrel, and indeed I hope we shall see a great deal of him in the future, for his visits will always be welcome in our house. Of course, father, you will know best, but perhaps we should do better to leave Mr. Will's house for the present. I believe, after what has passed, we should hardly be agreeable inmates for some days."

Will, who had commanded himself with difficulty from the first, broke out upon this into an inarticulate noise, and raised one hand with an appearance of real dismay, as if he were about to interfere and contradict. But she checked him at once, looking up at him with a swift glance and an angry flush upon her cheek.

"You will perhaps have the good grace," she said, "to let me explain these matters for myself."

Will was put entirely out of countenance by her expression and the ring of her voice. He held his peace, concluding that there were some things about this girl beyond his comprehension, in which he was exactly right.

The poor parson was quite crestfallen. He tried to prove that this was no more than a true lovers' tiff, which would pass off before night; and when he was dislodged from that position, he went on to argue that where there was no quarrel there could be no call for a separation; for the good man liked both his entertainment and his host. It was curious to see how the girl managed them, saying little all the time, and that very quietly, and yet twisting them round her finger and insensibly leading them wherever she would by feminine tact and generalship. It scarcely seemed to have been her doing—it seemed as if things had merely so fallen out—that she and her father took their departure that same afternoon in a farm-cart, and went farther down the valley, to wait, until their own house was ready for them, in another hamlet. But Will had been observing closely, and was well aware of her dexterity and resolution. When he found himself alone he had a great many curious matters to turn over in his mind. He was very sad and solitary, to begin with. All the interest had gone out of his life; and he might look up at the stars as long as he pleased, he somehow failed to find support or consolation. And then he was in such a turmoil of spirit about Marjory. He had been puzzled and irritated at her behaviour, and yet he could not keep himself from admiring it. He thought he recognised a fine perverse angel in that still soul which he had never hitherto suspected; and though he saw it was an influence that would fit but ill with his own life of artificial calm, he could not keep himself from ardently desiring to possess it. Like a man who has lived among shadows and now meets the sun, he was both pained and delighted.

As the days went forward he passed from one extreme to another; now pluming himself on the strength of his determination, now despising his timid and silly caution. The former was, perhaps, the true thought of his heart, and represented the regular tenor of the man's reflections; but the latter burst forth from time to time with an unruly violence, and then he would forget all consideration, and go up and down his house and garden or walk among the fir woods like one who is beside himself with remorse. To equable, steady-minded Will this state of matters was intolerable; and he determined, at whatever cost, to bring it to an end. So, one warm summer afternoon he put on his best clothes, took a thorn switch in his hand, and set out down the valley by the river. As soon as he had taken his determination, he had regained at a bound his customary peace of heart, and he enjoyed the bright weather and the variety of the scene without any admixture of alarm or unpleasant eagerness. It was nearly the same to him how the matter turned out. If she accepted him, he would have to marry her this time, which perhaps was all for the best. If she refused him, he would have done his utmost, and might follow his own way in the future with an untroubled conscience. He hoped, on the whole, she would refuse him; and then, again, as he saw the brown roof which sheltered her, peeping through some willows at an angle of the stream, he was half inclined to reverse the wish, and more than half ashamed of himself for this infirmity of purpose.

Marjory seemed glad to see him, and gave him her hand without affectation or delay.

'I have been thinking about this marriage," he began.

"So have I," she answered. "And I respect you more and more for a very wise man. You understood me better than I understood myself; and I am now quite certain that things are all for the best as they are."

"At the same time—" ventured Will.

"You must be tired," she interrupted. ' Take a seat and let me fetch you a glass of wine. The afternoon is so warm; and I wish you not to be displeased with your visit. You must come quite often; once a week, if you can spare the time; I am always so glad to see my friends."

"Oh, very well," thought Will to himself. "It appears I was right after all." And he paid a very agreeable visit, walked home again in capital spirits, and gave himself no further concern about the matter.

For nearly three years Will and Marjory continued on these terms, seeing each other once or twice a week without any word of love between them; and for all that time I believe Will was nearly as happy as a man can be. He rather stinted himself the pleasure of seeing her; and he would often walk half-way over to the parsonage, and then back again, as if to whet his appetite. Indeed there was one corner of the road, whence he could see the church-spire wedged into a crevice of the valley between sloping fir woods, with a triangular snatch of plain by way of background, which he greatly affected as a place to sit and moralise in before returning homewards; and the peasants got so much into the habit of finding him there in the twilight that they gave it the name of "Will o' the Mill's Corner."

At the end of the three years Marjory played him a sad trick by suddenly marrying somebody else. Will kept his countenance bravely, and merely remarked that, for as little as he knew of women, he had acted very prudently in not marrying her himself three years before. She plainly knew very little of her own mind, and, in spite of a deceptive manner, was as fickle and flighty as the rest of them. He had to congratulate himself on an escape, he said, and would take a higher opinion of his own wisdom in consequence. But at heart, he was reasonably displeased, moped a good deal for a month or two, and fell away in flesh, to the astonishment of his serving-lads.

It was perhaps a year after this marriage that Will was awakened late one night by the sound of a horse galloping on the road, followed by precipitate knocking at the inn-door. He opened his window and saw a farm servant, mounted and holding a led horse by the bridle, who told him to make what haste he could and go along with him; for Marjory was dying, and had sent urgently to fetch him to her bedside. Will was no horseman, and made so little speed upon the way that the poor young wife was very near her end before he arrived. But they had some minutes' talk in private, and he was present and wept very bitterly while she breathed her last.

### DEATH

Year after year went away into nothing, with great explosions and outcries in the cities on the plain; red revolt springing up and being suppressed in blood, battle swaying hither and thither, patient astronomers in observatory towers picking out and christening new stars, plays being performed in lighted theatres, people being carried into hospitals on stretchers, and all the usual turmoil and agitation of men's lives in crowded centres. Up in Will's valley only the winds and seasons made an epoch; the fish hung in the swift stream, the birds circled overhead, the pine-tops rustled underneath the stars, the tall hills stood over all; and Will went to and fro, minding his wayside inn, until the snow began to thicken on his head. His heart was young and vigorous and if his pulses kept a sober time, they still beat strong and steady in his wrists. He carried a ruddy stain on either cheek, like a ripe apple; he stooped a little, but his step was still firm; and his sinewy hands were reached out to all men with a friendly pressure. His face was covered with those wrinkles which are got in open air, and which, rightly looked at, are no more than a sort of permanent sun-burning; such wrinkles heighten the stupidity of stupid faces; but to a person like Will, with his clear eyes and smiling mouth, only give another charm by testifying to a simple and easy life. His talk was full of wise sayings. He had a taste for other people; and other people had a taste for him. When the valley was full of tourists in the season, there were merry nights in Will's arbour; and his views, which seemed whimsical to his neighbours, were often enough admired by learned people out of towns and colleges. Indeed, he had a very noble old age, and grew daily better known; so that his fame was heard of in the cities of the plain; and young men who had been summer travellers spoke together in *cafés* of Will o' the Mill and his rough philosophy. Many and many an invitation, you may be sure, he had; but nothing could tempt him from his upland valley. He would shake his head and smile over his tobacco-pipe with a deal of meaning. "You come too late," he would answer. "I am a dead man now: I have lived and died already. Fifty years ago you would have brought my heart into my mouth; and now you do not even tempt me. But that is the object of long living, that man should cease to care about life." And again: "There is only one difference between a long life and a good dinner: that, in the dinner, the sweets come last." Or once more: "When I was a boy, I was a bit puzzled, and hardly knew whether it was myself or the world that was curious and worth

looking into.  Now, I know it is myself, and stick to
that."

He never showed any symptoms of frailty, but kept
stalwart and firm to the last; but they say he grew less
talkative towards the end, and would listen to other people by the hour in an amused and sympathetic silence.
Only, when he did speak, it was more to the point and
more charged with old experience.  He drank a bottle
of wine gladly; above all, at sunset on the hill-top or
quite late at night under the stars in the arbour.  The
sight of something attractive and unattainable seasoned
his enjoyment, he would say; and he professed he had
lived long enough to admire a candle all the more when
he could compare it with a planet.

One night, in his seventy-second year, he awoke in
bed, in such uneasiness of body and mind that he arose
and dressed himself and went out to meditate in the
arbour.  It was pitch dark, without a star; the river
was swollen, and the wet woods and meadows loaded
the air with perfume.  It had thundered during the day,
and it promised more thunder for the morrow.  A
murky, stifling night for a man of seventy-two!  Whether
it was the weather or the wakefulness, or some little
touch of fever in his old limbs, Will's mind was besieged
by tumultuous and crying memories.  His boyhood, the
night with the fat young man, the death of his adopted
parents, the summer days with Marjory, and many of
those small circumstances, which seem nothing to another, and are yet the very gist of a man's own life to
himself—things seen, words heard, looks misconstrued
—arose from their forgotten corners and usurped his
attention.  The dead themselves were with him, not
merely taking part in this thin show of memory that de-
filed before his brain, but revisiting his bodily senses as
they do in profound and vivid dreams.  The fat young

man leaned his elbows on the table opposite; Marjory came and went with an apronful of flowers between the garden and the arbour; he could hear the old parson knocking out his pipe or blowing his resonant nose. The tide of his consciousness ebbed and flowed; he was sometimes half asleep and drowned in his recollections of the past; and sometimes he was broad awake, wondering at himself. But about the middle of the night he was startled by the voice of the dead miller calling to him out of the house as he used to do on the arrival of custom. The hallucination was so perfect that Will sprang from his seat and stood listening for the summons to be repeated; and as he listened he became conscious of another noise besides the brawling of the river and the ringing in his feverish ears. It was like the stir of the horses and the creaking of harness, as though a carriage with an impatient team had been brought up upon the road before the court-yard gate. At such an hour, upon this rough and dangerous pass, the supposition was no better than absurd; and Will dismissed it from his mind, and resumed his seat upon the arbour chair; and sleep closed over him again like running water. He was once again awakened by the dead miller's call, thinner and more spectral than before; and once again he heard the noise of an equipage upon the road. And so thrice and four times, the same dream, or the same fancy, presented itself to his senses: until at length, smiling to himself as when one humours a nervous child, he proceeded towards the gate to set his uncertainty at rest.

From the arbour to the gate was no great distance, and yet it took Will some time; it seemed as if the dead thickened around him in the court, and crossed his path at every step. For, first, he was suddenly surprised by an overpowering sweetness of heliotropes; it was as if his garden had been planted with this flower from end to end, and the hot, damp night had drawn forth all their perfumes in a breath. Now the heliotrope had been Marjory's favourite flower, and since her death not one of them had ever been planted in Will's ground.

"I must be going crazy," he thought. "Poor Marjory and her heliotropes!"

And with that he raised his eyes towards the window that had once been hers. If he had been bewildered before, he was now almost terrified; for there was a light in the room; the window was an orange oblong as of yore; and the corner of the blind was lifted and let fall as on the night when he stood and shouted to the stars in his perplexity. The illusion only endured an instant; but it left him somewhat unmanned, rubbing his eyes and staring at the outline of the house and the black night behind it. While he thus stood, and it seemed as if he must have stood there quite a long time, there came a renewal of the noises on the road: and he turned in time to meet a stranger, who was advancing to meet him across the court. There was something like the outline of a great carriage discernible on the road behind the stranger, and, above that, a few black pine-tops, like so many plumes.

"Master Will?" asked the new-comer, in brief military fashion.

"That same, sir," answered Will. "Can I do anything to serve you?"

"I have heard you much spoken of, Master Will," returned the other; "much spoken of, and well. And though I have both hands full of business, I wish to drink a bottle of wine with you in your arbour. Before I go, I shall introduce myself."

Will led the way to the trellis, and got a lamp lighted and a bottle uncorked. He was not altogether unused

to such complimentary interviews, and hoped little
enough from this one, being schooled by many disap-
pointments. A sort of cloud had settled on his wits
and prevented him from remembering the strangeness
of the hour. He moved like a person in his sleep; and
it seemed as if the lamp caught fire and the bottle came
uncorked with the facility of thought. Still, he had
some curiosity about the appearance of his visitor, and
tried in vain to turn the light into his face; either he
handled the lamp clumsily, or there was a dimness over
his eyes; but he could make out little more than a
shadow at table with him. He stared and stared at this
shadow, as he wiped out the glasses, and began to feel
cold and strange about the heart. The silence weighed
upon him, for he could hear nothing now, not even the
river, but the drumming of his own arteries in his ears.

"Here's to you," said the stranger roughly.

"Here is my service, sir," replied Will, sipping his
wine, which somehow tasted oddly.

"I understand you are a very positive fellow," pursued the stranger.

Will made answer with a smile of some satisfaction
and a little nod.

"So am I," continued the other; "and it is the delight of my heart to tramp on people's corns. I will
have nobody positive but myself; not one. I have
crossed the whims, in my time, of kings and generals
and great artists. And what would you say," he went
on, "if I had come up here on purpose to cross yours?"

Will had it on his tongue to make a sharp rejoinder;
but the politeness of an old innkeeper prevailed; and he
held his peace and made answer with a civil gesture of
the hand.

"I have," said the stranger. "And if I did not hold
you in a particular esteem, I should make no words

about the matter. It appears you pride yourself on staying where you are. You mean to stick by your inn. Now I mean you shall come for a turn with me in my barouche; and before this bottle's empty, so you shall."

"That would be an odd thing, to be sure," replied Will, with a chuckle. "Why, sir, I have grown here like an old oak tree; the Devil himself could hardly root me up; and for all I perceive you are a very entertaining old gentleman, I would wager you another bottle you lose your pains with me."

The dimness of Will's eyesight had been increasing all this while; but he was somehow conscious of a sharp and chilling scrutiny which irritated and yet overmastered him.

"You need not think," he broke out suddenly, in an explosive, febrile manner that startled and alarmed himself, "that I am a stay-at-home, because I fear anything under God. God knows I am tired enough of it all; and when the time comes for a longer journey than ever you dream of, I reckon I shall find myself prepared."

The stranger emptied his glass and pushed it away from him. He looked down for a little, and then, leaning over the table, tapped Will three times upon the forearm with a single finger. "The time has come!" he said solemnly.

An ugly thrill spread from the spot he touched. The tones of his voice were dull and startling, and echoed strangely in Will's heart.

"I beg your pardon," he said, with some discomposure. "What do you mean?"

"Look at me, and you will find your eyesight swim. Raise your hand; it is dead-heavy. This is your last bottle of wine, Master Will, and your last night upon the earth."

"You are a doctor?" quavered Will.

"The best that ever was," replied the other; "for I cure both mind and body with the same prescription. I take away all pain and I forgive all sins; and where my patients have gone wrong in life, I smooth out all complications and set them free again upon their feet."

"I have no need of you," said Will.

"A time comes for all men, Master Will," replied the doctor, "when the helm is taken out of their hands. For you, because you were prudent and quiet, it has been long of coming, and you have had long to discipline yourself for its reception. You have seen what is to be seen about your mill; you have sat close all your days like a hare in its form; but now that is at an end; and," added the doctor, getting on his feet, "you must arise and come with me."

"You are a strange physician," said Will, looking steadfastly upon his guest.

"I am a natural law," he replied, "and people call me Death."

"Why did you not tell me so at first?" cried Will. "I have been waiting for you these many years. Give me your hand, and welcome."

"Lean upon my arm," said the stranger, "for already your strength abates. Lean on me heavily as you need; for though I am old, I am very strong. It is but three steps to my carriage, and there all your trouble ends. Why, Will," he added, "I have been yearning for you as if you were my own son; and of all the men that ever I came for in my long days, I have come for you most gladly. I am caustic, and sometimes offend people at first sight; but I am a good friend at heart to such as you."

"Since Marjory was taken," returned Will, "I declare before God you were the only friend I had to look for."

So the pair went arm in arm across the court-yard.

One of the servants awoke about this time and heard the noise of horses pawing before he dropped asleep again; all down the valley that night there was a rushing as of a smooth and steady wind descending towards the plain; and when the world rose next morning, sure enough Will o' the Mill had gone at last upon his travels.

# THE SIRE DE MALÉTROIT'S DOOR [1]

DENIS DE BEAULIEU was not yet two-and-twenty, but he counted himself a grown man, and a very accomplished cavalier into the bargain. Lads were early formed in that rough, warfaring epoch; and when one has been in a pitched battle and a dozen raids, has killed one's man in an honourable fashion, and knows a thing or two of strategy and mankind, a certain swagger in the gait is surely to be pardoned. He had put up his horse with due care, and supped with due deliberation; and then, in a very agreeable frame of mind, went out to pay a visit in the grey of the evening. It was not a very wise proceeding on the young man's part. He would have done better to remain beside the fire or go decently to bed. For the town was full of the troops of Burgundy and England under a mixed command; and though Denis was there on safe-conduct, his safe-conduct was like to serve him little on a chance encounter.

[1] "Invented in France, first told over the fire one evening in Paris, and ultimately written at Penzance." It was published in *Temple Bar*, in January, 1878, and reprinted in the volume entitled *New Arabian Nights*, 1882. The scene is Chateau Landon, a town southeast of Paris and not far from the borders of the old duchy of Burgundy. The time is September, 1429, presumably a little after Charles VII and Jeanne d'Arc had made their ill-fated attack upon Paris and had marched southward through this very district. The English troops of the Duke of Bedford, with the Burgundians, their allies, were following, retaking the towns which the French had deserted. Chateau Landon was in the line of march, and Denis de Beaulieu must have come into it, with his safe-conduct, from the French king's forces. It is to be noted that in 1875, with Sir Walter Simpson, who afterwards accompanied him upon the Inland Voyage, Stevenson walked up the Valley of the Loing, and probably passed through Chateau Landon.

It was September, 1429; the weather had fallen sharp;
a flighty piping wind, laden with showers, beat about
the township; and the dead leaves ran riot along the
streets.  Here and there a window was already lighted
up; and the noise of men-at-arms making merry over
supper within, came forth in fits and was swallowed up
and carried away by the wind.  The night fell swiftly;
the flag of England, fluttering on the spire-top, grew
ever fainter and fainter against the flying clouds—a
black speck like a swallow in the tumultuous, leaden
chaos of the sky.  As the night fell the wind rose, and
began to hoot under archways and roar amid the tree-
tops in the valley below the town.

Denis de Beaulieu walked fast and was soon knocking
at his friend's door; but though he promised himself to
stay only a little while and make an early return, his welcome was so pleasant, and he found so much to delay
him, that it was already long past midnight before he
said good-bye upon the threshold.  The wind had fallen
again in the meanwhile; the night was as black as the
grave; not a star, nor a glimmer of moonshine, slipped
through the canopy of cloud.  Denis was ill-acquainted
with the intricate lanes of Chateau Landon; even by
daylight he had found some trouble in picking his way;
and in this absolute darkness he soon lost it altogether.
He was certain of one thing only—to keep mounting
the hill; for his friend's house lay at the lower end, or
tail, of Chateau Landon, while the inn was up at the
head, under the great church spire.  With this clue to go
upon he stumbled and groped forward, now breathing
more freely in open places where there was a good slice
of sky overhead, now feeling along the wall in stifling
closes.  It is an eerie and mysterious position to be thus
submerged in opaque blackness in an almost unknown
town.  The silence is terrifying in its possibilities.  The

touch of cold window bars to the exploring hand startles the man like the touch of a toad; the inequalities of the pavement shake his heart into his mouth; a piece of denser darkness threatens an ambuscade or a chasm in the pathway; and where the air is brighter, the houses put on strange and bewildering appearances, as if to lead him farther from his way. For Denis, who had to regain his inn without attracting notice, there was real danger as well as mere discomfort in the walk; and he went warily and boldly at once, and at every corner paused to make an observation.

He had been for some time threading a lane so narrow that he could touch a wall with either hand when it began to open out and go sharply downward. Plainly this lay no longer in the direction of his inn; but the hope of a little more light tempted him forward to reconnoitre. The lane ended in a terrace with a bartizan wall,[1] which gave an outlook between high houses, as out of an embrasure, into the valley lying dark and formless several hundred feet below. Denis looked down, and could discern a few tree-tops waving and a single speck of brightness where the river ran across a weir. The weather was clearing up, and the sky had lightened, so as to show the outline of the heavier clouds and the dark margin of the hills. By the uncertain glimmer, the house on his left hand should be a place of some pretensions; it was surmounted by several pinnacles and turret-tops; the round stern of a chapel, with a fringe of flying buttresses, projected boldly from the main block; and the door was sheltered under a deep porch carved with figures and overhung by two long gargoyles. The windows of the chapel gleamed through their intricate tracery with a light as of many tapers, and threw out the buttresses and the peaked roof in a more intense black-

---

[1] A wall with jutting turrets.

ness against the sky.  It was plainly the hotel of some
great family of the neighbourhood; and as it reminded
Denis of a town house of his own at Bourges, he stood
for some time gazing up at it and mentally gauging the
skill of the architects and the consideration of the two
families.

There seemed to be no issue to the terrace but the
lane by which he had reached it; he could only retrace
his steps, but he had gained some notion of his whereabouts, and hoped by this means to hit the main thor-
ough-fare and speedily regain the inn.  He was reckon-
ing without that chapter of accidents which was to make
this night memorable above all others in his career; for
he had not gone back above a hundred yards before he
saw a light coming to meet him, and heard loud voices
speaking together in the echoing narrows of the lane.
It was a party of men-at-arms going the night round
with torches.  Denis assured himself that they had all
been making free with the wine-bowl, and were in no
mood to be particular about safe-conducts or the nice-
ties of chivalrous war.  It was as like as not that they
would kill him like a dog and leave him where he fell.
The situation was inspiriting but nervous.  Their own
torches would conceal him from sight, he reflected; and
he hoped that they would drown the noise of his footsteps with their own empty voices.  If he were but fleet
and silent, he might evade their notice altogether.

Unfortunately, as he turned to beat a retreat, his foot
rolled upon a pebble; he fell against the wall with an
ejaculation, and his sword rang loudly on the stones.
Two or three voices demanded who went there—some
in French, some in English; but Denis made no reply,
and ran the faster down the lane.  Once upon the terrace, he paused to look back.  They still kept calling
after him, and just then began to double the pace in

pursuit, with a considerable clank of armour, and great
tossing of the torchlight to and fro in the narrow jaws
of the passage.

Denis cast a look around and darted into the porch.
There he might escape observation, or—if that were
too much to expect—was in a capital posture whether
for parley or defence. So thinking, he drew his sword
and tried to set his back against the door. To his
surprise, it yielded behind his weight; and though he
turned in a moment, continued to swing back on oiled
and noiseless hinges, until it stood wide open on a black
interior. When things fall out opportunely for the person concerned, he is not apt to be critical about the how
or why, his own immediate personal convenience seem-
ing a sufficient reason for the strangest oddities and revolutions in our sublunary things; and so Denis, without
a moment's hesitation, stepped within and partly closed
the door behind him to conceal his place of refuge.
Nothing was further from his thoughts than to close it
altogether; but for some inexplicable reason—perhaps
by a spring or a weight—the ponderous mass of oak
whipped itself out of his fingers and clanked to, with a
formidable rumble and a noise like the falling of an
automatic bar.

The round, at that very moment, debouched upon the
terrace and proceeded to summon him with shouts and
curses. He heard them ferreting in the dark corners;
the stock of a lance even rattled along the outer surface
of the door behind which he stood; but these gentlemen
were in too high a humour to be long delayed, and soon
made off down a corkscrew pathway which had escaped
Denis's observation, and passed out of sight and hearing
along the battlements of the town.

Denis breathed again. He gave them a few minutes'
grace for fear of accidents, and then groped about for

some means of opening the door and slipping forth again.
The inner surface was quite smooth, not a handle, not
a moulding, not a projection of any sort. He got his
finger-nails round the edges and pulled, but the mass
was immovable. He shook it, it was as firm as a rock.
Denis de Beaulieu frowned and gave vent to a little
noiseless whistle. What ailed the door? he wondered.
Why was it open? How came it to shut so easily and
so effectually after him? There was something obscure
and underhand about all this, that was little to the
young man's fancy. It looked like a snare; and yet
who could suppose a snare in such a quiet by-street and
in a house of so prosperous and even noble an exterior?
And yet—snare or no snare, intentionally or uninten-
tionally—here he was, prettily trapped; and for the
life of him he could see no way out of it again. The
darkness began to weigh upon him. He gave ear; all
was silence without, but within and close by he seemed
to catch a faint sighing, a faint sobbing rustle, a little
stealthy creak—as though many persons were at his
side, holding themselves quite still, and governing even
their respiration with the extreme of slyness. The idea
went to his vitals with a shock, and he faced about
suddenly as if to defend his life. Then, for the first
time, he became aware of a light about the level of his
eyes and at some distance in the interior of the house—a
vertical thread of light, widening towards the bottom,
such as might escape between two wings of arras over a
doorway. To see anything was a relief to Denis; it
was like a piece of solid ground to a man labouring in a
morass; his mind seized upon it with avidity; and he
stood staring at it and trying to piece together some
logical conception of his surroundings. Plainly there
was a flight of steps ascending from his own level to
that of this illuminated doorway; and indeed he thought

he could make out another thread of light, as fine as a
needle, and as faint as phosphorescence, which might
very well be reflected along the polished wood of a
handrail. Since he had begun to suspect that he was
not alone, his heart had continued to beat with smother-
ing violence, and an intolerable desire for action of any
sort had possessed itself of his spirit. He was in deadly
peril, he believed. What could be more natural than to
mount the staircase, lift the curtain, and confront his
difficulty at once? At least he would be dealing with
something tangible; at least he would be no longer in
the dark. He stepped slowly forward with outstretched
hands, until his foot struck the bottom step; then he
rapidly scaled the stairs, stood for a moment to compose
his expression, lifted the arras, and went in.

He found himself in a large apartment of polished
stone. There were three doors; one on each of three
sides; all similarly curtained with tapestry. The fourth
side was occupied by two large windows and a great
stone chimney-piece, carved with the arms of the Malé-
troits. Denis recognised the bearings, and was gratified
to find himself in such good hands. The room was
strongly illuminated; but it contained little furniture except a heavy table and a chair or two, the hearth was
innocent of fire, and the pavement was but sparsely
strewn with rushes clearly many days old.

On a high chair beside the chimney, and directly fac-
ing Denis as he entered, sat a little old gentleman in a
fur tippet. He sat with his legs crossed and his hands
folded, and a cup of spiced wine stood by his elbow on
a bracket on the wall. His countenance had a strongly
masculine cast; not properly human, but such as we see
in the bull, the goat, or the domestic boar; something
equivocal and wheedling, something greedy, brutal, and
dangerous. The upper lip was inordinately full, as

though swollen by a blow or a toothache; and the smile,
the peaked eyebrows, and the small, strong eyes were
quaintly and almost comically evil in expression. Beautiful white hair hung straight all round his head, like a
saint's, and fell in a single curl upon the tippet. His
beard and moustache were the pink of venerable sweetness. Age, probably in consequence of inordinate precautions, had left no mark upon his hands; and the
Malétroit hand was famous. It would be difficult to
imagine anything at once so fleshy and so delicate in
design; the taper, sensual fingers were like those of one
of Leonardo's [1] women; the fork of the thumb made a
dimpled protuberance when closed; the nails were perfectly shaped, and of a dead, surprising whiteness. It
rendered his aspect tenfold more redoubtable, that a
man with hands like these should keep them devoutly
folded like a virgin martyr—that a man with so intent
and startling an expression of face should sit patiently
on his seat and contemplate people with an unwinking
stare, like a god, or a god's statue. His quiescence
seemed ironical and treacherous, it fitted so poorly with
his looks.

Such was Alain, Sire de Malétroit.

Denis and he looked silently at each other for a second
or two.

"Pray step in," said the Sire de Malétroit. "I have
been expecting you all the evening."

He had not risen, but he accompanied his words with
a smile and a slight but courteous inclination of the
head. Partly from the smile, partly from the strange
musical murmur with which the Sire prefaced his observation, Denis felt a strong shudder of disgust go through
his marrow. And what with disgust and honest con-

---

[1] Leonardo da Vinci, famous Italian painter of the time of the
Renaissance.

fusion of mind, he could scarcely get words together in reply.

"I fear," he said, "that this is a double accident. I am not the person you suppose me. It seems you were looking for a visit; but for my part, nothing was further from my thoughts—nothing could be more contrary to my wishes—than this intrusion."

"Well, well," replied the old gentleman indulgently, "here you are, which is the main point. Seat yourself, my friend, and put yourself entirely at your ease. We shall arrange our little affairs presently."

Denis perceived that the matter was still complicated with some misconception, and he hastened to continue his explanations.

"Your door . . ." he began.

"About my door?" asked the other, raising his peaked eyebrows. "A little piece of ingenuity." And he shrugged his shoulders. "A hospitable fancy! By your own account, you were not desirous of making my acquaintance. We old people look for such reluctance now and then; when it touches our honour, we cast about until we find some way of overcoming it. You arrive uninvited, but believe me, very welcome."

"You persist in error, sir," said Denis. "There can be no question between you and me. I am a stranger in this countryside. My name is Denis, damoiseau de Beaulieu. If you see me in your house, it is only——"

"My young friend," interrupted the other, "you will permit me to have my own ideas on that subject. They probably differ from yours at the present moment," he added, with a leer, "but time will show which of us is in the right."

Denis was convinced he had to do with a lunatic. He seated himself with a shrug, content to wait the upshot; and a pause ensued, during which he thought he could distinguish a hurried gabbling as of prayer from behind the arras immediately opposite him. Sometimes there seemed to be but one person engaged, sometimes two; and the vehemence of the voice, low as it was, seemed to indicate either great haste or an agony of spirit. It occurred to him that this piece of tapestry covered the entrance to the chapel he had noticed from without.

The old gentleman meanwhile surveyed Denis from head to foot with a smile, and from time to time emitted little noises like a bird or a mouse, which seemed to indicate a high degree of satisfaction. This state of matters became rapidly insupportable; and Denis, to put an end to it, remarked politely that the wind had gone down.

The old gentleman fell into a fit of silent laughter, so prolonged and violent that he became quite red in the face. Denis got upon his feet at once, and put on his hat with a flourish.

"Sir," he said, "if you are in your wits, you have affronted me grossly. If you are out of them, I flatter myself I can find better employment for my brains than to talk with lunatics. My conscience is clear; you have made a fool of me from the first moment; you have refused to hear my explanations; and now there is no power under God will make me stay here any longer; and if I cannot make my way out in a more decent fashion, I will hack your door in pieces with my sword."

The Sire de Malétroit raised his right hand and wagged it at Denis with the fore and little fingers extended.

"My dear nephew," he said, "sit down."

"Nephew!" retorted Denis, "you lie in your throat:" and he snapped his fingers in his face.

"Sit down, you rogue!" cried the old gentleman, in a sudden, harsh voice, like the barking of a dog. "Do you fancy," he went on, "that when I had made my little contrivance for the door I had stopped short with that? If you prefer to be bound hand and foot till your bones ache, rise and try to go away. If you choose to remain a free young buck, agreeably conversing with an old gentleman—why, sit where you are in peace, and God be with you."

"Do you mean I am a prisoner?" demanded Denis.

"I state the facts," replied the other. "I would rather leave the conclusion to yourself."

Denis sat down again. Externally he managed to keep pretty calm, but within, he was now boiling with anger, now chilled with apprehension. He no longer felt convinced that he was dealing with a madman. And if the old gentleman was sane, what, in God's name, had he to look for? What absurd or tragical adventure had befallen him? What countenance was he to assume?

While he was thus unpleasantly reflecting, the arras that overhung the chapel door was raised, and a tall priest in his robes came forth and, giving a long, keen stare at Denis, said something in an undertone to Sire de Malétroit.

"She is in a better frame of spirit?" asked the latter.

"She is more resigned, messire," replied the priest.

"Now the Lord help her, she is hard to please!" sneered the old gentleman. "A likely stripling—not ill-born—and of her own choosing, too? Why, what more would the jade have?"

"The situation is not usual for a young damsel," said the other, "and somewhat trying to her blushes."

"She should have thought of that before she began the dance! It was none of my choosing, God knows that: but since she is in it, by our lady, she shall carry it to the end." And then addressing Denis, "Monsieur de Beaulieu," he asked, "may I present you to my niece?

She has been waiting your arrival, I may say, with even greater impatience than myself."

Denis had resigned himself with a good grace—all he desired was to know the worst of it as speedily as possible; so he rose at once, and bowed in acquiescence. The Sire de Malétroit followed his example and limped, with the assistance of the chaplain's arm, towards the chapel door. The priest pulled aside the arras, and all three entered. The building had considerable architectural pretensions. A light groining sprang from six stout columns, and hung down in two rich pendants from the centre of the vault. The place terminated behind the altar in a round end, embossed and honeycombed with a superfluity of ornament in relief, and pierced by many little windows shaped like stars, trefoils, or wheels. These windows were imperfectly glazed, so that the night air circulated freely in the chapel. The tapers, of which there must have been half a hundred burning on the altar, were unmercifully blown about; and the light went through many different phases of brilliancy and semi-eclipse. On the steps in front of the altar knelt a young girl richly attired as a bride. A chill settled over Denis as he observed her costume; he fought with desperate energy against the conclusion that was being thrust upon his mind; it could not—it should not—be as he feared.

"Blanche," said the Sire, in his most flute-like tones, "I have brought a friend to see you, my little girl; turn round and give him your pretty hand. It is good to be devout; but it is necessary to be polite, my niece."

The girl rose to her feet and turned toward the newcomers. She moved all of a piece; and shame and exhaustion were expressed in every line of her fresh young body; and she held her head down and kept her eyes upon the pavement, as she came slowly forward. In the course of her advance, her eyes fell upon Denis de Beaulieu's feet—feet of which he was justly vain, be it remarked, and wore in the most elegant accoutrement even while travelling. She paused—started, as if his yellow boots had conveyed some shocking meaning—and glanced suddenly up into the wearer's countenance. Their eyes met; shame gave place to horror and terror in her looks; the blood left her lips; with a piercing scream she covered her face with her hands and sank upon the chapel floor.

"That is not the man!" she cried. "My uncle, that is not the man!"

The Sire de Malétroit chirped agreeably. "Of course not," he said. "I expected as much. It was so unfortunate you could not remember his name."

"Indeed," she cried, "indeed, I have never seen this person till this moment—I have never so much as set eyes upon him—I never wish to see him again. Sir," she said, turning to Denis, "if you are a gentleman, you will bear me out. Have I ever seen you—have you ever seen me—before this accursed hour?"

"To speak for myself, I have never had that pleasure," answered the young man. "This is the first time, messire, that I have met with your engaging niece."

The old gentleman shrugged his shoulders.

"I am distressed to hear it," he said. "But it is never too late to begin. I had little more acquaintance with my own late lady ere I married her; which proves," he added, with a grimace, "that these impromptu marriages may often produce an excellent understanding in the long run. As the bridegroom is to have a voice in the matter, I will give him two hours to make up for lost time before we proceed with the ceremony." And he turned toward the door, followed by the clergyman.

The girl was on her feet in a moment. "My uncle, you cannot be in earnest," she said. "I declare before God I will stab myself rather than be forced on that young man. The heart rises at it; God forbids such marriages; you dishonour your white hair. Oh, my uncle, pity me! There is not a woman in all the world but would prefer death to such a nuptial. Is it possible," she added, faltering—"is it possible that you do not believe me—that you still think this"—and she pointed at Denis with a tremor of anger and contempt —"that you still think *this* to be the man?"

"Frankly," said the old gentleman, pausing on the threshold, "I do. But let me explain to you once for all, Blanche de Malétroit, my way of thinking about this affair. When you took it into your head to dishonour my family and the name that I have borne, in peace and war, for more than three-score years, you forfeited not only the right to question my designs, but that of looking me in the face. If your father had been alive, he would have spat on you and turned you out of doors. His was the hand of iron. You may bless your God you have only to deal with the hand of velvet, mademoiselle. It was my duty to get you married without delay. Out of pure good-will, I have tried to find your own gallant for you. And I believe I have succeeded. But before God and all the holy angels, Blanche de Malétroit, if I have not, I care not one jack-straw. So let me recommend you to be polite to our young friend; for upon my word, your next groom may be less appetising."

And with that he went out, with the chaplain at his heels; and the arras fell behind the pair.

The girl turned upon Denis with flashing eyes.

"And what, sir," she demanded, "may be the meaning of all this?"

"God knows," returned Denis, gloomily. "I am a

prisoner in this house, which seems full of mad people. More I know not; and nothing do I understand."

"And pray how came you here?" she asked.

He told her as briefly as he could. "For the rest," he added, "perhaps you will follow my example, and tell me the answer to all these riddles, and what, in God's name, is like to be the end of it."

She stood silent for a little, and he could see her lips tremble and her tearless eyes burn with a feverish lustre. Then she pressed her forehead in both hands.

"Alas, how my head aches!" she said wearily—"to say nothing of my poor heart! But it is due to you to know my story, unmaidenly as it must seem. I am called Blanche de Malétroit; I have been without father or mother for—oh! for as long as I can recollect, and indeed I have been most unhappy all my life. Three months ago a young captain began to stand near me every day in church. I could see that I pleased him; I am much to blame, but I was so glad that any one should love me; and when he passed me a letter, I took it home with me and read it with great pleasure. Since that time he has written many. He was so anxious to speak with me, poor fellow! and kept asking me to leave the door open some evening that we might have two words upon the stair. For he knew how much my uncle trusted me." She gave something like a sob at that, and it was a moment before she could go on. "My uncle is a hard man, but he is very shrewd," she said at last. "He has performed many feats in war, and was a great person at court, and much trusted by Queen Isabeau in old days. How he came to suspect me I cannot tell; but it is hard to keep anything from his knowledge; and this morning, as we came from mass, he took my hand into his, forced it open, and read my little billet, walking by my side all the while. When he finished, he gave it back to me with great politeness.  It contained another request to have the door left open; and this has been the ruin of us all.  My uncle kept me strictly in my room until evening, and then ordered me to dress myself as you see me—a hard mockery for a young girl, do you not think so?  I suppose, when he could not prevail with me to tell him the young captain's name, he must have laid a trap for him: into which, alas! you have fallen in the anger of God.  I looked for much confusion; for how could I tell whether he was willing to take me for his wife on these sharp terms?  He might have been trifling with me from the first; or I might have made myself too cheap in his eyes.  But truly I had not looked for such a shameful punishment as this! I could not think that God would let a girl be so disgraced before a young man.  And now I tell you all; and I can scarcely hope that you will not despise me."

Denis made her a respectful inclination.

"Madam," he said, "you have honoured me by your confidence.  It remains for me to prove that I am not unworthy of the honour.  Is Messire de Malétroit at hand?"

"I believe he is writing in the salle without," she answered.

"May I lead you thither, madam?" asked Denis, offering his hand with his most courtly bearing.

She accepted it; and the pair passed out of the chapel, Blanche in a very drooping and shamefast condition, but Denis strutting and ruffling in the consciousness of a mission, and the boyish certainty of accomplishing it with honour.

The Sire de Malétroit rose to meet them with an ironica' obeisance.

"Sir," said Denis, with the grandest possible air, "I believe I am to have some say in the matter of this marriage; and let me tell you at once, I will be no party to forcing the inclination of this young lady. Had it been freely offered to me, I should have been proud to accept her hand, for I perceive she is as good as she is beautiful; but as things are, I have now the honour, messire, of refusing."

Blanche looked at him with gratitude in her eyes; but the old gentleman only smiled and smiled, until his smile grew positively sickening to Denis.

"I am afraid," he said, "Monsieur de Beaulieu, that you do not perfectly understand the choice I have offered you. Follow me, I beseech you, to this window." And he led the way to one of the large windows which stood open on the night. "You observe," he went on, "there is an iron ring in the upper masonry, and reeved through that, a very efficacious rope. Now, mark my words: if you should find your disinclination to my niece's person insurmountable, I shall have you hanged out of this window before sunrise. I shall only proceed to such an extremity with the greatest regret, you may believe me. For it is not at all your death that I desire, but my niece's establishment in life. At the same time, it must come to that if you prove obstinate. Your family, Monsieur de Beaulieu, is very well in its way; but if you sprang from Charlemagne, you should not refuse the hand of a Malétroit with impunity—not if she had been as common as the Paris road—not if she were as hideous as the gargoyle over my door. Neither my niece nor you, nor my own private feelings, move me at all in this matter. The honour of my house has been compromised; I believe you to be the guilty person, at least you are now in the secret; and you can hardly wonder if I request you to wipe out the stain. If you will not, your blood be on your own head! It will be no great satisfaction to me to have your interesting relics kicking their heels in the breeze below my windows, but half a loaf is better than no bread, and if I cannot cure the dishonour, I shall at least stop the scandal."

There was a pause.

"I believe there are other ways of settling such imbroglios among gentlemen," said Denis. "You wear a sword, and I hear you have used it with distinction."

The Sire de Malétroit made a signal to the chaplain, who crossed the room with long silent strides and raised the arras over the third of the three doors. It was only a moment before he let it fall again; but Denis had time to see a dusky passage full of armed men.

"When I was a little younger, I should have been delighted to honour you, Monsieur de Beaulieu," said Sire Alain; "but I am now too old. Faithful retainers are the sinews of age, and I must employ the strength I have. This is one of the hardest things to swallow as a man grows up in years; but with a little patience, even this becomes habitual. You and the lady seem to prefer the salle for what remains of your two hours; and as I have no desire to cross your preference, I shall resign it to your use with all the pleasure in the world. No haste!" he added, holding up his hand, as he saw a dangerous look come into Denis de Beaulieu's face. "If your mind revolt against hanging, it will be time enough two hours hence to throw yourself out of the window or upon the pikes of my retainers. Two hours of life are always two hours. A great many things may turn up in even as little a while as that. And, besides, if I understand her appearance, my niece has something to say to you. You will not disfigure your last hours by a want of politeness to a lady?"

Denis looked at Blanche, and she made him an imploring gesture.

It is likely that the old gentleman was hugely pleased

at this symptom of an understanding; for he smiled on both, and added sweetly: "If you will give me your word of honour, Monsieur de Beaulieu, to await my return at the end of the two hours before attempting anything desperate, I shall withdraw my retainers, and let you speak in greater privacy with mademoiselle."

Denis again glanced at the girl, who seemed to beseech him to agree.

"I give you my word of honour," he said.

Messire de Malétroit bowed, and proceeded to limp about the apartment, clearing his throat the while with that odd musical chirp which had already grown so irritating in the ears of Denis de Beaulieu. He first possessed himself of some papers which lay upon the table; then he went to the mouth of the passage and appeared to give an order to the men behind the arras; and lastly he hobbled out through the door by which Denis had come in, turning upon the threshold to address a last smiling bow to the young couple, and followed by the chaplain with a hand-lamp.

No sooner were they alone than Blanche advanced towards Denis with her hands extended. Her face was flushed and excited, and her eyes shone with tears.

"You shall not die!" she cried, "you shall marry me after all."

"You seem to think, madam," replied Denis, "that I stand much in fear of death."

"Oh, no, no," she said, "I see you are no poltroon. It is for my own sake—I could not bear to have you slain for such a scruple."

"I am afraid," returned Denis, "that you underrate the difficulty, madam. What you may be too generous to refuse, I may be too proud to accept. In a moment of noble feeling towards me, you forgot what you perhaps owe to others."

He had the decency to keep his eyes on the floor as he said this, and after he had finished, so as not to spy upon her confusion. She stood silent for a moment, then walked suddenly away, and falling on her uncle's chair, fairly burst out sobbing. Denis was in the acme of embarrassment. He looked round, as if to seek for inspiration, and seeing a stool, plumped down upon it for something to do. There he sat playing with the guard of his rapier, and wishing himself dead a thousand times over, and buried in the nastiest kitchen-heap in France. His eyes wandered round the apartment, but found nothing to arrest them. There were such wide spaces between the furniture, the light fell so badly and cheerlessly over all, the dark outside air looked in so coldly through the windows, that he thought he had never seen a church so vast, nor a tomb so melancholy. The regular sobs of Blanche de Malétroit measured out the time like the ticking of a clock. He read the device upon the shield over and over again, until his eyes became obscured; he stared into shadowy corners until he imagined they were swarming with horrible animals; and every now and again he awoke with a start, to remember that his last two hours were running, and death was on the march.

Oftener and oftener, as the time went on, did his glance settle on the girl herself. Her face was bowed forward and covered with her hands, and she was shaken at intervals by the convulsive hiccup of grief. Even thus she was not an unpleasant object to dwell upon, so plump and yet so fine, with a warm brown skin, and the most beautiful hair, Denis thought, in the whole world of womankind. Her hands were like her uncle's; but they were more in place at the end of her young arms, and looked infinitely soft and caressing. He remembered how her blue eyes had shone upon him, full of anger, pity, and innocence. And the more he dwelt on her perfections, the uglier death looked, and the more deeply was he smitten with penitence at her continued tears. Now he felt that no man could have the courage to leave a world which contained so beautiful a creature; and now he would have given forty minutes of his last hour to have unsaid his cruel speech.

Suddenly a hoarse and ragged peal of cockcrow rose to their ears from the dark valley below the windows. And this shattering noise in the silence of all around was like a light in a dark place, and shook them both out of their reflections.

"Alas, can I do nothing to help you?" she said, looking up.

"Madam," replied Denis, with a fine irrelevancy, "if I have said anything to wound you, believe me, it was for your own sake and not for mine."

She thanked him with a tearful look.

"I feel your position cruelly," he went on. "The world has been bitter hard on you. Your uncle is a disgrace to mankind. Believe me, madam, there is no young gentleman in all France but would be glad of my opportunity, to die in doing you a momentary service."

"I know already that you can be very brave and generous," she answered. "What I *want* to know is whether I can serve you—now or afterwards," she added, with a quaver.

"Most certainly," he answered with a smile. "Let me sit beside you as if I were a friend, instead of a foolish intruder; try to forget how awkwardly we are placed to one another; make my last moments go pleasantly; and you will do me the chief service possible."

"You are very gallant," she added, with a yet deeper sadness . . . "very gallant . . . and it somehow pains me. But draw nearer, if you please; and if you find anything to say to me, you will at least make certain of a very friendly listener. Ah! Monsieur de Beaulieu," she broke forth—"ah! Monsieur de Beaulieu, how can I look you in the face?" And she fell to weeping again with a renewed effusion.

"Madam," said Denis, taking her hand in both of his, "reflect on the little time I have before me, and the great bitterness into which I am cast by the sight of your distress. Spare me, in my last moments, the spectacle of what I cannot cure even with the sacrifice of my life."

"I am very selfish," answered Blanche. "I will be braver, Monsieur de Beaulieu, for your sake. But think if I can do you no kindness in the future—if you have no friends to whom I could carry your adieux. Charge me as heavily as you can; every burden will lighten, by so little, the invaluable gratitude I owe you. Put it in my power to do something more for you than weep."

"My mother is married again, and has a young family to care for. My brother Guichard will inherit my fiefs; and if I am not in error, that will content him amply for my death. Life is a little vapour that passeth away, as we are told by those in holy orders. When a man is in a fair way and sees all life open in front of him, he seems to himself to make a very important figure in the world. His horse whinnies to him; the trumpets blow and the girls look out of window as he rides into town before his company; he receives many assurances of trust and regard—sometimes by express in a letter—sometimes face to face, with persons of great consequence falling on his neck. It is not wonderful if his head is turned for a time. But once he is dead, were he as brave as Hercules or as wise as Solomon, he is soon forgotten. It is not ten years since my father fell, with many other knights around him, in a very fierce encounter, and I do not think that any one of them, nor so much as the name of the fight, is now remembered. No, no, madam, the nearer you come to it, you see that death is a dark and dusty corner, where a man gets into his tomb and has the door shut after him till the judgment day. I have few friends just now, and once I am dead I shall have none."

"Ah, Monsieur de Beaulieu!" she exclaimed, "you forget Blanche de Malétroit."

"You have a sweet nature, madam, and you are pleased to estimate a little service far beyond its worth."

"It is not that," she answered. "You mistake me if you think I am easily touched by my own concerns. I say so, because you are the noblest man I have ever met; because I recognise in you a spirit that would have made even a common person famous in the land."

"And yet here I die in a mousetrap—with no more noise about it than my own squeaking," answered he.

A look of pain crossed her face, and she was silent for a little while. Then a light came into her eyes, and with a smile she spoke again.

"I cannot have my champion think meanly of himself. Anyone who gives his life for another will be met in Paradise by all the heralds and angels of the Lord God. And you have no such cause to hang your head. For . . . pray, do you think me beautiful?" she asked, with a deep flush.

"Indeed, madam, I do," he said.

"I am glad of that," she answered heartily. "Do you think there are many men in France who have been asked in marriage by a beautiful maiden—with her own lips—and who have refused her to her face? I know you men would half despise such a triumph; but believe me, we women know more of what is precious in love. There is nothing that should set a person higher in his own esteem; and we women would prize nothing more dearly."

"You are very good," he said; "but you cannot make me forget that I was asked in pity and not for love."

"I am not so sure of that," she replied, holding down her head. "Hear me to an end, Monsieur de Beaulieu. I know how you must despise me; I feel you are right to do so; I am too poor a creature to occupy one thought of your mind, although, alas! you must die for me this morning. But when I asked you to marry me, indeed, and indeed, it was because I respected and admired you, and loved you with my whole soul, from the very moment that you took my part against my uncle. If you had seen yourself, and how noble you looked, you would pity rather than despise me. And now," she went on, hurriedly checking him with her hand, "although I have laid aside all reserve and told you so much, remember that I know your sentiments towards me already. I would not, believe me, being nobly born, weary you with importunities into consent. I too have a pride of my own: and I declare before the holy mother of God, if you should now go back from your word already given] I would no more marry you than I would marry my uncle's groom."

Denis smiled a little bitterly.

"It is a small love," he said, "that shies at a little pride."

She made no answer, although she probably had her own thoughts.

"Come hither to the window," he said with a sigh. "Here is the dawn."

And indeed the dawn was already beginning. The hollow of the sky was full of essential daylight, colourless and clean; and the valley underneath was flooded with a grey reflection. A few thin vapours clung in the coves of the forest or lay along the winding course of the river. The scene disengaged a surprising effect of stillness, which was hardly interrupted when the cocks began once more to crow among the steadings. Perhaps the same fellow who had made so horrid a clangour in the darkness not half an hour before, now sent up the merriest cheer to greet the coming day. A little wind went bustling and eddying among the tree-tops underneath the windows. And still the daylight kept flooding insensibly out of the east, which was soon to grow incandescent and cast up that red-hot cannon-ball, the rising sun.

Denis looked out over all this with a bit of a shiver. He had taken her hand, and retained it in his almost unconsciously.

"Has the day begun already?" she said; and then, illogically enough: "the night has been so long! Alas! what shall we say to my uncle when he returns?"

"What you will," said Denis, and he pressed her fingers in his.

She was silent.

"Blanche," he said, with a swift, uncertain, passionate utterance, "you have seen whether I fear death. You must know well enough that I would as gladly leap out of that window into the empty air as to lay a finger on you without your free and full consent. But if you care for me at all, do not let me lose my life in a misapprehension; for I love you better than the whole world; and though I will die for you blithely, it would be like all the joys of Paradise to live on and spend my life in your service."

As he stopped speaking, a bell began to ring loudly in the interior of the house; and a clatter of armour in the corridor showed that the retainers were returning to their post, and the two hours were at an end.

"After all that you have heard?" she whispered, leaning towards him with her lips and eyes.

"I have heard nothing," he replied.

"The captain's name was Florimond de Champdivers," she said in his ear.

"I did not hear it," he answered, taking her supple body in his arms, and covering her wet face with kisses.

A melodious chirping was audible behind, followed by a beautiful chuckle, and the voice of Messire de Malétroit wished his new nephew a good morning.

# THE MERRY MEN[1]

## CHAPTER I

### EILEAN AROS

IT was a beautiful morning in the late July when I set
forth on foot for the last time for Aros. A boat had put
me ashore the night before at Grisapol; I had such
breakfast as the little inn afforded, and, leaving all my
baggage till I had an occasion to come round for it by
sea, struck right across the promontory with a cheerful
heart.

I was far from being a native of these parts, springing,
as I did, from an unmixed lowland stock. But an uncle
of mine, Gordon Darnaway, after a poor, rough youth,
and some years at sea, had married a young wife in the

[1] Written in 1881, at Pitlochry in the Scottish Highlands, where
Stevenson and his wife were staying with his parents in the year
after his return from California, and published in *The Cornhill
Magazine*, June, July, 1882. The scene is Earraid (Aros), an island
off the north-west coast of Scotland, where he had spent some time
in 1870 before beginning a tour of the Western Islands in the course
of an attempt to follow his father in the profession of civil engineering. Grisapol is Mull, a larger island of the inner Hebrides. Ben
Kyaw is Ben More, the highest summit of this island. It was upon
Earraid that David Balfour was cast away, and it was upon Earraid
that he nearly starved, as is recounted in Chapters XIII and XIV
of Stevenson's *Kidnapped*. In a letter to W. E. Henley (July, 1881),
Stevenson called this tale "my favourite work," saying later, "It's
really a story of wrecks as they appear to dwellers on the coast."
Graham Balfour, his biographer, reports another remark about this
story: "You may take a certain atmosphere," said Stevenson, "and
get actions and persons to realise it. I'll give you an example—
The Merry Men. There I began with the feeling of one of those
islands on the west coast of Scotland, and I gradually developed the
story to express the sentiment with which that coast affected me."
Republished in *The Merry Men, and other Tales*, 1887.

islands; Mary Maclean she was called, the last of her family; and when she died in giving birth to a daughter, Aros, the sea-girt farm, had remained in his possession. It brought him in nothing but the means of life, as I was well aware; but he was a man whom ill-fortune had pursued; he feared, cumbered as he was with the young child, to make a fresh adventure upon life; and remained in Aros, biting his nails at destiny. Years passed over his head in that isolation, and brought neither help nor contentment. Meantime our family was dying out in the lowlands; there is little luck for any of that race; and perhaps my father was the luckiest of all, for not only was he one of the last to die, but he left a son to his name and a little money to support it. I was a student of Edinburgh University, living well enough at my own charges, but without kith or kin; when some news of me found its way to Uncle Gordon on the Ross of Grisapol; and he, as he was a man who held blood thicker than water, wrote to me the day he heard of my existence, and taught me to count Aros as my home. Thus it was that I came to spend my vacations in that part of the country, so far from all society and comfort, between the codfish and the moorcocks; and thus it was that now, when I had done with my classes, I was returning thither with so light a heart that July day.

The Ross, as we call it, is a promontory neither wide nor high, but as rough as God made it to this day; the deep sea on either hand of it, full of rugged isles and reefs most perilous to seamen—all overlooked from the eastward by some very high cliffs and the great peak of Ben Kyaw. *The Mountain of the Mist,* they say the words signify in the Gaelic tongue; and it is well named. For that hill-top, which is more than three thousand feet in height, catches all the clouds that come blowing from the seaward; and, indeed, I used often to think that it must make them for itself; since when all heave was clear to the sea level, there would ever be a streamer on Ben Kyaw. It brought water, too, and was mossy[1] to the top in consequence. I have seen us sitting in broad sunshine on the Ross, and the rain falling black like crape upon the mountain. But the wetness of it made it often appear more beautiful to my eyes; for when the sun struck upon the hill sides, there were many wet rocks and watercourses that shone like jewels even as far as Aros, fifteen miles away.

The road that I followed was a cattle-track. It twisted so as nearly to double the length of my journey; it went over rough boulders so that a man had to leap from one to another, and through soft bottoms where the moss came nearly to the knee. There was no cultivation anywhere, and not one house in the ten miles from Grisapol to Aros. Houses of course there were—three at least; but they lay so far on the one side or the other that no stranger could have found them from the track. A large part of the Ross is covered with big granite rocks, some of them larger than a two-roomed house, one beside another, with fern and deep heather in between them where the vipers breed. Anyway the wind was, it was always sea air, as salt as on a ship; the gulls were as free as moorfowl over all the Ross; and whenever the way rose a little, your eye would kindle with the brightness of the sea. From the very midst of the land, on a day of wind and a high spring, I have heard the Roost roaring like a battle where it runs by Aros, and the great and fearful voices of the breakers that we call the Merry Men.

Aros itself—Aros Jay, I have heard the natives call it, and they say it means *the House of God*—Aros itself was not properly a piece of the Ross, nor was it quite an islet.

[1] Boggy.

It formed the south-west corner of the land, fitted close to it, and was in one place only separated from the coast by a little gut of the sea, not forty feet across the narrowest. When the tide was full, this was clear and still, like a pool on a land river; only there was a difference in the weeds and fishes, and the water itself was green instead of brown; but when the tide went out, in the bottom of the ebb, there was a day or two in every month when you could pass dryshod from Aros to the mainland. There was some good pasture, where my uncle fed the sheep he lived on; perhaps the feed was better because the ground rose higher on the islet than the main level of the Ross, but this I am not skilled enough to settle. The house was a good one for that country, two storeys high. It looked westward over a bay, with a pier hard by for a boat, and from the door you could watch the vapours blowing on Ben Kyaw.

On all this part of the coast, and especially near Aros, these great granite rocks that I have spoken of go down together in troops into the sea, like cattle on a summer's day. There they stand, for all the world like their neighbours ashore; only the salt water sobbing between them instead of the quiet earth, and clots of sea-pink blooming on their sides instead of heather; and the great sea conger to wreathe about the base of them instead of the poisonous viper of the land. On calm days you can go wandering between them in a boat for hours, echoes following you about the labyrinth; but when the sea is up, Heaven help the man that hears that cauldron boiling.

Off the south-west end of Aros these blocks are very many, and much greater in size. Indeed, they must grow monstrously bigger out to sea, for there must be ten sea miles of open water sown with them as thick as a country place with houses, some standing thirty feet above the tides, some covered, but all perilous to ships;

so that on a clear, westerly blowing day, I have counted, from the top of Aros, the great rollers breaking white and heavy over as many as six-and-forty buried reefs. But it is nearer inshore that the danger is worst; for the tide, here running like a mill race, makes a long belt of broken water—a *Roost* we call it—at the tail of the land. I have often been out there in a dead calm at the slack of the tide; and a strange place it is, with the sea swirling and combing up and boiling like the cauldrons of a linn, and now and again a little dancing mutter of sound as though the *Roost* were talking to itself. But when the tide begins to run again, and above all in heavy weather, there is no man could take a boat within half a mile of it, nor a ship afloat that could either steer or live in such a place. You can hear the roaring of it six miles away. At the seaward end there comes the strongest of the bubble; and it 's here that these big breakers dance together—the dance of death, it may be called—that have got the name, in these parts, of the Merry Men. I have heard it said that they run fifty feet high; but that must be the green water only, for the spray runs twice as high as that. Whether they got the name from their movements, which are swift and antic, or from the shouting they make about the turn of the tide, so that all Aros shakes with it, is more than I can tell.

The truth is, that in a south-westerly wind, that part of our archipelago is no better than a trap. If a ship got through the reefs, and weathered the Merry Men, it would be to come ashore on the south coast of Aros, in Sandag Bay, where so many dismal things befell our family, as I propose to tell. The thought of all these dangers, in the place I knew so long, makes me particularly welcome the works now going forward to set lights upon the headlands and buoys along the channels of our iron-bound, inhospitable islands.

The country people had many a story about Aros, as I used to hear from my uncle's man, Rorie, an old servant of the Macleans, who had transferred his services without afterthought on the occasion of the marriage. There was some tale of an unlucky creature, a sea-kelpie, that dwelt and did business in some fearful manner of his own among the boiling breakers of the Roost. A mermaid had once met a piper on Sandag beach, and there sang to him a long, bright midsummer's night, so that in the morning he was found stricken crazy, and from thenceforward, till the day he died, said only one form of words; what they were in the original Gaelic I cannot tell, but they were thus translated: "Ah, the sweet singing out of the sea." Seals that haunted on that coast have been known to speak to man in his own tongue, presaging great disasters. It was here that a certain saint first landed on his voyage out of Ireland to convert the Hebrideans. And, indeed, I think he had some claim to be called saint; for, with the boats of that past age, to make so rough a passage, and land on such a ticklish coast, was surely not far short of the miraculous. It was to him, or to some of his monkish underlings who had a cell there, that the islet owes its holy and beautiful name, the House of God.

Among these old wives' stories there was one which I was inclined to hear with more credulity. As I was told, in that tempest which scattered the ships of the Invincible Armada over all the north and west of Scotland, one great vessel came ashore on Aros, and before the eyes of some solitary people on a hill-top, went down in a moment with all hands, her colours flying even as she sank. There was some likelihood in this tale; for another of that fleet lay sunk on the north side, twenty miles from Grisapol. It was told, I thought, with more detail and gravity than its companion stories, and there was one particularity which went far to convince me of its truth: the name, that is, of the ship was still remembered, and sounded, in my ears Spanishly. The *Espirito Santo* they called it, a great ship of many decks of guns, laden with treasure and grandees of Spain, and fierce soldadoes, that now lay fathom deep to all eternity, done with her wars and voyages, in Sandag Bay, upon the west of Aros. No more salvos of ordnance for that tall ship, the "Holy Spirit," no more fair winds or happy ventures; only to rot there deep in the sea-tangle and hear the shoutings of the Merry Men as the tide ran high about the island. It was a strange thought to me first and last, and only grew stranger as I learned the more of the way in which she had set sail with so proud a company, and King Philip, the wealthy king, that sent her on that voyage.

And now I must tell you, as I walked from Grisapol that day, the *Espirito Santo* was very much in my reflections. I had been favourably remarked by our then Principal in Edinburgh College, that famous writer, Dr. Robertson, and by him had been set to work on some papers of an ancient date to rearrange and sift of what was worthless; and in one of these, to my great wonder, I found a note of this very ship, the *Espirito Santo*, with her captain's name, and how she carried a great part of the Spaniard's treasure, and had been lost upon the Ross of Grisapol; but in what particular spot, the wild tribes of that place and period would give no information to the king's inquiries. Putting one thing with another, and taking our island tradition together with this note of old King Jamie's perquisitions after wealth, it had come strongly on my mind that the spot for which he sought in vain could be no other than the small bay of Sandag on my uncle's land; and being a fellow of a mechanical turn, I had ever since been plotting how to weigh that good ship up again with all her ingots, ounces, and doubloons, and bring back our house of Darnaway to its long-forgotten dignity and wealth.

This was a design of which I soon had reason to repent. My mind was sharply turned on different reflections; and since I became the witness of a strange judgment of God's, the thought of dead men's treasures has been intolerable to my conscience. But even at that time I must acquit myself of sordid greed; for if I desired riches, it was not for their own sake, but for the sake of a person who was dear to my heart—my uncle's daughter, Mary Ellen. She had been educated well, and had been a time to school upon the mainland; which, poor girl, she would have been happier without. For Aros was no place for her, with old Rorie the servant, and her father, who was one of the unhappiest men in Scotland, plainly bred up in a country place among Cameronians, long a skipper sailing out of the Clyde about the islands, and now, with infinite discontent, managing his sheep and a little 'longshore fishing for the necessary bread. If it was sometimes weariful to me, who was there but a month or two, you may fancy what it was to her who dwelt in that same desert all the year round, with the sheep and flying seagulls, and the Merry Men singing and dancing in the Roost!

## CHAPTER II

### WHAT THE WRECK HAD BROUGHT TO AROS

It was half-flood when I got the length of Aros; and there was nothing for it but to stand on the far shore and whistle for Rorie with the boat. I had no need to repeat the signal. At the first sound, Mary was at the door flying a handkerchief by way of answer, and the old long-legged serving-man was shambling down the gravel to the pier. For all his hurry, it took him a long while to pull across the bay; and I observed him several times to pause, go into the stern, and look over curiously into the wake. As he came nearer, he seemed to me aged and haggard, and I thought he avoided my eye. The coble had been repaired, with two new thwarts and several patches of some rare and beautiful foreign wood, the name of it unknown to me.

"Why, Rorie," said I, as we began the return voyage, "this is fine wood. How came you by that?"

"It will be hard to cheesel," Rorie opined reluctantly; and just then, dropping the oars, he made another of those dives into the stern which I had remarked as he came across to fetch me, and, leaning his hand on my shoulder, stared with an awful look into the waters of the bay.

"What is wrong?" I asked, a good deal startled.

"It will be a great feesh," said the old man, returning to his oars; and nothing more could I get out of him, but strange glances and an ominous nodding of the head. In spite of myself, I was infected with a measure of uneasiness; I turned also, and studied the wake. The water was still and transparent, but, out here in the middle of the bay, exceeding deep. For some time I could see naught; but at last it did seem to me as if something dark—a great fish, or perhaps only a shadow —followed studiously in the track of the moving coble. And then I remembered one of Rorie's superstitions: how in a ferry in Morven, in some great, exterminating feud among the clans, a fish, the like of it unknown in all our waters, followed for some years the passage of the ferry-boat, until no man dared to make the crossing.

"He will be waiting for the right man," said Rorie.

Mary met me on the beach, and led me up the brae

and into the house of Aros. Outside and inside there were many changes. The garden was fenced with the same wood that I had noted in the boat; there were chairs in the kitchen covered with strange brocade; curtains of brocade hung from the window; a clock stood silent on the dresser; a lamp of brass was swinging from the roof; the table was set for dinner with the finest of linen and silver; and all these new riches were displayed in the plain old kitchen that I knew so well, with the high-backed settle, and the stools, and the closet-bed for Rorie; with the wide chimney the sun shone into, and the clear-smouldering peats; with the pipes on the mantelshelf and the three-cornered spittoons, filled with sea-shells instead of sand, on the floor; with the bare stone walls and the bare wooden floor, and the three patchwork rugs that were of yore its sole adornment— poor man's patchwork, the like of it unknown in cities, woven with homespun, and Sunday black, and sea-cloth polished on the bench of rowing. The room, like the house, had been a sort of wonder in that country-side, it was so neat and habitable; and to see it now, shamed by these incongruous additions, filled me with indignation and a kind of anger. In view of the errand I had come upon to Aros, the feeling was baseless and unjust; but it burned high, at the first moment, in my heart."

"Mary, girl," said I, "this is the place I had learned to call my home, and I do not know it."

"It is my home by nature, not by the learning," she replied; "the place I was born and the place I 'm like to die in; and I neither like these changes, nor the way they came, nor that which came with them. I would have liked better, under God's pleasure, they had gone down into the sea, and the Merry Men were dancing on them now."

Mary was always serious; it was perhaps the only

trait that she shared with her father; but the tone with which she uttered these words was even graver than of custom.

"Ay," said I, "I feared it came by wreck, and that's by death; yet when my father died, I took his goods without remorse."

"Your father died a clean strae death,[1] as the folk say," said Mary.

"True," I returned; "and a wreck is like a judgment. What was she called?"

"They ca'd her the *Christ-Anna*," said a voice behind me; and, turning round, I saw my uncle standing in the doorway.

He was a sour, small, bilious man, with a long face and very dark eyes; fifty-six years old, sound and active in body, and with an air somewhat between that of a shepherd and that of a man following the sea. He never laughed, that I heard; read long at the Bible; prayed much, like the Cameronians he had been brought up among; and indeed, in many ways, used to remind me of one of the hill-preachers in the killing times before the Revolution. But he never got much comfort, nor even, as I used to think, much guidance, by his piety. He had his black fits when he was afraid of hell; but he had led a rough life, to which he would look back with envy, and was still a rough, cold, gloomy man.

As he came in at the door out of the sunlight, with his bonnet on his head and a pipe hanging in his button-hole, he seemed, like Rorie, to have grown older and paler, the lines were deeplier ploughed upon his face, and the whites of his eyes were yellow, like old stained ivory, or the bones of the dead.

"Ay," he repeated, dwelling upon the first part of the word, "the *Christ-Anna*. It's an awfu' name."

[1] That is, he died in his bed.

I made him my salutations, and complimented him upon his look of health; for I feared he had perhaps been ill.

"I 'm in the body," he replied, ungraciously enough; "aye in the body and the sins of the body, like yoursel'. Denner," he said abruptly to Mary, and then ran on to me: "They 're grand braws,[1] thir that we hae gotten, are they no? Yon 's a bonny knock,[2] but it 'll no gang; and the napery 's by ordnar. Bonny, bairnly braws; it 's for the like o' them folk sells the peace of God that passeth understanding; it 's for the like o' them, an' maybe no even sae muckle worth, folk daunton God to His face and burn in muckle hell; and it 's for that reason the Scripture ca's them, as I read the passage, the accursed thing. Mary, ye girzie," he interrupted himself to cry with some asperity, "what for hae ye no put out the twa candlesticks?"

"Why should we need them at high noon?" she asked.

But my uncle was not to be turned from his idea. "We'll bruik[3] them while we may," he said; and so two massive candlesticks of wrought silver were added to the table equipage, already so unsuited to that rough sea-side farm.

"She cam' ashore Februar' 10, about ten at nicht," he went on to me. "There was nae wind, and a sair run o' sea; and she was in the sook o' the Roost, as I jaloose.[4] We had seen her a' day, Rorie and me, beating to the wind. She wasnae a handy craft, I 'm thinking, that *Christ-Anna;* for she would neither steer nor stey wi' them. A sair day they had of it; their hands was never aff the sheets, and it perishin' cauld—ower cauld to snaw; and aye they would get a bit nip o' wind, and awa' again, to pit the emp'y hope into them. Eh,

---

[1] Fineries.     [2] Clock.     [3] Enjoy.     [4] Suspect.

man! but they had a sair day for the last o't! He would have had a prood, prood heart that won ashore upon the back o' that."

"And were all lost?" I cried. "God help them!"

"Wheesht!" he said sternly. "Nane shall pray for the deid on my hearth-stane."

I disclaimed a Popish sense for my ejaculation; and he seemed to accept my disclaimer with unusual facility, and ran on once more upon what had evidently become a favourite subject.

"We fand her in Sandag Bay, Rorie an' me, and a' thae braws in the inside of her. There's a kittle bit, ye see, about Sandag; whiles the sook rins strong for the Merry Men; an' whiles again, when the tide's makin' hard an' ye can hear the Roost blawin' at the far-end of Aros, there comes a back-spang of current straucht into Sandag Bay. Weel, there's the thing that got the grip on the *Christ-Anna*. She but[1] to have come in ram-stam[2] an' stern forrit; for the bows of her are aften under, and the back-side of her is clear at hie-water o' neaps.[3] But, man! the dunt that she cam' doon wi' when she struck! Lord save us a'! but it's an unco life to be a sailor—a cauld, wanchancy[4] life. Mony's the gliff[5] I got mysel' in the great deep; and why the Lord should hae made yon unco water is mair than ever I could win to understand. He made the vales and the pastures, the bonny green yaird,[6] the halesome, canty[7] land—

> And now they shout and sing to Thee,
> For Thou hast made them glad,

as the Psalms say in the metrical version. No that I would preen[8] my faith to that clink[9] neither; but it's

---

[1] Must.  [2] Rapidly.  [3] At the lowest tides.
[4] Unlucky.  [5] Fright.  [6] Earth.
[7] Cheerful.  [8] Pin.  [9] Rhyme.

bonny, and easier to mind. 'Who go to sea in ships,'
they hae 't again—

> And in
> Great waters trading be,
> Within the deep these men God's works
> And His great wonders see.

Weel, it 's easy sayin' sae. Maybe Dauvit wasnae very
weel acquant wi' the sea. But troth, if it wasnae pren-
tit in the Bible, I wad whiles be temp'it to think it wasnae
the Lord, but the muckle, black deil that made the sea.
There 's naething good comes oot o't but the fish; an'
the spentacle o' God riding on the tempest, to be shure,
whilk would be what Dauvit was likely ettling at.[1] But,
man, they were sair wonders that God showed to the
*Christ-Anna*—wonders, do I ca' them? Judgments,
rather: judgments in the mirk nicht among the draygons
o' the deep. And their souls—to think o' that—their
souls, man, maybe no prepared! The sea—a muckle
yett[2] to hell!"

I observed, as my uncle spoke, that his voice was unnaturally moved and his manner unwontedly demon-
strative. He leaned forward at these last words, for
example, and touched me on the knee with his spread
fingers, looking up into my face with a certain pallor,
and I could see that his eyes shone with a deep-seated
fire, and that the lines about his mouth were drawn and
tremulous.

Even the entrance of Rorie, and the beginning of our
meal, did not detach him from his train of thought beyond a moment. He condescended, indeed, to ask me
some questions as to my success at college, but I thought
it was with half his mind; and even in his extempore
grace, which was, as usual, long and wandering, I could

[1] Trying for.          [2] Gate.

find the trace of his preoccupation, praying, as he did, that God would "remember in mercy fower puir, feckless,[1] fiddling, sinful creatures here by their lee-lane beside the great and dowie[2] waters."

Soon there came an interchange of speeches between him and Rorie.

"Was it there?" asked my uncle.

"Ou, ay!" said Rorie.

I observed that they both spoke in a manner of aside, and with some show of embarrassment, and that Mary herself appeared to colour, and looked down on her plate. Partly to show my knowledge, and so relieve the party from an awkward strain, partly because I was curious, I pursued the subject.

"You mean the fish?" I asked.

"Whatten fish?" cried my uncle. "Fish, quo' he! Fish! Your een are fu' o' fatness, man; your heid dozened wi' carnal leir.[3] Fish! it 's a bogle!"

He spoke with great vehemence, as though angry; and perhaps I was not very willing to be put down so shortly, for young men are disputatious. At least I remember I retorted hotly, crying out upon childish superstitions.

"And ye come frae the College!" sneered Uncle Gordon. "Gude kens what they learn folk there; it 's no muckle service onyway. Do ye think, man, that there 's naething in a' yon saut wilderness o' a world oot wast[4] there, wi' the sea grasses growin', an' the sea beasts fechtin', an' the sun glintin' down into it, day by day? Na; the sea 's like the land, but fearsomer. If there 's folk ashore, there 's folk in the sea—deid they may be, but they 're folk whatever; and as for deils, there 's nane that 's like the sea deils. There 's no sae muckle harm

[1] Feeble.                          [2] Mad.
[3] Made stupid by worldly learning.    [4] West.

in the land deils, when a's said and done. Lang syne, when I was a callant[1] in the south country, I mind there was an auld, bald bogle in the Peewie Moss.[2] I got a glisk o' him mysel', sittin' on his hunkers in a hag, as gray 's a tombstane. ·An', troth, he was a fearsome-like taed. But he steered[3] naebody. Nae doobt, if ane that was a reprobate, ane the Lord hated, had gane by there wi' his sin still upon his stamach, nae doobt the creature would hae lowped upo' the likes o' him. But there 's deils in the deep sea would yoke on[4] a communicant! Eh, sirs, if ye had gane doon wi' the puir lads in the *Christ-Anna*, ye would ken by now the mercy o' the seas. If ye had sailed it for as lang as me, ye would hate the thocht of it as I do. If ye had but used the een God gave ye, ye would hae learned the wickedness o' that fause, saut, cauld, bullering[5] creature, and of a' that 's in it by the Lord's permission: labsters an' partans,[6] an' sic like, howking[7] in the deid; muckle, gutsy,[8] blawing whales; an' fish—the hale clan o' them—cauld-wamed, blind-eed uncanny ferlies.[9] O, sirs," he cried, "the horror—the horror o' the sea!"

We were all somewhat staggered by this outburst; and the speaker himself, after that last hoarse apostrophe, appeared to sink gloomily into his own thoughts. But Rorie, who was greedy of superstitious lore, recalled him to the subject by a question.

"You will not ever have seen a teevil of the sea?" he asked.

"No clearly," replied the other, "I misdoobt if a mere man could see ane clearly and conteenue in the body. I hae sailed wi' a lad—they ca'd him Sandy Gabart; he saw ane, shüre eneuch, an' shüre eneuch it was the end

---

[1] Young fellow.   [2] Bog.   [3] Meddled with.
[4] Grip hold of.   [5] Gurgling.   [6] Crabs.
[7] Digging.   [8] Voracious.   [9] Wonders.

of him.  We were seeven days oot frae the Clyde—a
sair wark we had had—gaun north wi' seeds an' braws
an' things for the Macleod.  We had got in ower near
under the Cutchull'ns, an' had just gane about by Soa,
an' were off on a lang tack, we thocht would maybe
hauld as far 's Copnahow.  I mind the nicht weel; a
mune smoored[1] wi' mist; a fine gaun[2] breeze upon the
water, but no steedy; an'—what nane o' us likit to hear
—anither wund gurlin'[3] owerheid, amang thae fearsome,
auld stane craigs o' the Cutchull'ns.  Weel, Sandy was
forrit wi' the jib sheet; we couldnae see him for the
mains'l, that had just begude to draw, when a' at ance
he gied a skirl.[4]   I luffed for my life, for I thocht we were
ower near Soa;  but na, it wasnae that, it was puir Sandy
Gabart's deid skreigh,[5] or near hand, for he was deid in
half an hour.   A't he could tell was that a sea deil, or sea
bogle, or sea spenster, or sic-like, had clum up by the
bowsprit, an' gi'en him ae cauld, uncanny look.  An',
or the life was oot o' Sandy's body, we kent weel what the
thing betokened, and why the wund gurled in the taps
o' the Cutchull'ns; for doon it cam'—a wund do I ca'
it! it was the wund o' the Lord's anger—an' a' that nicht
we foucht like men dementit, and the niest that we
kenned we were ashore in Loch Uskevagh, an' the cocks
were crawing in Benbecula.''

"It will have been a merman,'' Rorie said.

"A merman!'' screamed my uncle, with immeasurable
scorn.   "Auld wives' clavers![6]   There 's nae sic things
as mermen.''

"But what was the creature like?'' I asked.

"What like was it?  Gude forbid that we suld ken
what like it was!  It had a kind of a heid upon it—man
could say nae mair.''

---

[1] Smothered.           [2] Moving.            [3] Growling.
[4] Shriek.              [5] Death scream.      [6] Idle tales.

Then Rorie, smarting under the affront, told several tales of mermen, mermaids, and sea-horses that had come ashore upon the islands and attacked the crews of boats upon the sea; and my uncle, in spite of his incredulity, listened with uneasy interest.

"Aweel, aweel," he said, "it may be sae; I may be wrang; but I find nae word o' mermen in the Scriptures."

"And you will find nae word of Aros Roost, maybe," objected Rorie, and his argument appeared to carry weight.

When dinner was over, my uncle carried me forth with him to a bank behind the house. It was a very hot and quiet afternoon; scarce a ripple anywhere upon the sea, nor any voice but the familiar voice of sheep and gulls; and perhaps in consequence of this repose in nature, my kinsman showed himself more rational and tranquil than before. He spoke evenly and almost cheerfully of my career, with every now and then a reference to the lost ship or the treasures it had brought to Aros. For my part, I listened to him in a sort of trance, gazing with all my heart on that remembered scene, and drinking gladly the sea-air and the smoke of peats that had been lit by Mary.

Perhaps an hour had passed when my uncle, who had all the while been covertly gazing on the surface of the little bay, rose to his feet, and bade me follow his example. Now I should say that the great run of tide at the south-west end of Aros exercises a perturbing influence round all the coast. In Sandag Bay, to the south, a strong current runs at certain periods of the flood and ebb respectively; but in this northern bay—Aros Bay, as it is called—where the house stands and on which my uncle was now gazing, the only sign of disturbance is towards the end of the ebb, and even then it is too slight to be remarkable. When there is any swell, nothing can be seen at all; but when it is calm, as it often is, there appear certain strange, undecipherable marks—sea-runes, as we may name them—on the glassy surface of the bay. The like is common in a thousand places on the coast; and many a boy must have amused himself as I did, seeking to read in them some reference to himself or those he loved. It was to these marks that my uncle now directed my attention, struggling as he did so, with an evident reluctance.

"Do ye see yon scart[1] upo' the water?" he inquired; "yon ane wast the gray stane? Ay? Weel, it 'll no be like a letter, wull it?"

"Certainly it is," I replied. "I have often remarked it. It is like a C."

He heaved a sigh as if heavily disappointed with my answer, and then added below his breath: "Ay, for the *Christ-Anna*."

"I used to suppose, sir, it was for myself," said I; "for my name is Charles."

"And so ye saw 't afore?" he ran on, not heeding my remark. "Weel, weel, but that 's unco strange. Maybe, it 's been there waitin', as a man wad say, through a' the weary ages. Man, but that 's awfu'." And then, breaking off: "Ye 'll no see anither, will ye?" he asked.

"Yes," said I. "I see another very plainly, near the Ross side, where the road comes down—an M."

"An M," he repeated very low; and then, again after another pause: "An' what wad ye make o' that?" he inquired.

"I had always thought it to mean Mary, sir," I answered, growing somewhat red, convinced as I was in my own mind that I was on the threshold of a decisive explanation.

But we were each following his own train of thought to the exclusion of the other's. My uncle once more

[1] Scratch.

paid no attention to my words; only hung his head and
held his peace; and I might have been led to fancy that
he had not heard me, if his next speech had not contained a kind of echo from my own.

"I would say naething o' thae clavers to Mary," he
observed, and began to walk forward.

There is a belt of turf along the side of Aros Bay
where walking is easy; and it was along this that I
silently followed my silent kinsman. I was perhaps a
little disappointed at having lost so good an opportunity
to declare my love; but I was at the same time far more
deeply exercised at the change that had befallen my
uncle. He was never an ordinary, never, in the strict
sense, an amiable, man; but there was nothing in even
the worst that I had known of him before, to prepare
me for so strange a transformation. It was impossible
to close the eyes against one fact; that he had, as the
saying goes, something on his mind; and as I mentally
ran over the different words which might be represented
by the letter M—misery, mercy, marriage, money, and
the like—I was arrested with a sort of start by the word
murder. I was still considering the ugly sound and fatal
meaning of the word, when the direction of our walk
brought us to a point from which a view was to be had
to either side, back towards Aros Bay and homestead,
and forward on the ocean, dotted to the north with isles,
and lying to the southward blue and open to the sky.
There my guide came to a halt, and stood staring for a
while on that expanse. Then he turned to me and laid
a hand on my arm.

"Ye think there's naething there?" he said, pointing
with his pipe; and then cried out aloud, with a kind of
exultation: "I'll tell ye, man! The deid are down
there—thick like rattons!"[1]

[1] Rats.

He turned at once, and, without another word, we retraced our steps to the house of Aros.

I was eager to be alone with Mary; yet it was not till after supper, and then but for a short while, that I could have a word with her. I lost no time beating about the bush, but spoke out plainly what was on my mind.

"Mary," I said, "I have not come to Aros without a hope. If that should prove well founded, we may all leave and go somewhere else, secure of daily bread and comfort; secure, perhaps, of something far beyond that, which it would seem extravagant in me to promise. But there's a hope that lies nearer to my heart than money." And at that I paused. "You can guess fine what that is, Mary," I said. She looked away from me in silence, and that was small encouragement, but I was not to be put off. "All my days I have thought the world of you," I continued; "the time goes on and I think always the more of you; I could not think to be happy or hearty in my life without you: you are the apple of my eye." Still she looked away, and said never a word; but I thought I saw that her hands shook. "Mary," I cried in fear, "do ye no like me?"

"O, Charlie man," she said, "is this a time to speak of it? Let me be, a while; let me be the way I am; it'll not be you that loses by the waiting!"

I made out by her voice that she was nearly weeping, and this put me out of any thought but to compose her. "Mary Ellen," I said, "say no more; I did not come to trouble you: your way shall be mine, and your time too; and you have told me all I wanted. Only just this one thing more: what ails you?"

She owned it was her father, but would enter into no particulars, only shook her head, and said he was not well and not like himself, and it was a great pity. She knew nothing of the wreck. "I havenae been near it," said she. "What for would I go near it, Charlie lad? The poor souls are gone to their account long syne; and I would just have wished they had ta'en their gear with them—poor souls!"

This was scarcely any great encouragement for me to tell her of the *Espirito Santo;* yet I did so, and at the very first word she cried out in surprise. "There was a man at Grisapol," she said, "in the month of May— a little, yellow, black-avised[1] body, they tell me, with gold rings upon his fingers, and a beard; and he was speiring high and low for that same ship."

It was towards the end of April that I had been given these papers to sort out by Dr. Robertson: and it came suddenly back upon my mind that they were thus prepared for a Spanish historian, or a man calling himself such, who had come with high recommendations to the Principal, on a mission of inquiry as to the dispersion of the great Armada. Putting one thing with another, I fancied that the visitor "with the gold rings upon his fingers" might be the same with Dr. Robertson's historian from Madrid. If that were so, he would be more likely after treasure for himself than information for a learned society. I made up my mind, I should lose no time over my undertaking; and if the ship lay sunk in Sandag Bay, as perhaps both he and I supposed, it should not be for the advantage of this ringed adventurer, but for Mary and myself, and for the good, old, honest, kindly family of the Darnaways.

## CHAPTER III

### LAND AND SEA IN SANDAG BAY

I was early afoot next morning; and as soon as I had a bite to eat, set forth upon a tour of exploration. Some-

[1] Dark-complexioned.

thing in my heart distinctly told me that I should find the ship of the Armada; and although I did not give way entirely to such hopeful thoughts, I was still very light in spirits and walked upon air. Aros is a very rough islet, its surface strewn with great rocks and shaggy with fern and heather; and my way lay almost north and south across the highest knoll; and though the whole distance was inside of two miles, it took more time and exertion than four upon a level road. Upon the summit, I paused. Although not very high—not three hundred feet, as I think—it yet outtops all the neighbouring low-lands of the Ross, and commands a great view of sea and islands. The sun, which had been up some time, was already hot upon my neck; the air was listless and thun-dery, although purely clear; away over the north-west, where the isles lie thickliest congregated, some half-a-dozen small and ragged clouds hung together in a covey; and the head of Ben Kyaw wore, not merely a few streamers, but a solid hood of vapour. There was a threat in the weather. The sea, it is true, was smooth like glass: even the Roost was but a seam on that wide mirror, and the Merry Men no more than caps of foam; but to my eye and ear, so long familiar with these places, the sea also seemed to lie uneasily; a sound of it, like a long sigh, mounted to me where I stood; and, quiet as it was, the Roost itself appeared to be revolving mischief. For I ought to say that all we dwellers in these parts attributed, if not prescience, at least a quality of warning, to that strange and dangerous creature of the tides.

I hurried on, then, with the greater speed, and had soon descended the slope of Aros to the part that we call Sandag Bay. It is a pretty large piece of water compared with the size of the isle; well sheltered from all but the prevailing wind; sandy and shoal and bounded by low sand-hills to the west, but to the eastward lying several fathoms deep along a ledge of rocks. It is upon that

side that, at a certain time each flood, the current mentioned by my uncle sets so strong into the bay; a little
later, when the Roost begins to work higher, an undertow
runs still more strongly in the reverse direction; and it is
the action of this last, as I suppose, that has scoured
that part so deep. Nothing is to be seen out of Sandag
Bay but one small segment of the horizon and, in heavy
weather, the breakers flying high over a deep sea reef.

From half-way down the hill, I had perceived the
wreck of February last, a brig of considerable tonnage,
lying, with her back broken, high and dry on the east
corner of the sands; and I was making directly towards
it, and already almost on the margin of the turf, when
my eyes were suddenly arrested by a spot, cleared of
fern and heather, and marked by one of those long, low,
and almost human-looking mounds that we see so
commonly in graveyards. I stopped like a man shot.
Nothing had been said to me of any dead man or inter-
ment on the island; Rorie, Mary, and my uncle had all
equally held their peace; of her at least, I was certain
that she must be ignorant; and yet here, before my eyes,
was proof indubitable of the fact. Here was a grave;
and I had to ask myself, with a chill, what manner of
man lay there in his last sleep, awaiting the signal of the
Lord in that solitary, sea-beat resting-place? My mind
supplied no answer but what I feared to entertain.
Shipwrecked, at least, he must have been; perhaps, like
the old Armada mariners, from some far and rich land
over-sea; or perhaps one of my own race, perishing
within eyesight of the smoke of home. I stood awhile
uncovered by his side, and I could have desired that it
had lain in our religion to put up some prayer for that
unhappy stranger, or, in the old classic way, outwardly
to honour his misfortune. I knew, although his bones
lay there, a part of Aros, till the trumpet sounded, his

imperishable soul was forth and far away, among the raptures of the everlasting Sabbath or the pangs of hell; and yet my mind misgave me even with a fear, that perhaps he was near me where I stood, guarding his sepulchre, and lingering on the scene of his unhappy fate.

Certainly it was with a spirit somewhat overshadowed that I turned away from the grave to the hardly less melancholy spectacle of the wreck. Her stem was above the first arc of the flood; she was broken in two a little abaft the foremast—though indeed she had none, both masts having broken short in her disaster; and as the pitch of the beach was very sharp and sudden, and the bows lay many feet below the stern, the fracture gaped widely open, and you could see right through her poor hull upon the farther side. Her name was much defaced, and I could not make out clearly whether she was called *Christiania*, after the Norwegian city, or *Christiana*, after the good woman, Christian's wife, in that old book the "Pilgrim's Progress." By her build she was a foreign ship, but I was not certain of her nationality. She had been painted green, but the colour was faded and weathered, and the paint peeling off in strips. The wreck of the mainmast lay alongside, half buried in sand. She was a forlorn sight, indeed, and I could not look without emotion at the bits of rope that still hung about her, so often handled of yore by shouting seamen; or the little scuttle where they had passed up and down to their affairs; or that poor noseless angel of a figurehead that had dipped into so many running billows.

I do not know whether it came most from the ship or from the grave, but I fell into some melancholy scruples, as I stood there, leaning with one hand against the battered timbers. The homelessness of men and even of inanimate vessels, cast away upon strange shores, came strongly in upon my mind. To make a profit of such

pitiful misadventures seemed an unmanly and a sordid
act; and I began to think of my then quest as of something sacrilegious in its nature.   But when I remembered
Mary, I took heart again.   My uncle would never consent to an imprudent marriage, nor would she, as I was
persuaded, wed without his full approval.   It behoved
me, then, to be up and doing for my wife; and I thought
with a laugh how long it was since that great sea-castle,
the *Espirito Santo*, had left her bones in Sandag Bay,
and how weak it would be to consider rights so long
extinguished and misfortunes so long forgotten in the
process of time.

I had my theory of where to seek for her remains.
The set of the current and the soundings both pointed
to the east side of the bay under the ledge of rocks.   If
she had been lost in Sandag Bay, and if, after these centuries, any portion of her held together, it was there that
I should find it.   The water deepens, as I have said,
with great rapidity, and even close alongside the rocks
several fathoms may be found.   As I walked upon the
edge I could see far and wide over the sandy bottom of
the bay; the sun shone clear and green and steady in the
deeps; the bay seemed rather like a great transparent
crystal, as one sees them in a lapidary's shop; there was
naught to show that it was water but an internal trembling, a hovering within of sun-glints and netted shadows,
and now and then a faint lap and a dying bubble round
the edge.   The shadows of the rocks lay out for some
distance at their feet, so that my own shadow, moving,
pausing, and stooping on the top of that, reached sometimes half across the bay.   It was above all in this belt
of shadows that I hunted for the *Espirito Santo;* since
it was there the undertow ran strongest, whether in or
out.   Cool as the whole water seemed this broiling day,
it looked, in that part, yet cooler, and had a mysterious

invitation for the eyes. Peer as I pleased, however, I
could see nothing but a few fishes or a bush of sea-tangle,
and here and there a lump of rock that had fallen from
above and now lay separate on the sandy floor. Twice
did I pass from one end to the other of the rocks, and in
the whole distance I could see nothing of the wreck, nor
any place but one where it was possible for it to be.
This was a large terrace in five fathoms of water, raised
off the surface of the sand to a considerable height, and
looking from above like a mere outgrowth of the rocks on
which I walked. It was one mass of great sea-tangles
like a grove, which prevented me judging of its nature,
but in shape and size it bore some likeness to a vessel's
hull. At least it was my best chance. If the *Espirito
Santo* lay not there under the tangles, it lay nowhere at
all in Sandag Bay; and I prepared to put the question
to the proof, once and for all, and either go back to Aros
a rich man or cured for ever of my dreams of wealth.

I stripped to the skin, and stood on the extreme margin with my hands clasped, irresolute. The bay at that
time was utterly quiet; there was no sound but from a
school of porpoises somewhere out of sight behind the
point; yet a certain fear withheld me on the threshold
of my venture. Sad sea-feelings, scraps of my uncle's
superstitions, thoughts of the dead, of the grave, of the
old broken ships, drifted through my mind. But the
strong sun upon my shoulders warmed me to the heart,
and I stooped forward and plunged into the sea.

It was all that I could do to catch a trail of the sea-
tangle that grew so thickly on the terrace; but once so
far anchored I secured myself by grasping a whole armful of these thick and slimy stalks, and, planting my feet
against the edge, I looked around me. On all sides the
clear sand stretched forth unbroken; it came to the foot
of the rocks, scoured into the likeness of an alley in a

garden by the action of the tides; and before me, for as
far as I could see, nothing was visible but the same
many-folded sand upon the sun-bright bottom of the
bay. Yet the terrace to which I was then holding was
as thick with strong sea-growths as a tuft of heather,
and the cliff from which it bulged hung draped below
the water-line with brown lianas. In this complexity of
forms, all swaying together in the current, things were
hard to be distinguished; and I was still uncertain
whether my feet were pressed upon the natural rock or
upon the timbers of the Armada treasure-ship, when the
whole tuft of tangle came away in my hand, and in an
instant I was on the surface, and the shores of the bay
and the bright water swam before my eyes in a glory of
crimson.

I clambered back upon the rocks, and threw the plant
of tangle at my feet. Something at the same moment
rang sharply, like a falling coin. I stooped, and there,
sure enough, crusted with the red rust, there lay an iron
shoe-buckle. The sight of this poor human relic thrilled
me to the heart, but not with hope nor fear, only with a
desolate melancholy. I held it in my hand, and the
thought of its owner appeared before me like the presence of an actual man. His weather-beaten face, his
sailor's hand, his sea-voice hoarse with singing at the
capstan, the very foot that had once worn that buckle
and trod so much along the swerving decks—the whole
human fact of him, as a creature like myself, with hair
and blood and seeing eyes, haunted me in that sunny,
solitary place, not like a spectre, but like some friend
whom I had basely injured. Was the great treasure-ship
indeed below there, with her guns and chain and treasure,
as she had sailed from Spain; her decks a garden for the
sea-weed, her cabin a breeding-place for fish, soundless
but for the dredging water, motionless but for the waving

of the tangle upon her battlements—that old, populous sea-riding castle, now a reef in Sandag Bag? Or, as I thought it likelier, was this a waif from the disaster of the foreign brig—was this shoe-buckle bought but the other day and worn by a man of my own period in the world's history, hearing the same news from day to day, thinking the same thoughts, praying, perhaps, in the same temple with myself? However it was, I was assailed with dreary thoughts; my uncle's words, "the dead are down there," echoed in my ears; and though I determined to dive once more, it was with a strong repugnance that I stepped forward to the margin of the rocks.

A great change passed at that moment over the appearance of the bay. It was no more that clear, visible interior, like a house roofed with glass, where the green, submarine sunshine slept so stilly. A breeze, I suppose, had flawed the surface, and a sort of trouble and blackness filled its bosom, where flashes of light and clouds of shadow tossed confusedly together. Even the terrace below obscurely rocked and quivered. It seemed a graver thing to venture on this place of ambushes; and when I leaped into the sea the second time it was with a quaking in my soul.

I secured myself as at first, and groped among the waving tangle. All that met my touch was cold and soft and gluey. The thicket was alive with crabs and lobsters, trundling to and fro lopsidedly, and I had to harden my heart against the horror of their carrion neighbourhood. On all sides I could feel the grain and the clefts of hard, living stone; no planks, no iron, not a sign of any wreck; the *Espirito Santo* was not there. I remember I had almost a sense of relief in my disappointment, and I was about ready to leave go, when something happened that sent me to the surface with my

heart in my mouth. I had already stayed somewhat
late over my explorations; the current was freshening
with the change of the tide, and Sandag Bay was no
longer a safe place for a single swimmer. Well, just at
the last moment there came a sudden flush of current,
dredging through the tangles like a wave. I lost one
hold, was flung sprawling on my side, and, instinctively
grasping for a fresh support, my fingers closed on something hard and cold. I think I knew at that moment
what it was. At least I instantly left hold of the tangle,
leaped for the surface, and clambered out next moment
on the friendly rocks with the bone of a man's leg in my
grasp.

Mankind is a material creature, slow to think and dull
to perceive connections. The grave, the wreck of the
brig, and the rusty shoe-buckle were surely plain adver-
tisements. A child might have read their dismal story,
and yet it was not until I touched that actual piece of
mankind that the full horror of the charnel ocean burst
upon my spirit. I laid the bone beside the buckle,
picked up my clothes, and ran as I was along the rocks
towards the human shore. I could not be far enough
from the spot; no fortune was vast enough to tempt me
back again. The bones of the drowned dead should
henceforth roll undisturbed by me, whether on tangle
or minted gold. But as soon as I trod the good earth
again and had covered my nakedness against the sun, I
knelt down over against the ruins of the brig, and out of
the fulness of my heart prayed long and passionately for
all poor souls upon the sea. A generous prayer is never
presented in' vain; the petition may be refused, but the
petitioner is always, I believe, rewarded by some gracious
visitation. The horror, at least, was lifted from my
mind; I could look with calm of spirit on that great
bright creature, God's ocean; and as I set off homeward

up the rough sides of Aros, nothing remained of any concern beyond a deep determination to meddle no more with the spoils of wrecked vessels or the treasures of the dead.

I was already some way up the hill before I paused to breathe and look behind me. The sight that met my eyes was doubly strange.

For, first, the storm that I had foreseen was now advancing with almost tropical rapidity. The whole surface of the sea had been dulled from its conspicuous brightness to an ugly hue of corrugated lead; already in the distance the white waves, the "skipper's daughters," had begun to flee before a breeze that was still insensible on Aros; and already along the curve of Sandag Bay there was a splashing run of sea that I could hear from where I stood. The change upon the sky was even more remarkable. There had begun to arise out of the south-west a huge and solid continent of scowling cloud; here and there, through rents in its contexture, the sun still poured a sheaf of spreading rays; and here and there, from all its edges, vast inky streamers lay forth along the yet unclouded sky. The menace was express and imminent. Even as I gazed, the sun was blotted out. At any moment the tempest might fall upon Aros in its might.

The suddenness of this change of weather so fixed my eyes on heaven that it was some seconds before they alighted on the bay, mapped out below my feet, and robbed a moment later of the sun. The knoll which I had just surmounted overflanked a little amphitheatre of lower hillocks sloping towards the sea, and beyond that the yellow arc of beach and the whole extent of Sandag Bay. It was a scene on which I had often looked down, but where I had never before beheld a human figure. I had but just turned my back upon it and left it empty, and my wonder may be fancied when I saw a boat and several men in that deserted spot. The boat was lying by the rocks. A pair of fellows, bareheaded, with their sleeves rolled up, and one with a boathook, kept her with difficulty to her moorings, for the current was growing brisker every moment. A little way off upon the ledge two men in black clothes, whom I judged to be superior in rank, laid their heads together over some task which at first I did not understand, but a second after I had made it out—they were taking bearings with the compass; and just then I saw one of them unroll a sheet of paper and lay his finger down, as though identifying features in a map. Meanwhile a third was walking to and fro, poking among the rocks and peering over the edge into the water. While I was still watching them with the stupefaction of surprise, my mind hardly yet able to work on what my eyes reported, this third person suddenly stooped and summoned his companions with a cry so loud that it reached my ears upon the hill. The others ran to him, even dropping the compass in their hurry, and I could see the bone and the shoe-buckle going from hand to hand, causing the most unusual gesticulations of surprise and interest. Just then I could hear the seamen crying from the boat, and saw them point westward to that cloud continent which was ever the more rapidly unfurling its blackness over heaven. The others seemed to consult; but the danger was too pressing to be braved, and they bundled into the boat carrying my relics with them, and set forth out of the bay with all speed of oars.

I made no more ado about the matter, but turned and ran for the house. Whoever these men were, it was fit my uncle should be instantly informed. It was not then altogether too late in the day for a descent of the Jacobites; and maybe Prince Charlie, whom I knew my uncle

to detest, was one of the three superiors whom I had
seen upon the rock. Yet as I ran, leaping from rock to
rock, and turned the matter loosely in my mind, this
theory grew ever the longer the less welcome to my
reason. The compass, the map, the interest awakened
by the buckle, and the conduct of that one among the
strangers who had looked so often below him in the
water, all seemed to point to a different explanation of
their presence on that outlying, obscure islet of the
western sea. The Madrid historian, the search insti-
tuted by Dr. Robertson, the bearded stranger with the
rings, my own fruitless search that very morning in the
deep water of Sandag Bay, ran together, piece by piece,
in my memory, and I made sure that these strangers
must be Spaniards in quest of ancient treasure and the
lost ship of the Armada. But the people living in outlying islands, such as Aros, are answerable for their own
security; there is none near by to protect or even to
help them; and the presence in such a spot of a crew of
foreign adventurers—poor, greedy, and most likely law-
less—filled me with apprehensions for my uncle's money,
and even for the safety of his daughter. I was still
wondering how we were to get rid of them when I came,
all breathless, to the top of Aros. The whole world was
shadowed over; only in the extreme east, on a hill of the
mainland, one last gleam of sunshine lingered like a
jewel; rain had begun to fall, not heavily, but in great
drops; the sea was rising with each moment, and already
a band of white encircled Aros and the nearer coasts of
Grisapol. The boat was still pulling seaward, but I now
became aware of what had been hidden from me lower
down—a large, heavily sparred, handsome schooner,
lying to at the south end of Aros. Since I had not seen
her in the morning when I had looked around so closely
at the signs of the weather, and upon these lone waters

where a sail was rarely visible, it was clear she must have lain last night behind the uninhabited Eilean Gour, and this proved conclusively that she was manned by strangers to our coast, for that anchorage, though good enough to look at, is little better than a trap for ships. With such ignorant sailors upon so wild a coast, the coming gale was not unlikely to bring death upon its wings.

## CHAPTER IV

### THE GALE

I found my uncle at the gable end, watching the signs of the weather, with a pipe in his fingers.

"Uncle," said I, "there were men ashore at Sandag Bay——"

I had no time to go further; indeed, I not only forgot my words, but even my weariness, so strange was the effect on Uncle Gordon. He dropped his pipe and fell back against the end of the house with his jaw fallen, his eyes staring, and his long face as white as paper. We must have looked at one another silently for a quarter of a minute, before he made answer in this extraordinary fashion: "Had he a hair kep on?"

I knew as well as if I had been there that the man who now lay buried at Sandag had worn a hairy cap, and that he had come ashore alive. For the first and only time I lost toleration for the man who was my benefactor and the father of the woman I hoped to call my wife.

"These were living men," said I, "perhaps Jacobites, perhaps the French, perhaps pirates, perhaps adventurers come here to seek the Spanish treasure-ship; but, whatever they may be, dangerous at least to your daughter and my cousin. As for your own guilty terrors, man, the dead sleeps well where you have laid him. I stood this morning by his grave; he will not wake before the trump of doom."

My kinsman looked upon me, blinking, while I spoke; then he fixed his eyes for a little on the ground, and pulled his fingers foolishly; but it was plain that he was past the power of speech.

"Come," said I. "You must think for others. You must come up the hill with me, and see this ship."

He obeyed without a word or a look, following slowly after my impatient strides. The spring seemed to have gone out of his body, and he scrambled heavily up and down the rocks, instead of leaping, as he was wont, from one to another. Nor could I, for all my cries, induce him to make better haste. Only once he replied to me complainingly, and like one in bodily pain: "Ay, ay, man, I'm coming." Long before we had reached the top, I had no other thought for him but pity. If the crime had been monstrous, the punishment was in proportion.

At last we emerged above the sky-line of the hill, and could see around us. All was black and stormy to the eye; the last gleam of sun had vanished; a wind had sprung up, not yet high, but gusty and unsteady to the point; the rain, on the other hand, had ceased. Short as was the interval, the sea already ran vastly higher than when I had stood there last; already it had begun to break over some of the outward reefs, and already it moaned aloud in the sea-caves of Aros. I looked, at first in vain, for the schooner.

"There she is," I said at last. But her new position, and the course she was now lying, puzzled me. "They cannot mean to beat to sea," I cried.

"That's what they mean," said my uncle, with something like joy; and just then the schooner went about and stood upon another tack, which put the question beyond the reach of doubt. These strangers, seeing a gale on hand, had thought first of sea-room. With the wind that threatened, in these reef-sown waters and contending against so violent a stream of tide, their course was certain death.

"Good God!" said I, "they are all lost."

"Ay," returned my uncle, "a'—a' lost. They hadnae a chance but to rin for Kyle Dona. The gate they 're gaun the noo, they couldnae win through an the muckle deil were there to pilot them. Eh, man," he continued, touching me on the sleeve, "it's a braw nicht for a shipwreck! Twa in ae twalmonth! Eh, but the Merry Men 'll dance bonny!"

I looked at him, and it was then that I began to fancy him no longer in his right mind. He was peering up to me, as if for sympathy, a timid joy in his eyes. All that had passed between us was already forgotten in the prospect of this fresh disaster.

"If it were not too late," I cried with indignation, "I would take the coble and go out to warn them."

"Na, na," he protested, "ye maunnae interfere; ye maunnae meddle wi' the like o' that. It 's His,"—doffing his bonnet—"His wull. And, eh, man! but it 's a braw nicht for 't!"

Something like fear began to creep into my soul; and, reminding him that I had not yet dined, I proposed we should return to the house. But no; nothing would tear him from his place of outlook.

"I maun see the hail thing, man, Cherlie," he explained; and then as the schooner went about a second time, "Eh, but they han'le her bonny!" he cried. "The *Christ-Anna* was naething to this."

Already the men on board the schooner must have

begun to realize some part, but not yet the twentieth, of the dangers that environed their doomed ship. At every lull of the capricious wind they must have seen how fast the current swept them back. Each tack was made shorter, as they saw how little it prevailed. Every moment the rising swell began to boom and foam upon another sunken reef; and ever and again a breaker would fall in sounding ruin under the very bows of her, and the brown reef and streaming tangle appear in the hollow of the wave. I tell you, they had to stand to their tackle: there was no idle man aboard that ship, God knows. It was upon the progress of a scene so horrible to any human-hearted man that my misguided uncle now pored and gloated like a connoisseur. As I turned to go down the hill, he was lying on his belly on the summit, with his hands stretched forth and clutching in the heather. He seemed rejuvenated, mind and body.

When I got back to the house already dismally affected, I was still more sadly downcast at the sight of Mary. She had her sleeves rolled up over her strong arms, and was quietly making bread. I got a bannock[1] from the dresser and sat down to eat it in silence.

"Are ye wearied, lad?" she asked after a while.

"I am not so much wearied, Mary," I replied, getting on my feet, "as I am weary of delay, and perhaps of Aros too. You know me well enough to judge me fairly, say what I like. Well, Mary, you may be sure of this: you had better be anywhere but here."

"I'll be sure of one thing," she returned: "I'll be where my duty is."

"You forget, you have a duty to yourself," I said.

"Ay, man?" she replied, pounding at the dough: "will you have found that in the Bible, now?"

---

[1] A cake made from coarse meal.

"Mary," I said solemnly, "you must not laugh at me just now. God knows I am in no heart for laughing. If we could get your father with us, it would be best; but with him or without him, I want you far away from here, my girl; for your own sake, and for mine, ay, and for your father's too, I want you far—far away from here. I came with other thoughts; I came here as a man comes home; now it is all changed, and I have no desire nor hope but to flee—for that's the word—flee, like a bird out of the fowler's snare, from this accursed island."

She had stopped her work by this time.

"And do you think, now," said she, "do you think, now, I have neither eyes nor ears? Do ye think I have-nae broken my heart to have these braws (as he calls them, God forgive him!) thrown into the sea? Do ye think I have lived with him, day in, day out, and not seen what you saw in an hour or two? No," she said, "I know there's wrong in it; what wrong, I neither know nor want to know. There was never an ill thing made better by meddling, that I could hear of. But, my lad, you must never ask me to leave my father. While the breath is in his body, I'll be with him. And he's not long for here, either: that I can tell you, Charlie —he's not long for here. The mark is on his brow; and better so—maybe better so."

I was a while silent, not knowing what to say; and when I roused my head at last to speak, she got before me.

"Charlie," she said, "what's right for me, neednae be right for you. There's sin upon this house and trouble; you are a stranger; take your things upon your back and go your ways to better places and to better folk, and if you were ever minded to come back, though it were twenty years syne, you would find me aye waiting."

"Mary Ellen," I said, "I asked you to be my wife, and

you said as good as yes. That's done for good. Where-ever you are, I am; as I shall answer to my God."

As I said the words, the winds suddenly burst out raving, and then seemed to stand still and shudder round the house of Aros. It was the first squall, or prologue, of the coming tempest, and as we started and looked about us, we found that a gloom, like the approach of evening, had settled round the house.

"God pity all poor folks at sea!" she said. "We'll see no more of my father till the morrow's morning."

And then she told me, as we sat by the fire and hearkened to the rising gusts, of how this change had fallen upon my uncle. All last winter he had been dark and fitful in his mind. Whenever the Roost ran high, or, as Mary said, whenever the Merry Men were dancing, he would lie out for hours together on the Head, if it were at night, or on the top of Aros by day, watching the tumult of the sea, and sweeping the horizon for a sail. After February the tenth, when the wealth-bringing wreck was cast ashore at Sandag, he had been at first unnaturally gay, and his excitement had never fallen in degree, but only changed in kind from dark to darker. He neglected his work, and kept Rorie idle. They two would speak together by the hour at the gable end, in guarded tones and with an air of secrecy and almost of guilt; and if she questioned either, as at first she sometimes did, her inquiries were put aside with confusion. Since Rorie had first remarked the fish that hung about the ferry, his master had never set foot but once upon the mainland of the Ross. That once—it was in the height of the springs—he had passed dryshod while the tide was out; but, having lingered overlong on the far side, found himself cut off from Aros by the returning waters. It was with a shriek of agony that he had leaped across the gut, and he had reached home thereafter in a fever-fit of fear. A fear of the sea, a constant haunting thought of the sea, appeared in his talk and devotions, and even in his looks when he was silent.

Rorie alone came in to supper; but a little later my uncle appeared, took a bottle under his arm, put some bread in his pocket, and set forth again to his outlook, followed this time by Rorie. I heard that the schooner was losing ground, but the crew were still fighting every inch with hopeless ingenuity and courage; and the news filled my mind with blackness.

A little after sundown the full fury of the gale broke forth, such a gale as I have never seen in summer, nor, seeing how swiftly it had come, even in winter. Mary and I sat in silence, the house quaking overhead, the tempest howling without, the fire between us sputtering with rain drops. Our thoughts were far away with the poor fellows on the schooner, or my not less unhappy uncle, houseless on the promontory; and yet ever and again we were startled back to ourselves, when the wind would rise and strike the gable like a solid body, or suddenly fall and draw away, so that the fire leaped into flame and our hearts bounded in our sides. Now the storm in its might would seize and shake the four corners of the roof, roaring like Leviathan in anger. Anon, in a lull, cold eddies of tempest moved shudderingly in the room, lifting the hair upon our heads and passing between us as we sat. And again the wind would break forth in a chorus of melancholy sounds, hooting low in the chimney, wailing with flutelike softness round the house.

It was perhaps eight o'clock when Rorie came in and pulled me mysteriously to the door. My uncle, it appeared, had frightened even his constant comrade; and Rorie, uneasy at his extravagance, prayed me to come out and share the watch. I hastened to do as I was asked; the more readily, as what with fear and horror, and the electrical tension of the night, I was myself restless and disposed for action. I told Mary to be under no alarm, for I should be a safeguard on her father; and wrapping myself warmly in a plaid, I followed Rorie into the open air.

The night, though we were so little past midsummer, was as dark as January. Intervals of a groping twilight alternated with spells of utter blackness; and it was impossible to trace the reason of these changes in the flying horror of the sky. The wind blew the breath out of a man's nostrils; all heaven seemed to thunder overhead like one huge sail; and when there fell a momentary lull on Aros, we could hear the gusts dismally sweeping in the distance. Over all the lowlands of the Ross, the wind must have blown as fierce as on the open sea; and God only knows the uproar that was raging around the head of Ben Kyaw. Sheets of mingled spray and rain were driven in our faces. All round the isle of Aros the surf, with an incessant, hammering thunder, beat upon the reefs and beaches. Now louder in one place, now lower in another, like the combinations of orchestral music, the constant mass of sound was hardly varied for a moment. And loud above all this hurly-burly I could hear the changeful voices of the Roost and the intermittent roaring of the Merry Men. At that hour, there flashed into my mind the reason of the name that they were called. For the noise of them seemed almost mirthful, as it out-topped the other noises of the night; or if not mirthful, yet instinct with a portentous joviality. Nay, and it seemed even human. As when savage men have drunk away their reason, and, discarding speech, bawl together in their madness by the hour; so, to my ears these deadly breakers shouted by Aros in the night.

Arm in arm, and staggering against the wind, Rorie and I won every yard of ground with conscious effort.

We slipped on the wet sod, we fell together sprawling on the rocks. Bruised, drenched, beaten, and breathless, it must have taken us near half an hour to get from the house down to the Head that overlooks the Roost. There, it seemed, was my uncle's favourite observatory. Right in the face of it, where the cliff is highest and most sheer, a hump of earth, like a parapet, makes a place of shelter from the common winds, where a man may sit in quiet and see the tide and the mad billows contending at his feet. As he might look down from the window of a house upon some street disturbance, so, from this post, he looks down upon the tumbling of the Merry Men. On such a night, of course, he peers upon a world of blackness, where the waters wheel and boil, where the waves joust together with the noise of an explosion, and the foam towers and vanishes in the twinkling of an eye. Never before had I seen the Merry Men thus violent. The fury, height and transiency of their spoutings was a thing to be seen and not recounted. High over our heads on the cliff rose their white columns in the darkness; and the same instant, like phantoms, they were gone. Sometimes three at a time would thus aspire and vanish; sometimes a gust took them, and the spray would fall about us, heavy as a wave. And yet the spectacle was rather maddening in its levity than impressive by its force. Thought was beaten down by the confounding uproar; a gleeful vacancy possessed the brains of men, a state akin to madness; and I found myself at times following the dance of the Merry Men as it were a tune upon a jigging instrument.

I first caught sight of my uncle when we were still some yards away in one of the flying glimpses of twilight that checkered the pitch darkness of the night. He was standing up behind the parapet, his head thrown back and the bottle to his mouth. As he put it down,

he saw and recognised us with a toss of one hand fleer-
ingly above his head.

"Has he been drinking?" shouted I to Rorie.

"He will aye be drunk when the wind blaws," returned Rorie in the same high key, and it was all that I
could do to hear him.

"Then—was he so—in February?" I inquired.

Rorie's "Ay" was a cause of joy to me. The murder,
then, had not sprung in cold blood from calculation; it
was an act of madness no more to be condemned than to
be pardoned. My uncle was a dangerous mad-man, if
you will, but he was not cruel and base as I had feared.
Yet what a scene for a carouse, what an incredible vice,
was this that the poor man had chosen! I have always
thought drunkenness a wild and almost fearful pleasure,
rather demoniacal than human; but drunkenness, out
here in the roaring blackness, on the edge of a cliff above
that hell of waters, the man's head spinning like the
Roost, his foot tottering on the edge of death, his ear
watching for the signs of shipwreck, surely that, if it
were credible in any one, was morally impossible in a
man like my uncle, whose mind was set upon a damna-
tory creed and haunted by the darkest superstitions.
Yet so it was; and, as we reached the bight[1] of shelter
and could breathe again, I saw the man's eyes shining
in the night with an unholy glimmer.

"Eh, Charlie, man, it's grand!" he cried. "See to
them!" he continued, dragging me to the edge of the
abyss from whence arose that deafening clamour and
those clouds of spray; "see to them dancin', man! Is
that no wicked?"

He pronounced the word with gusto, and I thought
it suited with the scene.

"They're yowlin' for thon schooner," he went on, his

[1] Bend in the cliff.

thin, insane voice clearly audible in the shelter of the
bank, "an' she's comin' aye nearer, aye nearer, aye
nearer an' nearer an' nearer; an' they ken 't, the folk
kens it, they ken weel it 's by wi' them.   Charlie, lad,
they 're a' drunk in yon schooner, a' dozened wi' drink.
They were a' drunk in the *Christ-Anna*, at the hinder
end.   There 's nane could droon at sea wantin' the
brandy.   Hoot awa, what do you ken?" with a sudden
blast of anger.   "I tell ye, it cannae be; they daurnae
droon withoot it.   Ha'e," holding out the bottle, "tak'
a sowp."

I was about to refuse, but Rorie touched me as if in
warning; and indeed I had already thought better of the
movement.   I took the bottle, therefore, and not only
drank freely myself, but contrived to spill even more as
I was doing so.   It was pure spirit, and almost strangled
me to swallow.   My kinsman did not observe the loss,
but, once more throwing back his head, drained the remainder to the dregs.   Then, with a loud laugh, he cast
the bottle forth among the Merry Men, who seemed to
leap up, shouting, to receive it.

"Ha'e, bairns!" he cried, "there 's your han'sel.[1]
Ye 'll get bonnier nor that, or morning."

Suddenly, out in the black night before us, and not
two hundred yards away, we heard, at a moment when
the wind was silent, the clear note of a human voice.
Instantly the wind swept howling down upon the Head,
and the Roost bellowed, and churned, and danced with
a new fury.   But we had heard the sound, and we knew,
with agony, that this was the doomed ship now close on
ruin, and that what we had heard was the voice of her
master issuing his last command.   Crouching together
on the edge, we waited, straining every sense, for the in-
evitable end.   It was long, however, and to us it seemed

[1] Gift.

like ages, ere the schooner suddenly appeared for one brief instant, relieved against a tower of glimmering foam. I still see her reefed mainsail flapping loose, as the boom fell heavily across the deck; I still see the black outline of the hull, and still think I can distinguish the figure of a man stretched upon the tiller. Yet the whole sight we had of her passed swifter than lightning; the very wave that disclosed her fell burying her for ever; the mingled cry of many voices at the point of death rose and was quenched in the roaring of the Merry Men. And with that the tragedy was at an end. The strong ship, with all her gear, and the lamp perhaps still burning in the cabin, the lives of so many men, precious surely to others, dear, at least, as heaven to themselves, had all, in that one moment, gone down into the surging waters. They were gone like a dream. And the wind still ran and shouted, and the senseless waters in the Roost still leaped and tumbled as before.

How long we lay there together, we three, speechless and motionless, is more than I can tell, but it must have been for long. At length, one by one, and almost mechanically, we crawled back into the shelter of the bank. As I lay against the parapet, wholly wretched and not entirely master of my mind, I could hear my kinsman maundering to himself in an altered and melancholy mood. Now he would repeat to himself with maudlin iteration, "Sic a fecht as they had—sic a sair fecht as they had, puir lads, puir lads!" and anon he would bewail that "a' the gear was as gude's tint," [1] because the ship had gone down among the Merry Men instead of stranding on the shore; and throughout, the name—the *Christ-Anna*—would come and go in his divagations, pronounced with shuddering awe. The storm all this time was rapidly abating. In half an hour

[1] Lost.

the wind had fallen to a breeze, and the change was accompanied or caused by a heavy, cold, and plumping rain. I must then have fallen asleep, and when I came to myself, drenched, stiff, and unrefreshed, day had already broken, grey, wet, discomfortable day; the wind blew in faint and shifting capfuls, the tide was out, the Roost was at its lowest, and only the strong beating surf round all the coasts of Aros remained to witness of the furies of the night.

## CHAPTER V

### A MAN OUT OF THE SEA

RORIE set out for the house in search of warmth and breakfast; but my uncle was bent upon examining the shores of Aros, and I felt it a part of duty to accompany him throughout. He was now docile and quiet, but tremulous and weak in mind and body; and it was with the eagerness of a child that he pursued his exploration. He climbed far down upon the rocks; on the beaches, he pursued the retreating breakers. The merest broken plank or rag of cordage was a treasure in his eyes to be secured at the peril of his life. To see him, with weak and stumbling footsteps, expose himself to the pursuit of the surf, or the snares and pitfalls of the weedy rock, kept me in a perpetual terror. My arm was ready to support him, my hand clutched him by the skirt, I helped him to draw his pitiful discoveries beyond the reach of the returning wave; a nurse accompanying a child of seven would have had no different experience.

Yet, weakened as he was by the reaction from his madness of the night before, the passions that smouldered in his nature were those of a strong man. His terror of the sea, although conquered for the moment, was still undiminished; had the sea been a lake of living flames, he could not have shrunk more panically from its touch; and once, when his foot slipped and he plunged to the midleg into a pool of water, the shriek that came up out of his soul was like the cry of death. He sat still for a while, panting like a dog, after that; but his desire for the spoils of shipwreck triumphed once more over his fears; once more he tottered among the curded foam; once more he crawled upon the rocks among the bursting bubbles; once more his whole heart seemed to be set on driftwood; fit, if it was fit for anything, to throw upon the fire. Pleased as he was with what he found, he still incessantly grumbled at his ill-fortune.

"Aros," he said, "is no a place for wrecks ava'—no ava'. A' the years I 've dwalt here, this ane maks the second; and the best o' the gear clean tint!"

"Uncle," said I, for we were now on a stretch of open sand, where there was nothing to divert his mind, "I saw you last night as I never thought to see you—you were drunk."

"Na, na," he said, "no as bad as that. I had been drinking, though. And to tell ye the God's truth, it 's a thing I cannae mend. There 's nae soberer man than me in my ordnar; but when I hear the wind blaw in my lug,[1] it 's my belief that I gang gyte." [2]

"You are a religious man," I replied, "and this is sin."

" Ou," he returned, "if it wasnae sin, I dinnae ken that I would care for 't. Ye see, man, it 's defiance. There 's a sair spang [3] o' the auld sin o' the warld in yon sea; it 's an unchristian business at the best o 't; an' whiles when it gets up, an' the wind skreighs—the wind

---

[1] Ear.                [2] Crazy.                [3] Grip.

an' her are a kind of sib,[1] I 'm thinkin'—an' thae Merry
Men, the daft callants, blawin' and lauchin', and puir
souls in the deid thraws[2] warstlin'[3] the leelang nicht wi'
their bit ships—weel, it comes ower me like a glamour.
I 'm a deil, I ken 't. But I think naething o' the puir
sailor lads; I 'm wi' the sea, I 'm just like ane o' her ain
Merry Men."

I thought I should touch him in a joint of his harness. I turned me towards the sea; the surf was running gaily, wave after wave, with their manes blowing
behind them, riding one after another up the beach,
towering, curving, falling one upon another on the
trampled sand. Without, the salt air, the scared gulls,
the widespread army of the sea-chargers, neighing to
each other, as they gathered together to the assault of
Aros; and close before us, that line on the flat sands
that, with all their number and their fury, they might
never pass.

"Thus far shalt thou go," said I, "and no farther."
And then I quoted as solemnly as I was able a verse that
I had often before fitted to the chorus of the breakers:—

> But yet the Lord that is on high,
>   Is more of might by far,
> Than noise of many waters is,
>   As great sea billows are.

"Ay," said my kinsman, "at the hinder end, the Lord
will triumph; I dinnae misdoobt that. But here on
earth, even silly men-folk daur Him to His face. It is
nae wise; I am nae sayin' that it 's wise; but it 's the
pride of the eye, and it 's the lust o' life, an' it 's the wale[4]
o' pleesures."

---

[1] Relatives.  [2] In the throes of death.
[3] Struggling.  [4] Choice.

I said no more, for we had now begun to cross a neck of land that lay between us and Sandag; and I withheld my last appeal to the man's better reason till we should stand upon the spot associated with his crime. Nor did he pursue the subject; but he walked beside me with a firmer step. The call that I had made upon his mind acted like a stimulant, and I could see that he had forgotten his search for worthless jetsam, in a profound, gloomy, and yet stirring train of thought. In three or four minutes we had topped the brae and begun to go down upon Sandag. The wreck had been roughly handled by the sea; the stem had been spun round and dragged a little lower down; and perhaps the stern had been forced a little higher, for the two parts now lay entirely separate on the beach. When we came to the grave I stopped, uncovered my head in the thick rain, and, looking my kinsman in the face, addressed him.

"A man," said I, "was in God's providence suffered to escape from mortal dangers; he was poor, he was naked, he was wet, he was weary, he was a stranger; he had every claim upon the bowels of your compassion; it may be that he was the salt of the earth, holy, helpful, and kind; it may be he was a man laden with iniquities to whom death was the beginning of torment. I ask you in the sight of heaven: Gordon Darnaway, where is the man for whom Christ died?"

He started visibly at the last words; but there came no answer, and his face expressed no feeling but a vague alarm.

"You were my father's brother," I continued; "you have taught me to count your house as if it were my father's house; and we are both sinful men walking before the Lord among the sins and dangers of this life. It is by our evil that God leads us into good ; we sin, I dare not say by His temptation, but I must say with

His consent; and to any but the brutish man his sins are the beginning of wisdom. God has warned you by this crime; He warns you still by the bloody grave between our feet; and if there shall follow no repentance, no improvement, no return to Him, what can we look for but the following of some memorable judgment?"

Even as I spoke the words, the eyes of my uncle wandered from my face. A change fell upon his looks that cannot be described; his features seemed to dwindle in size, the colour faded from his cheeks, one hand rose waveringly and pointed over my shoulder into the distance, and the oft-repeated name fell once more from his lips: "The *Christ-Anna!*"

I turned; and if I was not appalled to the same degree, as I return thanks to Heaven that I had not the cause, I was still startled by the sight that met my eyes. The form of a man stood upright on the cabin-hutch of the wrecked ship; his back was towards us; he appeared to be scanning the offing with shaded eyes, and his figure was relieved to its full height, which was plainly very great, against the sea and sky. I have said a thousand times that I am not superstitious; but at that moment, with my mind running upon death and sin, the unexplained appearance of a stranger on that sea-girt, solitary island filled me with a surprise that bordered close on terror. It seemed scarce possible that any human soul should have come ashore alive in such a sea as had raged last night along the coasts of Aros; and the only vessel within miles had gone down before our eyes among the Merry Men. I was assailed with doubts that made suspense unbearable, and, to put the matter to the touch at once, stepped forward and hailed the figure like a ship.

He turned about, and I thought he started to behold us. At this my courage instantly revived, and I called and signed to him to draw near, and he, on his part, dropped immediately to the sands, and began slowly to approach, with many stops and hesitations. At each repeated mark of the man's uneasiness I grew the more confident myself; and I advanced another step, encouraging him as I did so with my head and hand. It was plain the castaway had heard indifferent accounts of our island hospitality; and indeed, about this time, the people farther north had a sorry reputation.

"Why," I said, "the man is black!"

And just at that moment, in a voice that I could scarce have recognised, my kinsman began swearing and praying in a mingled stream. I looked at him; he had fallen on his knees, his face was agonised; at each step of the castaway's the pitch of his voice rose, the volubility of his utterance and the fervour of his language redoubled. I call it prayer, for it was addressed to God; but surely no such ranting incongruities were ever before addressed to the Creator by a creature: surely if prayer can be a sin, this mad harangue was sinful. I ran to my kinsman, I seized him by the shoulders, I dragged him to his feet.

"Silence, man," said I, "respect your God in words, if not in action. Here, on the very scene of your transgressions, He sends you an occasion of atonement. Forward and embrace it; welcome like a father yon creature who comes trembling to your mercy."

With that, I tried to force him towards the black; but he felled me to the ground, burst from my grasp, leaving the shoulder of his jacket, and fled up the hillside towards the top of Aros like a deer. I staggered to my feet again, bruised and somewhat stunned; the negro had paused in surprise, perhaps in terror, some halfway between me and the wreck; my uncle was already far away, bounding from rock to rock; and I thus found myself torn for a time between two duties. But I judged, and I pray Heaven that I judged rightly, in favour of **the poor wretch upon the** sands; his misfortune was at least not plainly of his own creation; it was one, besides, that I could certainly relieve; and I had begun by that time to regard my uncle as an incurable and dismal lunatic. I advanced accordingly towards the black, who now awaited my approach with folded arms, like one prepared for either destiny. As I came nearer, he reached forth his hand with a great gesture, such as I had seen from the pulpit, and spoke to me in something of a pulpit voice, but not a word was comprehensible. I tried him first in English, then in Gaelic, both in vain; so that it was clear we must rely upon the tongue of looks and gestures. Thereupon I signed to him to follow me, which he did readily and with a grave obeisance like a fallen king; all the while there had come no shade of alteration in his face, neither of anxiety while he was still waiting, nor of relief now that he was reassured; if he were a slave, as I supposed, I could not but judge he must have fallen from some high place in his own country, and fallen as he was, I could not but admire his bearing. As we passed the grave, I paused and raised my hands and eyes to heaven in token of respect and sorrow for the dead; and he, as if in answer, bowed low and spread his hands abroad; it was a strange motion, but done like a thing of common custom; and I supposed it was ceremonial in the land from which he came. At the same time he pointed to my uncle, whom we could just see perched upon a knoll, and touched his head to indicate that he was mad.

We took the long way round the shore, for I feared to excite my uncle if we struck across the island; and as we walked, I had time enough to mature the little dramatic exhibition by which I hoped to satisfy my doubts. Accordingly, pausing on a rock, I proceeded to imitate

before the negro the action of the man whom I had seen
the day before taking bearings with the compass at
Sandag. He understood me at once, and, taking the
imitation out of my hands, showed me where the boat
was, pointed out seaward as if to indicate the position of
the schooner, and then down along the edge of the rock
with the words "Espirito Santo," strangely pronounced,
but clear enough for recognition. I had thus been right
in my conjecture; the pretended historical inquiry had
been but a cloak for treasure-hunting; the man who had
played Dr. Robertson was the same as the foreigner who
visited Grisapol in spring, and now, with many others,
lay dead under the Roost of Aros: there had their greed
brought them, there should their bones be tossed for
evermore. In the meantime the black continued his
imitation of the scene, now looking up skyward as though
watching the approach of the storm; now, in the character of a seaman, waving the rest to come aboard; now
as an officer, running along the rock and entering the
boat; and anon bending over imaginary oars with the
air of a hurried boatman; but all with the same solemnity
of manner, so that I was never even moved to smile.
Lastly, he indicated to me, by a pantomime not to be
described in words, how he himself had gone up to examine the stranded wreck, and, to his grief and indignation, had been deserted by his comrades; and thereupon
folded his arms once more, and stooped his head, like
one accepting fate.

The mystery of his presence being thus solved for me,
I explained to him by means of a sketch the fate of the
vessel and of all aboard her. He showed no surprise
nor sorrow, and, with a sudden lifting of his open hand,
seemed to dismiss his former friends or masters (which-
ever they had been) into God's pleasure. Respect came
upon me and grew stronger, the more I observed him;

I saw he had a powerful mind and a sober and severe character, such as I loved to commune with; and before we reached the house of Aros I had almost forgotten, and wholly forgiven him, his uncanny colour.

To Mary I told all that had passed without suppression, though I own my heart failed me; but I did wrong to doubt her sense of justice.

"You did the right," she said. "God's will be done." And she set out meat for us at once.

As soon as I was satisfied, I bade Rorie keep an eye upon the castaway, who was still eating, and set forth again myself to find my uncle. I had not gone far before I saw him sitting in the same place, upon the very topmost knoll, and seemingly in the same attitude as when I had last observed him. From that point, as I have said, the most of Aros and the neighbouring Ross would be spread below him like a map; and it was plain that he kept a bright look-out in all directions, for my head had scarcely risen above the summit of the first ascent before he had leaped to his feet and turned as if to face me. I hailed him at once, as well as I was able, in the same tones and words as I had often used before, when I had come to summon him to dinner. He made not so much as a movement in reply. I passed on a little farther, and again tried parley, with the same result. But when I began a second time to advance, his insane fears blazed up again, and still in dead silence, but with incredible speed, he began to flee from before me along the rocky summit of the hill. An hour before, he had been dead weary, and I had been comparatively active. But now his strength was recruited by the fervour of insanity, and it would have been vain for me to dream of pursuit. Nay, the very attempt, I thought, might have inflamed his terrors, and thus increased the miseries of

our position.   And I had nothing left but to turn homeward and make my sad report to Mary.

She heard it, as she had heard the first, with a concerned composure, and, bidding me lie down and take
that rest of which I stood so much in need, set forth
herself in quest of her misguided father.   At that age it
would have been a strange thing that put me from either
meat or sleep;  I slept long and deep;  and it was already
long past noon before I awoke and came downstairs into
the kitchen.   Mary, Rorie, and the black castaway were
seated about the fire in silence;  and I could see that
Mary had been weeping.   There was cause enough, as
I soon learned, for tears.   First she, and then Rorie, had
been forth to seek my uncle;  each in turn had found
him perched upon the hill-top, and from each in turn he
had silently and swiftly fled.   Rorie had tried to chase
him, but in vain;  madness lent a new vigour to his
bounds;  he sprang from rock to rock over the widest
gullies;  he scoured like the wind along the hill-tops;  he
doubled and twisted like a hare before the dogs;  and
Rorie at length gave in;  and the last that he saw, my
uncle was seated as before upon the crest of Aros.   Even
during the hottest excitement of the chase, even when
the fleet-footed servant had come, for a moment, very
near to capture him, the poor lunatic had uttered not a
sound.   He fled, and he was silent, like a beast;  and
this silence had terrified his pursuer.

There was something heart-breaking in the situation.
How to capture the madman, how to feed him in the
meanwhile, and what to do with him when he was
captured, were the three difficulties that we had to
solve.

"The black," said I, "is the cause of this attack.   It
may even be his presence in the house that keeps my
uncle on the hill.   We have done the fair thing;  he has

been fed and warmed under this roof; now I propose that Rorie put him across the bay in the coble, and take him through the Ross as far as Grisapol."

In this proposal Mary heartily concurred; and bidding the black follow us, we all three descended to the pier. Certainly, Heaven's will was declared against Gordon Darnaway; a thing had happened, never paralleled before in Aros; during the storm, the coble had broken loose, and, striking on the rough splinters of the pier, now lay in four feet of water with one side stove in. Three days of work at least would be required to make her float. But I was not to be beaten. I led the whole party round to where the gut was narrowest, swam to the other side, and called to the black to follow me. He signed, with the same clearness and quiet as before, that he knew not the art; and there was truth apparent in his signals, it would have occurred to none of us to doubt his truth; and that hope being over, we must all go back even as we came to the house of Aros, the negro walking in our midst without embarrassment.

All we could do that day was to make one more attempt to communicate with the unhappy madman. Again he was visible on his perch; again he fled in silence. But food and a great cloak were at least left for his comfort; the rain, besides, had cleared away, and the night promised to be even warm. We might compose ourselves, we thought, until the morrow; rest was the chief requisite, that we might be strengthened for unusual exertions; and as none cared to talk, we separated at an early hour.

I lay long awake, planning a campaign for the morrow. I was to place the black on the side of Sandag, whence he should head my uncle towards the house; Rorie in the west, I on the east, were to complete the cordon, as best we might. It seemed to me, the more I recalled the configuration of the island, that it should be possible, though hard, to force him down upon the low ground along Aros Bay; and once there, even with the strength of his madness, ultimate escape was hardly to be feared. It was on his terror of the black that I relied; for I made sure, however he might run, it would not be in the direction of the man whom he supposed to have returned from the dead, and thus one point of the compass at least would be secure.

When at length I fell asleep, it was to be awakened shortly after by a dream of wrecks, black men, and submarine adventure; and I found myself so shaken and fevered that I arose, descended the stair, and stepped out before the house. Within, Rorie and the black were asleep together in the kitchen; outside was a wonderful clear night of stars, with here and there a cloud still hanging, last stragglers of the tempest. It was near the top of the flood, and the Merry Men were roaring in the windless quiet of the night. Never, not even in the height of the tempest, had I heard their song with greater awe. Now, when the winds were gathered home, when the deep was dandling itself back into its summer slumber, and when the stars rained their gentle light over land and sea, the voice of these tide-breakers was still raised for havoc. They seemed, indeed, to be a part of the world's evil and the tragic side of life. Nor were their meaningless vociferations the only sounds that broke the silence of the night. For I could hear, now shrill and thrilling and now almost drowned, the note of a human voice that accompanied the uproar of the Roost. I knew it for my kinsman's; and a great fear fell upon me of God's judgments, and the evil in the world. I went back again into the darkness of the house as into a place of shelter, and lay long upon my bed, pondering these mysteries.

It was late when I again woke, and I leaped into my clothes and hurried to the kitchen. No one was there; Rorie and the black had both stealthily departed long before; and my heart stood still at the discovery. I could rely on Rorie's heart, but I placed no trust in his discretion. If he had thus set out without a word, he was plainly bent upon some service to my uncle. But what service could he hope to render even alone, far less in the company of the man in whom my uncle found his fears incarnated? Even if I were not already too late to prevent some deadly mischief, it was plain I must delay no longer. With the thought I was out of the house; and often as I have run on the rough sides of Aros, I never ran as I did that fatal morning. I do not believe I put twelve minutes to the whole ascent.

My uncle was gone from his perch. The basket had indeed been torn open and the meat scattered on the turf; but, as we found afterwards, no mouthful had been tasted; and there was not another trace of human existence in that wide field of view. Day had already filled the clear heavens; the sun already lighted in a rosy bloom upon the crest of Ben Kyaw; but all below me the rude knolls of Aros and the shield of the sea lay steeped in the clear darkling twilight of the dawn.

"Rorie!" I cried; and again "Rorie!" My voice died in the silence, but there came no answer back. If there were indeed an enterprise afoot to catch my uncle, it was plainly not in fleetness of foot, but in dexterity of stalking, that the hunters placed their trust. I ran on farther, keeping the higher spurs, and looking right and left, nor did I pause again till I was on the mount above Sandag. I could see the wreck, the uncovered belt of sand, the waves idly beating, the long ledge of rocks, and on either hand the tumbled knolls, boulders, and gullies of the island. But still no human thing.

At a stride the sunshine fell on Aros, and the shadows and colours leaped into being. Not half a moment later, below me to the west, sheep began to scatter as in a panic. There came a cry. I saw my uncle running. I saw the black jump up in hot pursuit; and before I had time to understand, Rorie also had appeared, calling directions in Gaelic as to a dog herding sheep.

I took to my heels to interfere, and perhaps I had done better to have waited where I was, for I was the means of cutting off the madman's last escape. There was nothing before him from that moment but the grave, the wreck, and the sea in Sandag Bay. And yet heaven knows that what I did was for the best.

My uncle Gordon saw in what direction, horrible to him, the chase was driving him. He doubled, darting to the right and left; but high as the fever ran in his veins, the black was still the swifter. Turn where he would, he was still forestalled, still driven towards the scene of his crime. Suddenly he began to shriek aloud, so that the coast re-echoed; and now both I and Rorie were calling on the black to stop. But all was vain, for it was written otherwise. The pursuer still ran, the chase still sped before him screaming; they avoided the grave, and skimmed close past the timbers of the wreck; in a breath they had cleared the sand; and still my kinsman did not pause, but dashed straight into the surf; and the black, now almost within reach, still followed swiftly behind him. Rorie and I both stopped, for the thing was now beyond the hands of men, and these were the decrees of God that came to pass before our eyes. There was never a sharper ending. On that steep beach they were beyond their depth at a bound; neither could swim; the black rose once for a moment with a throttling cry; but the current had them, racing sea-ward; and if ever they came up again, which God alone can tell, it would be ten mintues after, at the far **end of** Aros Roost, where the sea-birds hover fishing.

# MARKHEIM [1]

"YES," said the dealer, "our windfalls are of various kinds. Some customers are ignorant, and then I touch a dividend on my superior knowledge. Some are dishonest," and here he held up the candle, so that the light fell strongly on his visitor, "and in that case," he continued, "I profit by my virtue."

Markheim had but just entered from the daylight streets, and his eyes had not yet grown familiar with the mingled shine and darkness in the shop. At these pointed words, and before the near presence of the flame, he blinked painfully and looked aside.

The dealer chuckled. "You come to me on Christmas Day," he resumed, "when you know that I am alone in my house, put up my shutters, and make a point of refusing business. Well, you will have to pay for that; you will have to pay for my loss of time, when I should be balancing my books; you will have to pay, besides, for a kind of manner that I remark in you to-day very strongly. I am the essence of discretion, and ask no awkward questions; but when a customer cannot look me in the eye, he has to pay for it." The dealer once more chuckled; and then, changing to his usual business voice, though still with a note of irony, "You can give, as usual, a clear account of how you

---

[1] Written in Bournemouth, in 1884, when Stevenson's body was enfeebled by illness, but his mind strongly wrestling with the problem of the duality of our moral nature, a problem afterwards worked out with more completeness in *The Strange Case of Dr. Jekyll and Mr. Hyde*. It was published in the Christmas number of *Unwin's Annual*, in 1885; and afterwards in the volume entitled *The Merry Men, and Other Tales*, 1887.

came into the possession of the object?" he continued.
"Still your uncle's cabinet? A remarkable collector,
sir!"

And the little pale, round-shouldered dealer stood almost on tip-toe, looking over the top of his gold spectacles, and nodding his head with every mark of disbelief.
Markheim returned his gaze with one of infinite pity,
and a touch of horror.

"This time," said he, "you are in error. I have not
come to sell, but to buy. I have no curios to dispose of;
my uncle's cabinet is bare to the wainscot; even were it
still intact, I have done well on the Stock Exchange, and
should more likely add to it than otherwise, and my
errand to-day is simplicity itself. I seek a Christmas
present for a lady," he continued, waxing more fluent as
he struck into the speech he had prepared; "and certainly I owe you every excuse for thus disturbing you
upon so small a matter. But the thing was neglected
yesterday; I must produce my little compliment at
dinner: and, as you very well know, a rich marriage is
not a thing to be neglected."

There followed a pause, during which the dealer
seemed to weigh this statement incredulously. The ticking of many clocks among the curious lumber of the shop,
and the faint rushing of the cabs in a near thoroughfare,
filled up the interval of silence.

"Well, sir," said the dealer, "be it so. You are an
old customer after all; and if, as you say, you have the
chance of a good marriage, far be it from me to be
an obstacle. Here is a nice thing for a lady now," he
went on, "this hand glass—fifteenth century, warranted;
comes from a good collection, too; but I reserve the
name, in the interests of my customer, who was just like
yourself, my dear sir, the nephew and sole heir of a remarkable collector."

The dealer, while he thus ran on in his dry and biting voice, had stooped to take the object from its place; and as he had done so a shock had passed through Markheim, a start both of hand and foot, a sudden leap of many tumultuous passions to the face. It passed as swiftly as it came, and left no trace beyond a certain trembling of the hand that now received the glass.

"A glass," he said hoarsely, and then paused, and repeated it more clearly. "A glass? For Christmas? Surely not?"

"And why not?" cried the dealer. "Why not a glass?"

Markheim was looking upon him with an indefinable expression. "You ask me why not?" he said. "Why, look here—look in it—look at yourself! Do you like to see it? No! nor I—nor any man."

The little man had jumped back when Markheim had so suddenly confronted him with the mirror; but now, perceiving there was nothing worse on hand, he chuckled. "Your future lady, sir, must be pretty hard favoured," said he.

"I ask you," said Markheim, "for a Christmas present, and you give me this—this damned reminder of years, and sins and follies—this hand-conscience! Did you mean it? Had you a thought in your mind? Tell me. It will be better for you if you do. Come, tell me about yourself. I hazard a guess now, that you are in secret a very charitable man?"

The dealer looked closely at his companion. It was very odd, Markheim did not appear to be laughing; there was something in his face like an eager sparkle of hope, but nothing of mirth.

"What are you driving at?" the dealer asked

"Not charitable?" returned the other, gloomily. "Not charitable; not pious; not scrupulous; unloving, unbeloved; a hand to get money, a safe to keep it. Is that all? Dear God, man, is that all?"

"I will tell you what it is," began the dealer, with some sharpness, and then broke off again into a chuckle. "But I see this is a love match of yours, and you have been drinking the lady's health."

"Ah!" cried Markheim, with a strange curiosity. "Ah, have you been in love? Tell me about that."

"I," cried the dealer. "I in love! I never had the time, nor have I the time to-day for all this nonsense. Will you take the glass?"

"Where is the hurry?" returned Markheim. "It is very pleasant to stand here talking; and life is so short and insecure that I would not hurry away from any pleasure—no, not even from so mild a one as this. We should rather cling, cling to what little we can get, like a man at a cliff's edge. Every second is a cliff, if you think upon it—a cliff a mile high—high enough, if we fall, to dash us out of every feature of humanity. Hence it is best to talk pleasantly. Let us talk of each other; why should we wear this mask? Let us be confidential. Who knows, we might become friends?"

"I have just one word to say to you," said the dealer. "Either make your purchase, or walk out of my shop."

"True, true," said Markheim. "Enough fooling. To business. Show me something else."

The dealer stooped once more, this time to replace the glass upon the shelf, his thin blond hair falling over his eyes as he did so. Markheim moved a little nearer, with one hand in the pocket of his greatcoat; he drew himself up and filled his lungs; at the same time many different emotions were depicted together on his face— terror, horror, and resolve, fascination and a physical repulsion; and through a haggard lift of his upper lip, his teeth looked out.

"This, perhaps, may suit," observed the dealer; and then, as he began to re-arise, Markheim bounded from behind upon his victim. The long, skewerlike dagger flashed and fell. The dealer struggled like a hen, striking his temple on the shelf, and then tumbled on the floor in a heap.

Time had some score of small voices in that shop, some stately and slow as was becoming to their great age; others garrulous and hurried. All these told out the seconds in an intricate chorus of tickings. Then the passage of a lad's feet, heavily running on the pavement, broke in upon these smaller voices and startled Markheim into the consciousness of his surroundings. He looked about him awfully. The candle stood on the counter, its flame solemnly wagging in a draught; and by that inconsiderable movement, the whole room was filled with noiseless bustle and kept heaving like a sea: the tall shadows nodding, the gross blots of darkness swelling and dwindling as with respiration, the faces of the portraits and the china gods changing and wavering like images in water. The inner door stood ajar, and peered into that leaguer[1] of shadows with a long slit of daylight like a pointing finger.

From these fear-stricken rovings, Markheim's eyes returned to the body of his victim, where it lay both humped and sprawling, incredibly small and strangely meaner than in life. In these poor, miserly clothes, in that ungainly attitude, the dealer lay like so much sawdust. Markheim had feared to see it, and lo! it was nothing. And yet, as he gazed, this bundle of old clothes and pool of blood began to find eloquent voices. There it must lie; there was none to work the cunning hinges or direct the miracle of locomotion—there it must lie till it was found. Found! ay, and then? Then

[1] Besieger's camp.

would this dead flesh lift up a cry that would ring over
England, and fill the world with the echoes of pursuit.
Ay, dead or not, this was still the enemy. "Time was
that when the brains were out," he thought; and the
first word struck into his mind. Time, now that the
deed was accomplished—time, which had closed for the
victim, had become instant and momentous for the
slayer.

The thought was yet in his mind, when, first one and
then another, with every variety of pace and voice—one
deep as the bell from a cathedral turret, another ringing
on its treble notes the prelude of a waltz—the clocks
began to strike the hour of three in the afternoon.

The sudden outbreak of so many tongues in that
dumb chamber staggered him. He began to bestir himself, going to and fro with the candle, beleaguered by
moving shadows, and startled to the soul by chance reflections. In many rich mirrors, some of home designs,
some from Venice or Amsterdam, he saw his face repeated and repeated, as it were an army of spies; his
own eyes met and detected him; and the sound of his
own steps, lightly as they fell, vexed the surrounding
quiet. And still as he continued to fill his pockets, his
mind accused him, with a sickening iteration, of the
thousand faults of his design. He should have chosen
a more quiet hour; he should have prepared an alibi;
he should not have used a knife; he should have been
more cautious, and only bound and gagged the dealer,
and not killed him; he should have been more bold,
and killed the servant also; he should have done all
things otherwise; poignant regrets, weary, incessant
toiling of the mind to change what was unchangeable,
to plan what was now useless, to be the architect of the
irrevocable past. Meanwhile, and behind all this activity, brute terrors, like the scurrying of rats in a deserted

attic, filled the more remote chambers of his brain with riot; the hand of the constable would fall heavy on his shoulder, and his nerves would jerk like a hooked fish; or he beheld, in galloping defile, the dock, the prison, the gallows, and the black coffin.

Terror of the people in the street sat down before his mind like a besieging army. It was impossible, he thought, but that some rumour of the struggle must have reached their ears and set on edge their curiosity; and now, in all the neighbouring houses, he divined them sitting motionless and with uplifted ear—solitary people, condemned to spend Christmas dwelling alone on memories of the past, and now startingly recalled from that tender exercise; happy family parties, struck into silence round the table, the mother still with raised finger: every degree and age and humour, but all, by their own hearts, prying and hearkening and weaving the rope that was to hang him. Sometimes it seemed to him he could not move too softly; the clink of the tall Bohemian goblets rang out loudly like a bell; and alarmed by the bigness of the ticking, he was tempted to stop the clocks. And then, again, with a swift transition of his terrors, the very silence of the place appeared a source of peril, and a thing to strike and freeze the passer-by; and he would step more boldly, and bustle aloud among the contents of the shop, and imitate, with elaborate bravado, the movements of a busy man at ease in his own house.

But he was now so pulled about by different alarms that, while one portion of his mind was still alert and cunning, another trembled on the brink of lunacy. One hallucination in particular took a strong hold on his credulity. The neighbour hearkening with white face beside his window, the passer-by arrested by a horrible surmise on the pavement—these could at worst suspect, they could not know; through the brick walls and shuttered windows only sounds could penetrate. But here, within the house, was he alone? He knew he was; he had watched the servant set forth sweethearting, in her poor best, "out for the day" written in every ribbon and smile. Yes, he was alone, of course; and yet, in the bulk of empty house above him, he could surely hear a stir of delicate footing—he was surely conscious, inexplicably conscious of some presence. Ay, surely; to every room and corner of the house his imagination followed it; and now it was a faceless thing, and yet had eyes to see with; and again it was a shadow of himself; and yet again behold the image of the dead dealer, reinspired with cunning and hatred.

At times, with a strong effort, he would glance at the open door which still seemed to repel his eyes. The house was tall, the skylight small and dirty, the day blind with fog; and the light that filtered down to the ground story was exceedingly faint, and showed dimly on the threshold of the shop. And yet, in that strip of doubtful brightness, did there not hang wavering a shadow?

Suddenly, from the street outside, a very jovial gentleman began to beat with a staff on the shop-door, accompanying his blows with shouts and railleries in which the dealer was continually called upon by name. Markheim, smitten into ice glanced at the dead man. But no! he lay quite still; he was fled away far beyond earshot of these blows and shoutings; he was sunk beneath seas of silence; and his name, which would once have caught his notice above the howling of a storm, had become an empty sound. And presently the jovial gentleman desisted from his knocking and departed.

Here was a broad hint to hurry what remained to be done, to get forth from this accusing neighbourhood, to plunge into a bath of London multitudes, and to reach, on the other side of day, that haven of safety and apparent innocence—his bed. One visitor had come: at any moment another might follow and be more obstinate. To have done the deed, and yet not to reap the profit, would be too abhorrent a failure. The money, that was now Markheim's concern; and as a means to that, the keys.

He glanced over his shoulder at the open door, where the shadow was still lingering and shivering; and with no conscious repugnance of the mind, yet with a tremour of the belly, he drew near the body of his victim. The human character had quite departed. Like a suit half-stuffed with bran, the limbs lay scattered, the trunk doubled, on the floor; and yet the thing repelled him. Although so dingy and inconsiderable to the eye, he feared it might have more significance to the touch. He took the body by the shoulders, and turned it on its back. It was strangely light and supple, and the limbs, as if they had been broken, fell into the oddest postures. The face was robbed of all expression; but it was as pale as wax, and shockingly smeared with blood about one temple. That was, for Markheim, the one displeasing circumstance. It carried him back, upon the instant, to a certain fair day in a fisher's village: a grey day, a piping wind, a crowd upon the street, the blare of brasses, the booming of drums, the nasal voice of a ballad singer; and a boy going to and fro, buried over head in the crowd and divided between interest and fear, until, coming out upon the chief place of concourse, he beheld a booth and a great screen with pictures, dismally designed, gar-ishly coloured: Brownrigg with her apprentice; the Mannings with their murdered guest; Weare in the death-grip of Thurtell; and a score besides of famous crimes. The thing was as clear as an illusion; he was once again that little boy; he was looking once again, and with the same sense of physical revolt, at these vile pictures; he was still stunned by the thumping of the drums. A bar of that day's music returned upon his memory; and at that, for the first time, a qualm came over him, a breath of nausea, a sudden weakness of the joints, which he must instantly resist and conquer.

He judged it more prudent to confront than to flee from these considerations; looking the more hardily in the dead face, bending his mind to realise the nature and greatness of his crime. So little a while ago that face had moved with every change of sentiment, that pale mouth had spoken, that body had been all on fire with governable energies; and now, and by his act, that piece of life had been arrested, as the horologist, with interjected finger, arrests the beating of the clock. So he reasoned in vain; he could rise to no more remorseful consciousness; the same heart which had shuddered before the painted effigies of crime, looked on its reality unmoved. At best, he felt a gleam of pity for one who had been endowed in vain with all those faculties that can make the world a garden of enchantment, one who had never lived and who was now dead. But of penitence, no, not a tremour.

With that, shaking himself clear of these considerations, he found the keys and advanced towards the open door of the shop. Outside, it had begun to rain smartly; and the sound of the shower upon the roof had banished silence. Like some dripping cavern, the chambers of the house were haunted by an incessant echoing, which filled the ear and mingled with the ticking of the clocks. And, as Markheim approached the door, he seemed to hear, in answer to his own cautious tread, the steps of another foot withdrawing up the stair. The shadow still palpitated loosely on the threshold. He threw a ton's weight of resolve upon his muscles, and drew back the door.

The faint, foggy daylight glimmered dimly on the
bare floor and stairs; on the bright suit of armour
posted, halbert in hand, upon the landing; and on the
dark wood-carvings, and framed pictures that hung
against the yellow panels of the wainscot. So loud was
the beating of the rain through all the house that, in
Markheim's ears, it began to be distinguished into many
different sounds. Footsteps and sighs, the tread of
regiments marching in the distance, the chink of money
in the counting, and the creaking of doors held stealthily
ajar, appeared to mingle with the patter of the drops
upon the cupola and the gushing of the water in the
pipes. The sense that he was not alone grew upon him
to the verge of madness. On every side he was haunted
and begirt by presences. He heard them moving in the
upper chambers; from the shop, he heard the dead man
getting to his legs; and as he began with a great effort
to mount the stairs, feet fled quietly before him and followed stealthily behind. If he were but deaf, he thought,
how tranquilly he would possess his soul! And then
again, and hearkening with ever fresh attention, he
blessed himself for that unresting sense which held the
outposts and stood a trusty sentinel upon his life. His
head turned continually on his neck; his eyes, which
seemed starting from their orbits, scouted on every side,
and on every side were half-rewarded as with the tail of
something nameless vanishing. The four-and-twenty
steps to the first floor were four-and-twenty agonies.

On that first storey, the doors stood ajar, three of
them like three ambushes, shaking his nerves like the
throats of cannon. He could never again, he felt, be
sufficiently immured and fortified from men's observing
eyes; he longed to be home, girt in by walls, buried
among bedclothes, and invisible to all but God. And at
that thought he wondered a little, recollecting tales of

other murderers and the fear they were said to entertain of heavenly avengers. It was not so, at least, with
him. He feared the laws of nature, lest, in their callous
and immutable procedure, they should preserve some
damning evidence of his crime. He feared tenfold
more, with a slavish, superstitious terror, some scission[1]
in the continuity of man's experience, some wilful ille-
gality of nature. He played a game of skill, depending
on the rules, calculating consequence from cause; and
what if nature, as the defeated tyrant overthrew the
chess-board, should break the mould of their succession?
The like had befallen Napoleon (so writers said) when
the winter changed the time of its appearance. The like
might befall Markheim: the solid walls might become
transparent and reveal his doings like those of bees in a
glass hive; the stout planks might yield under his foot
like quicksands and detain him in their clutch; ay, and
there were soberer accidents that might destroy him: if,
for instance, the house should fall and imprison him
beside the body of his victim; or the house next door
should fly on fire, and the firemen invade him from all
sides. These things he feared; and, in a sense, these
things might be called the hands of God reached forth
against sin. But about God himself he was at ease; his
act was doubtless exceptional, but so were his excuses,
which God knew; it was there, and not among men,
that he felt sure of justice.

When he had got safe into the drawing-room, and
shut the door behind him, he was aware of a respite
from alarms. The room was quite dismantled, uncar-
peted besides, and strewn with packing-cases and incongruous furniture; several great pier-glasses, in which he
beheld himself at various angles, like an actor on a stage;
many pictures, framed and unframed, standing with

---

[1] Literally cutting apart; here in the sense of gap.

their faces to the wall; a fine Sheraton sideboard, a cabinet of marquetry, and a great old bed, with tapestry hangings. The windows opened to the floor; but by great good fortune the lower part of the shutters had been closed, and this concealed him from the neighbours. Here, then, Markheim drew in a packing-case before the cabinet, and began to search among the keys. It was a long business, for there were many; and it was irksome, besides; for, after all, there might be nothing in the cabinet, and time was on the wing. But the closeness of the occupation sobered him. With the tail of his eye he saw the door—even glanced at it from time to time directly, like a besieged commander pleased to verify the good estate of his defences. But in truth he was at peace. The rain falling in the street sounded natural and pleasant. Presently, on the other side, the notes of a piano were wakened to the music of a hymn, and the voices of many children took up the air and words. How stately, how comfortable was the melody! How fresh the youthful voices! Markheim gave ear to it smilingly, as he sorted out the keys; and his mind was thronged with answerable ideas and images: churchgoing children and the pealing of the high organ; children afield, bathers by the brookside, ramblers on the brambly common, kite-fliers in the windy and cloud-navigated sky; and then, at another cadence of the hymn, back again to church, and the somnolence of summer Sundays, and the high genteel voice of the parson (which he smiled a little to recall) and the painted Jacobean tombs, and the dim lettering of the Ten Commandments in the chancel.

And as he sat thus, at once busy and absent, he was startled to his feet. A flash of ice, a flash of fire, a bursting gush of blood, went over him, and then he stood transfixed and thrilling. A step mounted the

stair slowly and steadily, and presently a hand was laid
upon the knob, and the lock clicked, and the door
opened.

Fear held Markheim in a vice. What to expect he
knew not, whether the dead man walking, or the official
ministers of human justice, or some chance witness
blindly stumbling in to consign him to the gallows. But
when a face was thrust into the aperture, glanced round
the room, looked at him, nodded and smiled as if in
friendly recognition, and then withdrew again, and the
door closed behind it, his fear broke loose from his control in a hoarse cry. At the sound of this the visitant
returned.

"Did you call me?" he asked, pleasantly, and with
that he entered the room and closed the door behind him.

Markheim stood and gazed at him with all his eyes.
Perhaps there was a film upon his sight, but the outlines
of the new comer seemed to change and waver like those
of the idols in the wavering candle-light of the shop;
and at times he thought he knew him; and at times he
thought he bore a likeness to himself; and always, like
a lump of living terror, there lay in his bosom the conviction that this thing was not of the earth and not of
God.

And yet the creature had a strange air of the commonplace, as he stood looking on Markheim with a
smile; and when he added: "You are looking for the
money, I believe?" it was in the tones of everyday
politeness.

Markheim made no answer.

"I should warn you," resumed the other, "that the
maid has left her sweetheart earlier than usual and will
soon be here. If Mr. Markheim be found in this house,
I need not describe to him the consequences."

"You know me?" cried the murderer.

The visitor smiled. "You have long been a favourite of mine," he said; "and I have long observed and often sought to help you."

"What are you?" cried Markheim: "the devil?"

"What I may be," returned the other, "cannot affect the service I propose to render you."

"It can," cried Markheim; "it does! Be helped by you? No, never; not by you! You do not know me yet; thank God, you do not know me!"

"I know you," replied the visitant, with a sort of kind severity or rather firmness. "I know you to the soul."

"Know me!" cried Markheim. "Who can do so? My life is but a travesty and slander on myself. I have lived to belie my nature. All men do; all men are better than this disguise that grows about and stifles them. You see each dragged away by life, like one whom bravos have seized and muffled in a cloak. If they had their own control—if you could see their faces, they would be altogether different, they would shine out for heroes and saints! I am worse than most; my self is more overlaid; my excuse is known to me and God. But, had I the time, I could disclose myself."

"To me?" inquired the visitant.

"To you before all," returned the murderer. "I supposed you were intelligent. I thought—since you exist —you would prove a reader of the heart. And yet you would propose to judge me by my acts! Think of it; my acts! I was born and I have lived in a land of giants; giants have dragged me by the wrists since I was born out of my mother—the giants of circumstance. And you would judge me by my acts! But can you not look within? Can you not understand that evil is hateful to me? Can you not see within me the clear writing of conscience, never blurred by any wilful sophistry, although too often disregarded? Can you not read me for a thing that surely must be common as humanity—the unwilling sinner?"

"All this is very feelingly expressed," was the reply, "but it regards me not. These points of consistency are beyond my province, and I care not in the least by what compulsion you may have been dragged away, so as you are but carried in the right direction. But time flies; the servant delays, looking in the faces of the crowd and at the pictures on the hoardings, but still she keeps moving nearer; and remember, it is as if the gallows itself was striding towards you through the Christmas streets! Shall I help you; I, who know all? Shall I tell you where to find the money?"

"For what price?" asked Markheim.

"I offer you the service for a Christmas gift," returned the other.

Markheim could not refrain from smiling with a kind of bitter triumph. "No," said he, "I will take nothing at your hands; if I were dying of thirst, and it was your hand that put the pitcher to my lips, I should find the courage to refuse. It may be credulous, but I will do nothing to commit myself to evil."

"I have no objection to a death-bed repentance," observed the visitant.

"Because you disbelieve their efficacy!" Markheim cried.

"I do not say so," returned the other; "but I look on these things from a different side, and when the life is done my interest falls. The man has lived to serve me, to spread black looks under colour of religion, or to sow tares in the wheat-field, as you do, in a course of weak compliance with desire. Now that he draws so near to his deliverance, he can add but one act of service—to repent, to die smiling, and thus to build up in confidence and hope the more timorous of my surviving followers.

I am not so hard a master. Try me. Accept my help. Please yourself in life as you have done hitherto; please yourself more amply, spread your elbows at the board; and when the night begins to fall and the curtains to be drawn, I tell you, for your greater comfort, that you will find it even easy to compound your quarrel with your conscience, and to make a truckling peace with God. I came but now from such a death-bed, and the room was full of sincere mourners, listening to the man's last words: and when I looked into that face, which had been set as a flint against mercy, I found it smiling with hope."

"And do you, then, suppose me such a creature?" asked Markheim. "Do you think I have no more generous aspirations than to sin, and sin, and sin, and, at last, sneak into heaven? My heart rises at the thought. Is this, then, your experience of mankind? or is it because you find me with red hands that you presume such baseness? and is this crime of murder indeed so impious as to dry up the very springs of good?"

"Murder is to me no special category," replied the other. "All sins are murder, even as all life is war. I behold your race, like starving mariners on a raft, plucking crusts out of the hands of famine and feeding on each other's lives. I follow sins beyond the moment of their acting; I find in all that the last consequence is death; and to my eyes, the pretty maid who thwarts her mother with such taking graces on a question of a ball, drips no less visibly with human gore than such a murderer as yourself. Do I say that I follow sins? I follow virtues also; they differ not by the thickness of a nail, they are both scythes for the reaping angel of Death. Evil, for which I live, consists not in action but in character. The bad man is dear to me; not the bad act, whose fruits, if we could follow them far enough down the hurtling cataract of the ages, might yet be found more blessed than those of the rarest virtues. And it is not because you have killed a dealer, but because you are Markheim, that I offered to forward your escape."

"I will lay my heart open to you," answered Markheim. "This crime on which you find me is my last. On my way to it I have learned many lessons; itself is a lesson, a momentous lesson. Hitherto I have been driven with revolt to what I would not; I was a bond-slave to poverty, driven and scourged. There are robust virtues that can stand in these temptations; mine was not so: I had a thirst of pleasure. But to-day, and out of this deed, I pluck both warning and riches—both the power and a fresh resolve to be myself. I become in all things a free actor in the world; I begin to see myself all changed, these hands the agents of good, this heart at peace. Something comes over me out of the past; something of what I have dreamed on Sabbath evenings to the sound of the church organ, of what I forecast when I shed tears over noble books, or talked, an innocent child, with my mother. There lies my life; I have wandered a few years, but now I see once more my city of destination."

"You are to use this money on the Stock Exchange, I think?" remarked the visitor; "and there, if I mistake not, you have already lost some thousands?"

"Ah," said Markheim, "but this time I have a sure thing."

"This time, again, you will lose," replied the visitor quietly.

"Ah, but I keep back the half!" cried Markheim.

"That also you will lose," said the other.

The sweat started upon Markheim's brow. "Well, then, what matter?" he exclaimed. "Say it be lost, say I am plunged again in poverty, shall one part of me, and that the worst, continue until the end to override the better? Evil and good run strong in me, haling me both ways. I do not love the one thing, I love all. I can conceive great deeds, renunciations, martyrdoms; and though I be fallen to such a crime as murder, pity is no stranger to my thoughts. I pity the poor; who knows their trials better than myself? I pity and help them; I prize love, I love honest laughter; there is no good thing nor true thing on earth but I love it from my heart. And are my vices only to direct my life, and my virtues to lie without effect, like some passive lumber of the mind? Not so; good, also, is a spring of acts."

But the visitant raised his finger. "For six-and-thirty years that you have been in this world," said he, "through many changes of fortune and varieties of humour, I have watched you steadily fall. Fifteen years ago you would have started at a theft. Three years back you would have blenched at the name of murder. Is there any crime, is there any cruelty or meanness, from which you still recoil?—five years from now I shall detect you in the fact! Downward, downward, lies your way; nor can anything but death avail to stop you."

"It is true," Markheim said huskily, "I have in some degree complied with evil. But it is so with all; the very saints, in the mere exercise of living, grow less dainty, and take on the tone of their surroundings."

"I will propound to you one simple question," said the other; "and as you answer, I shall read to you your moral horoscope. You have grown in many things more lax; possibly you do right to be so; and at any account, it is the same with all men. But granting that, are you in any one particular, however trifling, more difficult to please with your own conduct, or do you go in all things with a looser rein?"

"In any one?" repeated Markheim, with an anguish of consideration. "No," he added, with despair, "in none! I have gone down in all."

"Then," said the visitor, "content yourself with what you are, for you will never change; and the words of your part on this stage are irrevocably written down."

Markheim stood for a long while silent, and indeed it was the visitor who first broke the silence. "That being so," he said, "shall I show you the money?"

"And grace?" cried Markheim.

"Have you not tried it?" returned the other. "Two or three years ago, did I not see you on the platform of revival meetings, and was not your voice the loudest in the hymn?"

"It is true," said Markheim; "and I see clearly what remains for me by way of duty. I thank you for these lessons from my soul; my eyes are opened, and I behold myself at last for what I am."

At this moment, the sharp note of the door-bell rang through the house; and the visitant, as though this were some concerted signal for which he had been waiting, changed at once in his demeanour.

"The maid!" he cried. "She has returned, as I forewarned you, and there is now before you one more difficult passage. Her master, you must say, is ill; you must let her in, with an assured but rather serious countenance —no smiles, no overacting, and I promise you success! Once the girl within, and the door closed, the same dexterity that has already rid you of the dealer will relieve you of this last danger in your path. Thenceforward you have the whole evening—the whole night, if needful—to ransack the treasures of the house and to make good your safety. This is help that comes to you with the mask of danger. Up!" he cried: "up, friend; your life hangs trembling in the scales: up, and act!"

Markheim steadily regarded his counsellor. "If I be condemned to evil acts," he said, "there is still one door of freedom open—I can cease from action. If my life be an ill thing, I can lay it down. Though I be, as you say truly, at the beck of every small temptation, I can yet, by one decisive gesture, place myself beyond the reach of all. My love of good is damned to barrenness; it may, and let it be! But I have still my hatred of evil; and from that, to your galling disappointment, you shall see that I can draw both energy and courage."

The features of the visitor began to undergo a wonderful and lovely change: they brightened and softened with a tender triumph; and, even as they brightened, faded and dislimned. But Markheim did not pause to watch or understand the transformation. He opened the door and went downstairs very slowly, thinking to himself. His past went soberly before him; he beheld it as it was, ugly and strenuous like a dream, random as chance-medley—a scene of defeat. Life, as he thus reviewed it, tempted him no longer; but on the further side he perceived a quiet haven for his bark. He paused in the passage, and looked into the shop, where the candle still burned by the dead body. It was strangely silent. Thoughts of the dealer swarmed into his mind, as he stood gazing. And then the bell once more broke out into impatient clamour.

He confronted the maid upon the threshold with something like a smile.

"You had better go for the police," said he: "I have killed your master."

# STRANGE CASE OF DR. JEKYLL AND MR. HYDE [1]

TO

## KATHARINE DE MATTOS [2]

It's ill to loose the bands that God decreed to bind;
Still will we be the children of the heather and the wind.
Far away from home, O it's still for you and me
That the broom is blowing bonnie in the north countrie.

### STORY OF THE DOOR

MR. UTTERSON the lawyer was a man of a rugged
countenance, that was never lighted by a smile; cold,
scanty and embarrassed in discourse; backward in sentiment; lean, long, dusty, dreary and yet somehow lovable.
At friendly meetings, and when the wine was to his
taste, something eminently human beaconed from his
eye; something indeed which never found its way into
his talk; but which spoke not only in these silent symbols of the after-dinner face, but more often and loudly
in the acts of his life. He was austere with himself;
drank gin when he was alone, to mortify a taste for
vintages; and though he enjoyed the theatre, had not

[1] Written at Bournemouth at the close of 1885, while Stevenson
was struggling with ill-health, and published in January, 1886, in
book form. The problem of the duality of the moral nature,
which had already worked itself into story form in his *Markheim*,
here is given more complete expression. A dream gave him the
plot. Mrs. Stevenson was awakened one night by cries of horror
from Stevenson. He said angrily, "Why did you wake me? I
was dreaming a fine bogey tale." She had aroused him at the first
transformation scene of what afterward became *Dr. Jekyll and Mr.
Hyde.* It was this story which first gave him reputation in America.
[2] A favourite cousin.

crossed the doors of one for twenty years. But he had
an approved tolerance for others; sometimes wondering, almost with envy, at the high pressure of spirits involved in their misdeeds; and in any extremity inclined
to help rather than to reprove. "I incline to Cain's
heresy," he used to say quaintly: "I let my brother go
to the devil in his own way." In this character, it was
frequently his fortune to be the last reputable acquaintance and the last good influence in the lives of down-
going men. And to such as these, so long as they came
about his chambers, he never marked a shade of change
in his demeanour.

No doubt the feat was easy to Mr. Utterson; for he
was undemonstrative at the best, and even his friendship
seemed to be founded in a similar catholicity of good-
nature. It is the mark of a modest man to accept his
friendly circle ready-made from the hands of opportunity;
and that was the lawyer's way. His friends were those
of his own blood or those whom he had known the
longest; his affections, like ivy, were the growth of time,
they implied no aptness in the object. Hence, no doubt,
the bond that united him to Mr. Richard Enfield, his
distant kinsman, the well-known man about town. It
was a nut to crack for many, what these two could
see in each other, or what subject they could find in
common. It was reported by those who encountered
them in their Sunday walks, that they said nothing,
looked singularly dull, and would hail with obvious relief the appearance of a friend. For all that, the two
men put the greatest store by these excursions, counted
them the chief jewel of each week, and not only set aside
occasions of pleasure, but even resisted the calls of
business, that they might enjoy them uninterrupted.

It chanced on one of these rambles that their way led
them down a by-street in a busy quarter of London.

The street was small and what is called quiet, but it drove a thriving trade on the week-days. The inhabitants were all doing well, it seemed, and all emulously hoping to do better still, and laying out the surplus of their gains in coquetry; so that the shop fronts stood along that thoroughfare with an air of invitation, like rows of smiling saleswomen. Even on Sunday, when it veiled its more florid charms and lay comparatively empty of passage, the street shone out in contrast to its dingy neighbourhood, like a fire in a forest; and with its freshly painted shutters, well-polished brasses and general cleanliness and gaiety of note, instantly caught and pleased the eye of the passenger.

Two doors from one corner, on the left hand going east, the line was broken by the entry of a court; and just at that point, a certain sinister block of building thrust forward its gable on the street. It was two storeys high; showed no window, nothing but a door on the lower storey and a blind forehead of discoloured wall on the upper; and bore in every feature, the marks of prolonged and sordid negligence. The door, which was equipped with neither bell nor knocker, was blistered and distained. Tramps slouched into the recess and struck matches on the panels; children kept shop upon the steps; the schoolboy had tried his knife on the mouldings; and for close on a generation, no one had appeared to drive away these random visitors or to repair their ravages.

Mr. Enfield and the lawyer were on the other side of the by-street; but when they came abreast of the entry, the former lifted up his cane and pointed.

"Did you ever remark that door?" he asked; and when his companion had replied in the affirmative, "It is connected in my mind," added he, "with a very odd story."

"Indeed?" said Mr. Utterson, with a slight change of voice, "and what was that?"

"Well, it was this way," returned Mr. Enfield: "I was coming home from some place at the end of the world, about three o'clock of a black winter morning, and my way lay through a part of town where there was literally nothing to be seen but lamps. Street after street, and all the folks asleep—street after street, all lighted up as if for a procession and all as empty as a church—till at last I got into that state of mind when a man listens and listens and begins to long for the sight of a policeman. All at once, I saw two figures: one a little man who was stumping along eastward at a good walk, and the other a girl of maybe eight or ten who was running as hard as she was able down a cross street. Well, sir, the two ran into one another naturally enough at the corner; and then came the horrible part of the thing; for the man trampled calmly over the child's body and left her screaming on the ground. It sounds nothing to hear, but it was hellish to see. It wasn't like a man; it was like some damned Juggernaut.[1] I gave a view halloa, took to my heels, collared my gentleman, and brought him back to where there was already quite a group about the screaming child. He was perfectly cool and made no resistance, but gave me one look, so ugly that it brought out the sweat on me like running. The people who had turned out were the girl's own family; and pretty soon, the doctor, for whom she had been sent, put in his appearance. Well, the child was not much the worse, more frightened, according to the Sawbones; and there you might have supposed would be an end to it. But there was one curious circumstance. I had taken a

---

[1] When the car containing the idol of Juggernaut, a Hindu god, was drawn in procession, fanatic worshippers threw themselves before it to be crushed.

loathing to my gentleman at first sight. So had the child's family, which was only natural. But the doctor's case was what struck me. He was the usual cut and dry apothecary, of no particular age and colour, with a strong Edinburgh accent, and about as emotional as a bagpipe. Well, sir, he was like the rest of us; every time he looked at my prisoner, I saw that Sawbones turn sick and white with the desire to kill him. I knew what was in his mind, just as he knew what was in mine; and killing being out of the question, we did the next best. We told the man we could and would make such a scandal out of this, as should make his name stink from one end of London to the other. If he had any friends or any credit, we undertook that he should lose them. And all the time, as we were pitching it in red hot, we were keeping the women off him as best we could for they were as wild as harpies. I never saw a circle of such hateful faces; and there was the man in the middle, with a kind of black, sneering coolness—frightened too, I could see that—but carrying it off, sir, really like Satan. 'If you choose to make capital out of this accident,' said he, 'I am naturally helpless. No gentleman but wishes to avoid a scene,' says he. 'Name your figure.' Well, we screwed him up to a hundred pounds for the child's family; he would have clearly liked to stick out; but there was something about the lot of us that meant mischief, and at last he struck. The next thing was to get the money; and where do you think he carried us but to that place with the door?—whipped out a key, went in, and presently came back with the matter of ten pounds in gold and a cheque for the balance on Coutts's, drawn payable to bearer and signed with a name that I can't mention, though it's one of the points of my story, but it was a name at least very well known and often printed. The figure was stiff; but the signature was good for more than that, if it was only genuine. I took the liberty of pointing out to my gentleman that the whole business looked apocryphal, and that a man does not, in real life, walk into a cellar door at four in the morning and come out of it with another man's cheque for close upon a hundred pounds. But he was quite easy and sneering. 'Set your mind at rest,' says he, 'I will stay with you till the banks open and cash the cheque myself.' So we all set off, the doctor, and the child's father, and our friend and myself, and passed the rest of the night in my chambers; and next day, when we had breakfasted, went in a body to the bank. I gave in the check myself, and said I had every reason to believe it was a forgery. Not a bit of it. The cheque was genuine."

"Tut-tut," said Mr. Utterson.

"I see you feel as I do," said Mr. Enfield. "Yes, it's a bad story. For my man was a fellow that nobody could have to do with, a really damnable man; and the person that drew the cheque is the very pink of the proprieties, celebrated too, and (what makes it worse) one of your fellows who do what they call good. Black mail, I suppose; an honest man paying through the nose for some of the capers of his youth. Black Mail House is what I call that place with the door, in consequence. Though even that, you know, is far from explaining all," he added, and with the words fell into a vein of musing.

From this he was recalled by Mr. Utterson asking rather suddenly: "And you don't know if the drawer of the cheque lives there?"

"A likely place, isn't it?" returned Mr. Enfield. "But I happen to have noticed his address; he lives in some square or other."

"And you never asked about the—place with the door?" said Mr. Utterson.

"No, sir: I had a delicacy," was the reply. "I feel very strongly about putting questions; it partakes too much of the style of the day of judgment. You start a question, and it's like starting a stone. You sit quietly on the top of a hill; and away the stone goes, starting others; and presently some bland old bird (the last you would have thought of) is knocked on the head in his own back garden and the family have to change their name. No, sir, I make it a rule of mine: the more it looks like Queer Street, the less I ask."

"A very good rule, too," said the lawyer.

"But I have studied the place for myself," continued Mr. Enfield. "It seems scarcely a house. There is no other door, and nobody goes in or out of that one but, once in a great while, the gentleman of my adventure. There are three windows looking on the court on the first floor; none below; the windows are always shut but they're clean. And then there is a chimney which is generally smoking; so somebody must live there. And yet it's not so sure; for the buildings are so packed together about that court, that it's hard to say where one ends and another begins."

The pair walked on again for a while in silence; and then "Enfield," said Mr. Utterson, "that's a good rule of yours."

"Yes, I think it is," returned Enfield.

"But for all that," continued the lawyer, "there's one point I want to ask: I want to ask the name of that man who walked over the child."

"Well," said Mr. Enfield, "I can't see what harm it would do. It was a man of the name of Hyde."

"H'm," said Mr. Utterson. "What sort of a man is he to see?"

"He is not easy to describe. There is something wrong with his appearance; something displeasing, something downright detestable. I never saw a man I so disliked, and yet I scarce know why. He must be deformed somewhere; he gives a strong feeling of deformity, although I couldn't specify the point. He's an extraordinary looking man, and yet I really can name nothing out of the way. No, sir; I can make no hand of it; I can't describe him. And it's not want of memory; for I declare I can see him this moment."

Mr. Utterson again walked some way in silence and obviously under a weight of consideration. "You are sure he used a key?" he inquired at last.

"My dear sir . . ." began Enfield, surprised out of himself.

"Yes, I know," said Utterson; "I know it must seem strange. The fact is, if I do not ask you the name of the other party, it is because I know it already. You see, Richard, your tale has gone home. If you have been inexact in any point, you had better correct it."

"I think you might have warned me," returned the other with a touch of sullenness. "But I have been pedantically exact, as you call it. The fellow had a key; and what's more, he has it still. I saw him use it, not a week ago."

Mr. Utterson sighed deeply but said never a word; and the young man presently resumed. "Here is another lesson to say nothing," said he. "I am ashamed of my long tongue. Let us make a bargain never to refer to this again."

"With all my heart," said the lawyer. "I shake hands on that, Richard."

### SEARCH FOR MR. HYDE

That evening Mr. Utterson came home to his bachelor house in sombre spirits and sat down to dinner without relish. It was his custom of a Sunday, when this meal was over, to sit close by the fire, a volume of some dry divinity on his reading desk, until the clock of the neighbouring church rang out the hour of twelve, when he would go soberly and gratefully to bed. On this night, however, as soon as the cloth was taken away, he took up a candle and went into his business room. There he opened his safe, took from the most private part of it a document endorsed on the envelope as Dr. Jekyll's Will, and sat down with a clouded brow to study its contents. The will was holograph, for Mr. Utterson, though he took charge of it now that it was made, had refused to lend the least assistance in the making of it; it provided not only that, in case of the decease of Henry Jekyll, M.D., D.C.L., LL.D., F.R.S., etc., all his possessions were to pass into the hands of his "friend and benefactor Edward Hyde," but that in case of Dr. Jekyll's "disappearance or unexplained absence for any period exceeding three calendar months," the said Edward Hyde should step into the said Henry Jekyll's shoes without further delay and free from any burthen or obligation, beyond the payment of a few small sums to the members of the doctor's household. This document had long been the lawyer's eyesore. It offended him both as a lawyer and as a lover of the sane and customary sides of life, to whom the fanciful was the immodest. And hitherto it was his ignorance of Mr. Hyde that had swelled his indignation; now, by a sudden turn, it was his knowledge. It was already bad enough when the name was but a name of which he could learn no more. It was worse when it began to be clothed upon with detestable attributes; and out of the shifting, insubstantial mists that had so long baffled his eye, there leaped up the sudden, definite presentment of a fiend.

"I thought it was madness," he said, as he replaced

the obnoxious paper in the safe, "and now I begin to fear it is disgrace."

With that he blew out his candle, put on a greatcoat, and set forth in the direction of Cavendish Square, that citadel of medicine, where his friend, the great Dr. Lanyon, had his house and received his crowding patients. "If anyone knows, it will be Lanyon," he had thought.

The solemn butler knew and welcomed him; he was subjected to no stage of delay; but ushered direct from the door to the dining-room where Dr. Lanyon sat alone over his wine. This was a hearty, healthy, dapper, red-faced gentleman, with a shock of hair prematurely white, and a boisterous and decided manner. At sight of Mr. Utterson, he sprang up from his chair and welcomed him with both hands. The geniality, as was the way of the man, was somewhat theatrical to the eye; but it reposed on genuine feeling. For these two were old friends, old mates both at school and college, both thorough respecters of themselves and of each other, and, what does not always follow, men who thoroughly enjoyed each other's company.

After a little rambling talk, the lawyer led up to the subject which so disagreeably preoccupied his mind.

"I suppose, Lanyon," said he, "you and I must be the two oldest friends that Henry Jekyll has?"

"I wish the friends were younger," chuckled Dr. Lanyon. "But I suppose we are. And what of that? I see little of him now."

"Indeed?" said Utterson. "I thought you had a bond of common interest."

"We had," was the reply. "But it is more than ten years since Henry Jekyll became too fanciful for me. He began to go wrong, wrong in mind; and though of course I continue to take an interest in him for old sake's

sake, as they say, I see and I have seen devilish little of
the man. Such unscientific balderdash," added the
doctor, flushing suddenly purple, "would have estranged
Damon and Pythias."

This little spirit of temper was somewhat of a relief to
Mr. Utterson. "They have only differed on some point
of science," he thought; and being a man of no scientific
passions (except in the matter of conveyancing), he even
added: "It is nothing worse than that!" He gave his
friend a few seconds to recover his composure, and then
approached the question he had come to put. "Did
you ever come across a protégé of his—one Hyde?" he
asked.

"Hyde?" repeated Lanyon. "No. Never heard of
him. Since my time."

That was the amount of information that the lawyer
carried back with him to the great, dark bed on which
he tossed to and fro, until the small hours of the morning began to grow large. It was a night of little ease to
his toiling mind, toiling in mere darkness and besieged
by questions.

Six o'clock struck on the bells of the church that was
so conveniently near to Mr. Utterson's dwelling, and
still he was digging at the problem. Hitherto it had
touched him on the intellectual side alone; but now his
imagination also was engaged, or rather enslaved; and
as he lay and tossed in the gross darkness of the night and
the curtained room, Mr. Enfield's tale went by before his
mind in a scroll of lighted pictures. He would be aware
of the great field of lamps of a nocturnal city; then of
the figure of a man walking swiftly; then of a child running from the doctor's; and then these met, and that
human Juggernaut trod the child down and passed on
regardless of her screams. Or else he would see a room
a a rich house, where his friend lay asleep, dreaming

and smiling at his dreams; and then the door of that room would be opened, the curtains of the bed plucked apart, the sleeper recalled, and lo! there would stand by his side a figure to whom power was given, and even at that dead hour, he must rise and do its bidding. The figure in these two phases haunted the lawyer all night; and if at any time he dozed over, it was but to see it glide more stealthily through sleeping houses, or move the more swiftly and still the more swiftly, even to dizziness, through wider labyrinths of lamplighted city, and at every street corner crush a child and leave her screaming. And still the figure had no face by which he might know it; even in his dreams, it had no face, or one that baffled him and melted before his eyes; and thus it was that there sprang up and grew apace in the lawyer's mind a singularly strong, almost an inordinate, curiosity to behold the features of the real Mr. Hyde. If he could but once set eyes on him, he thought the mystery would lighten and perhaps roll altogether away, as was the habit of mysterious things when well examined. He might see a reason for his friend's strange preference or bondage (call it which you please) and even for the startling clause of the will. At least it would be a face worth seeing: the face of a man who was without bowels of mercy: a face which had but to show itself to raise up, in the mind of the unimpressionable Enfield, a spirit of enduring hatred.

From that time forward, Mr. Utterson began to haunt the door in the by-street of shops. In the morning before office hours, at noon when business was plenty, and time scarce, at night under the face of the fogged city moon, by all lights and at all hours of solitude or concourse, the lawyer was to be found on his chosen post.

"If he be Mr. Hyde," he had thought, "I shall be Mr. Seek."

And at last his patience was rewarded. It was a fine dry night; frost in the air; the streets as clean as a ball-room floor; the lamps, unshaken by any wind, drawing a regular pattern of light and shadow. By ten o'clock, when the shops were closed, the by-street was very solitary and, in spite of the low growl of London from all round, very silent. Small sounds carried far; domestic sounds out of the houses were clearly audible on either side of the roadway; and the rumour of the approach of any passenger preceded him by a long time. Mr. Utterson had been some minutes at his post, when he was aware of an odd, light footstep drawing near. In the course of his nightly patrols, he had long grown accustomed to the quaint effect with which the footfalls of a single person, while he is still a great way off, suddenly spring out distinct from the vast hum and clatter of the city. Yet his attention had never before been so sharply and decisively arrested; and it was with a strong, superstitious prevision of success that he withdrew into the entry of the court.

The steps drew swiftly nearer, and swelled out suddenly louder as they turned the end of the street. The lawyer, looking forth from the entry, could soon see what manner of man he had to deal with. He was small and very plainly dressed, and the look of him, even at that distance, went somehow strongly against the watcher's inclination. But he made straight for the door, crossing the roadway to save time; and as he came, he drew a key from his pocket like one approaching home.

Mr. Utterson stepped out and touched him on the shoulder as he passed. "Mr. Hyde, I think?"

Mr. Hyde shrank back with a hissing intake of the breath. But his fear was only momentary; and though he did not look the lawyer in the face, he answered coolly enough: "That is my name. What do you want?"

"I see you are going in," returned the lawyer. "I

am an old friend of Dr. Jekyll's—Mr. Utterson of Gaunt
Street—you must have heard my name; and meeting
you so conveniently, I thought you might admit me."

"You will not find Dr. Jekyll; he is from home," replied Mr. Hyde, blowing in the key. And then suddenly, but still without looking up, "How did you know
me?" he asked.

"On your side," said Mr. Utterson, "will you do me
a favour?"

"With pleasure," replied the other. "What shall it
be?"

"Will you let me see your face?" asked the lawyer.

Mr. Hyde appeared to hesitate, and then, as if upon
some sudden reflection, fronted about with an air of
defiance; and the pair stared at each other pretty fixedly
for a few seconds. "Now, I shall know you again,"
said Mr. Utterson. "It may be useful."

"Yes," returned Mr. Hyde, "it is as well we have
met; and à *propos*, you should have my address." And
he gave a number of a street in Soho.

"Good God!" thought Mr. Utterson, "can he, too,
have been thinking of the will." But he kept his feelings to himself and only grunted in acknowledgment of
the address.

"And now," said the other, "how did you know me?"

"By description," was the reply.

"Whose description?"

"We have common friends," said Mr. Utterson.

"Common friends?" echoed Mr. Hyde, a little
hoarsely. "Who are they?"

"Jekyll, for instance," said the lawyer.

"He never told you," cried Mr. Hyde, with a flush of
anger. "I did not think you would have lied."

"Come," said Mr. Utterson, "that is not fitting
language."

The other snarled aloud into a savage laugh; and the next moment, with extraordinary quickness, he had unlocked the door and disappeared into the house.

The lawyer stood awhile when Mr. Hyde had left him, the picture of disquietude. Then he began slowly to mount the street, pausing every step or two and putting his hand to his brow like a man in mental perplexity. The problem he was thus debating as he walked, was one of a class that is rarely solved. Mr. Hyde was pale and dwarfish, he gave an impression of deformity without any nameable malformation, he had a displeasing smile, he had borne himself to the lawyer with a sort of murderous mixture of timidity and boldness, and he spoke with a husky, whispering and somewhat broken voice; all these were points against him, but not all of these together could explain the hitherto unknown disgust, loathing and fear with which Mr. Utterson regarded him. "There must be something else," said the perplexed gentleman. "There *is* something more, if I could find a name for it. God bless me, the man seems hardly human! Something troglodytic,[1] shall we say? or can it be the old story of Dr. Fell?[2] or is it the mere radiance of a foul soul that thus transpires through, and transfigures, its clay continent? The last, I think; for, O my poor old Harry Jekyll, if I ever read Satan's signature upon a face, it is on that of your new friend."

Round the corner from the by-street, there was a square of ancient, handsome houses, now for the most part decayed from their high estate and let in flats and

---

[1] Characteristic of the cave-dwellers, or other primitive men.

[2] Dr. Fell was a seventeenth century divine whose reputation has been preserved in Tom Brown's lines:

> "I do not love thee, Doctor Fell,
> The reason why I cannot tell;
> But this alone I know full well,
> I do not love thee, Doctor Fell."

chambers to all sorts and conditions of men: map-engravers, architects, shady lawyers and the agents of obscure enterprises. One house, however, second from the corner, was still occupied entire; and at the door of this, which wore a great air of wealth and comfort, though it was now plunged in darkness except for the fanlight, Mr. Utterson stopped and knocked. A well-dressed, elderly servant opened the door.

"Is Dr. Jekyll at home, Poole?" asked the lawyer.

"I will see, Mr. Utterson," said Poole, admitting the visitor, as he spoke, into a large, low-roofed, comfortable hall, paved with flags, warmed (after the fashion of a country house) by a bright, open fire, and furnished with costly cabinets of oak. "Will you wait here by the fire, sir? or shall I give you a light in the dining-room?"

"Here, thank you," said the lawyer, and he drew near and leaned on the tall fender. This hall, in which he was now left alone, was a pet fancy of his friend the doctor's; and Utterson himself was wont to speak of it as the pleasantest room in London. But to-night there was a shudder in his blood; the face of Hyde sat heavy on his memory; he felt (what was rare with him) a nausea and distaste of life; and in the gloom of his spirits, he seemed to read a menace in the flickering of the firelight on the polished cabinets and the uneasy starting of the shadow on the roof. He was ashamed of his relief, when Poole presently returned to announce that Dr. Jekyll was gone out.

"I saw Mr. Hyde go in by the old dissecting-room door, Poole," he said. "Is that right, when Dr. Jekyll is from home?"

"Quite right, Mr. Utterson, sir," replied the servant. "Mr. Hyde has a key."

"Your master seems to repose a great deal of trust in that young man, Poole," resumed the other musingly.

"Yes, sir, he do indeed," said Poole. "We have all orders to obey him."

"I do not think I ever met Mr. Hyde?" asked Utterson.

"O, dear no, sir. He never *dines* here," replied the butler. "Indeed we see very little of him on this side of the house; he mostly comes and goes by the laboratory."

"Well, good-night, Poole."

"Good-night, Mr. Utterson."

And the lawyer set out homeward with a very heavy heart. "Poor Harry Jekyll," he thought, 'my mind misgives me he is in deep waters! He was wild when he was young; a long while ago to be sure; but in the law of God, there is no statute of limitations. Ay, it must be that; the ghost of some old sin, the cancer of some concealed disgrace: punishment coming, *pede claudo*,[1] years after memory has forgotten and self-love condoned the fault." And the lawyer, scared by the thought, brooded awhile on his own past, groping in all the corners of memory, lest by chance some Jack-in-the-Box of an old iniquity should leap to light there. His past was fairly blameless; few men could read the rolls of their life with less apprehension; yet he was humbled to the dust by the many ill things he had done, and raised up again into a sober and fearful gratitude by the many that he had come so near to doing, yet avoided. And then by a return on his former subject, he conceived a spark of hope. "This Master Hyde, if he were studied," thought he, "must have secrets of his own; black secrets, by the look of him; secrets compared to which poor Jekyll's worst would be like sunshine. Things cannot continue as they are. It turns me cold to think of this creature stealing like a thief to Harry's bedside;

[1] With limping foot.

poor Harry, what a wakening! And the danger of it;
for if this Hyde suspects the existence of the will, he
may grow impatient to inherit. Ay, I must put my
shoulder to the wheel—if Jekyll will but let me," he
added, "if Jekyll will only let me." For once more he
saw before his mind's eye, as clear as a transparency,
the strange clauses of the will.

### DR. JEKYLL WAS QUITE AT EASE

A fortnight later, by excellent good fortune, the doctor
gave one of his pleasant dinners to some five or six old
cronies, all intelligent, reputable men and all judges of
good wine; and Mr. Utterson so contrived that he remained behind after the others had departed. This was
no new arrangement, but a thing that had befallen
many scores of times. Where Utterson was liked, he
was liked well. Hosts loved to detain the dry lawyer,
when the light-hearted and the loose-tongued had already their foot on the threshold; they liked to sit awhile
in his unobtrusive company, practising for solitude,
sobering their minds in the man's rich silence after
the expense and strain of gaiety. To this rule, Dr.
Jekyll was no exception; and as he now sat on the opposite side of the fire—a large, well-made, smooth-faced
man of fifty, with something of a slyish cast perhaps, but
every mark of capacity and kindness—you could see by
his looks that he cherished for Mr. Utterson a sincere
and warm affection.

"I have been wanting to speak to you, Jekyll," began
the latter. "You know that will of yours?"

A close observer might have gathered that the topic
was distasteful; but the doctor carried it off gaily. "My
poor Utterson," said he, "you are unfortunate in such
a client. I never saw a man so distressed as you were

by my will; unless it were that hide-bound pedant, Lanyon, at what he called my scientific heresies. O, I know he's a good fellow—you needn't frown—an excellent fellow, and I always mean to see more of him; but a hide-bound pedant for all that; an ignorant, blatant pedant. I was never more disappointed in any man than Lanyon."

"You know I never approved of it," pursued Utterson, ruthlessly disregarding the fresh topic.

"My will? Yes, certainly, I know that," said the doctor, a trifle sharply. "You have told me so."

"Well, I tell you so again," continued the lawyer. "I have been learning something of young Hyde."

The large handsome face of Dr. Jekyll grew pale to the very lips, and there came a blackness about his eyes. "I do not care to hear more," said he. "This is a matter I thought we had agreed to drop."

"What I heard was abominable," said Utterson.

"It can make no change. You do not understand my position," returned the doctor, with a certain incoherency of manner. "I am painfully situated, Utterson; my position is a very strange—a very strange one. It is one of those affairs that cannot be mended by talking."

"Jekyll," said Utterson, "you know me: I am a man to be trusted. Make a clean breast of this in confidence; and I make no doubt I can get you out of it."

"My good Utterson," said the doctor, "this is very good of you, this is downright good of you, and I cannot find words to thank you in. I believe you fully; I would trust you before any man alive, ay, before myself, if I could make the choice; but indeed it isn't what you fancy; it is not so bad as that; and just to put your good heart at rest, I will tell you one thing: the moment I choose, I can be rid of Mr. Hyde. I give you my hand upon that; and I thank you again and again; and I will just add one little word, Utterson, that I 'm sure you 'll take in good part: this is a private matter, and I beg of you to let it sleep."

Utterson reflected a little, looking in the fire.

"I have no doubt you are perfectly right," he said at last, getting to his feet.

"Well, but since we have touched upon this business, and for the last time I hope," continued the doctor, "there is one point I should like you to understand. I have really a very great interest in poor Hyde. I know you have seen him; he told me so; and I fear he was rude. But I do sincerely take a great, a very great interest in that young man; and if I am taken away, Utterson, I wish you to promise me that you will bear with him and get his rights for him. I think you would, if you knew all; and it would be a weight off my mind if you would promise."

"I can't pretend that I shall ever like him," said the lawyer.

"I don't ask that," pleaded Jekyll, laying his hand upon the other's arm; "I only ask for justice; I only ask you to help him for my sake, when I am no longer here."

Utterson heaved an irrepressible sigh. "Well," said he, "I promise."

### THE CAREW MURDER CASE

Nearly a year later, in the month of October, 18—, London was startled by a crime of singular ferocity and rendered all the more notable by the high position of the victim. The details were few and startling. A maid servant living alone in a house not far from the river, had gone upstairs to bed about eleven. Although a fog

rolled over the city in the small hours, the early part of
the night was cloudless, and the lane, which the maid's
window overlooked, was brilliantly lit by the full moon.
It seems she was romantically given, for she sat down
upon her box, which stood immediately under the
window, and fell into a dream of musing.  Never (she
used to say, with streaming tears, when she narrated
that experience), never had she felt more at peace with
all men or thought more kindly of the world.  And as
she so sat she became aware of an aged and beautiful
gentleman with white hair, drawing near along the lane;
and advancing to meet him, another and very small
gentleman, to whom at first she paid less attention.
When they had come within speech (which was just
under the maid's eyes) the older man bowed and accosted
the other with a very pretty manner of politeness.  It
did not seem as if the subject of his address were of great
importance; indeed, from his pointing, it sometimes appeared as if he were only inquiring his way; but the
moon shone on his face as he spoke, and the girl was
pleased to watch it, it seemed to breathe such an innocent and old-world kindness of disposition, yet with
something high too, as of a well-founded self-content.
Presently her eye wandered to the other, and she was
surprised to recognize in him a certain Mr. Hyde, who
had once visited her master and for whom she had conceived a dislike.  He had in his hand a heavy cane, with
which he was trifling; but he answered never a word,
and seemed to listen with an ill-contained impatience.
And then all of a sudden he broke out in a great flame of
anger, stamping with his foot, brandishing the cane,
and carrying on (as the maid described it) like a madman.
The old gentleman took a step back, with the air of one
very much surprised and a trifle hurt; and at that Mr.
Hyde broke out of all bounds and clubbed him to the

earth. And next moment, with ape-like fury, he was trampling his victim under foot and hailing down a storm of blows, under which the bones were audibly shattered and the body jumped upon the roadway. At the horror of these sights and sounds, the maid fainted.

It was two o'clock when she came to herself and called for the police. The murderer was gone long ago; but there lay his victim in the middle of the lane, incredibly mangled. The stick with which the deed had been done, although it was of some rare and very tough and heavy wood, had broken in the middle under the stress of this insensate cruelty; and one splintered half had rolled in the neighbouring gutter—the other, without doubt, had been carried away by the murderer. A purse and a gold watch were found upon the victim: but no cards or papers, except a sealed and stamped envelope which he had been probably carrying to the post, and which bore the name and address of Mr. Utterson.

This was brought to the lawyer the next morning, before he was out of bed; and he had no sooner seen it, and been told the circumstances, than he shot out a solemn lip. "I shall say nothing till I have seen the body," said he; "this may be very serious. Have the kindness to wait while I dress." And with the same grave countenance he hurried through his breakfast and drove to the police station, whither the body had been carried. As soon as he came into the cell, he nodded.

"Yes," said he, "I recognise him. I am sorry to say that this is Sir Danvers Carew."

"Good God, sir," exclaimed the officer, "is it possible?" And the next moment his eye lighted up with professional ambition. "This will make a deal of noise," he said. "And perhaps you can help us to the man." And he briefly narrated what the maid had seen, and showed the broken stick.

Mr. Utterson had already quailed at the name of Hyde; but when the stick was laid before him, he could doubt no longer; broken and battered as it was, he recognised it for one that he had himself presented many years before to Henry Jekyll.

"Is this Mr. Hyde a person of small stature?" he inquired.

"Particularly small and particularly wicked-looking, is what the maid calls him," said the officer.

Mr. Utterson reflected; and then, raising his head, "If you will come with me in my cab," he said, "I think I can take you to his house."

It was by this time about nine in the morning, and the first fog of the season. A great chocolate-coloured pall lowered over heaven, but the wind was continually charging and routing these embattled vapours; so that as the cab crawled from street to street, Mr. Utterson beheld a marvellous number of degrees and hues of twilight; for here it would be dark like the back-end of evening; and there would be a glow of rich, lurid brown, like the light of some strange conflagration; and here, for a moment, the fog would be quite broken up, and a haggard shaft of daylight would glance in between the swirling wreaths. The dismal quarter of Soho seen under these changing glimpses, with its muddy ways, and slatternly passengers, and its lamps, which had never been extinguished or had been kindled afresh to combat this mournful reïnvasion of darkness, seemed, in the lawyer's eyes, like a district of some city in a nightmare. The thoughts of his mind, besides, were of the gloomiest dye; and when he glanced at the companion of his drive, he was conscious of some touch of that terror of the law and the law's officers, which may at times assail the most honest.

As the cab drew up before the address indicated, the

fog lifted a little and showed him a dingy street, a gin palace, a low French eating house, a shop for the retail of penny numbers and twopenny salads, many ragged children huddled in the doorways, and many women of many different nationalities passing out, key in hand, to have a morning glass; and the next moment the fog settled down again upon that part, as brown as umber, and cut him off from his blackguardly surroundings. This was the home of Henry Jekyll's favourite; of a man who was heir to quarter of a million sterling.

An ivory-faced and silvery-haired old woman opened the door. She had an evil face, smoothed by hypocrisy; but her manners were excellent. Yes, she said, this was Mr. Hyde's, but he was not at home; he had been in that night very late, but had gone away again in less than an hour; there was nothing strange in that; his habits were very irregular, and he was often absent; for instance, it was nearly two months since she had seen him till yesterday.

"Very well, then, we wish to see his rooms," said the lawyer; and when the woman began to declare it was impossible, "I had better tell you who this person is," he added. "This is Inspector Newcomen of Scotland Yard."

A flash of odious joy appeared upon the woman's face. "Ah!" said she, "he is in trouble! What has he done?"

Mr. Utterson and the inspector exchanged glances. "He don't seem a very popular character," observed the latter. "And now, my good woman, just let me and this gentleman have a look about us."

In the whole extent of the house, which but for the old woman remained otherwise empty, Mr. Hyde had only used a couple of rooms; but these were furnished with luxury and good taste. A closet was filled with wine; the plate was of silver, the napery elegant; a good picture hung upon the walls, a gift (as Utterson supposed) from Henry Jekyll, who was much of a connoisseur; and the carpets were of many plies and agreeable in colour. At this moment, however, the rooms bore every mark of having been recently and hurriedly ransacked; clothes lay about the floor, with their pockets inside out; lock-fast drawers stood open; and on the hearth there lay a pile of gray ashes, as though many papers had been burned. From these embers the inspector disinterred the butt end of a green cheque book, which had resisted the action of the fire; the other half of the stick was found behind the door; and as this clinched his suspicions, the officer declared himself delighted. A visit to the bank, where several thousand pounds were found to be lying to the murderer's credit, completed his gratification.

"You may depend upon it, sir," he told Mr. Utterson: "I have him in my hand. He must have lost his head, or he never would have left the stick or, above all, burned the cheque book. Why, money's life to the man. We have nothing to do but wait for him at the bank, and get out the handbills."

This last, however, was not so easy of accomplishment; for Mr. Hyde had numbered few familiars—even the master of the servant maid had only seen him twice; his family could nowhere be traced; he had never been photographed; and the few who could describe him differed widely, as common observers will. Only on one point, were they agreed; and that was the haunting sense of unexpressed deformity with which the fugitive impressed his beholders.

### INCIDENT OF THE LETTER

It was late in the afternoon, when Mr. Utterson found his way to Dr. Jekyll's door, where he was at once admitted by Poole, and carried down by the kitchen offices and across a yard which had once been a garden, to the building which was indifferently known as the laboratory or the dissecting rooms. The doctor had bought the house from the heirs of a celebrated surgeon; and his own tastes being rather chemical than anatomical, had changed the destination of the block at the bottom of the garden. It was the first time that the lawyer had been received in that part of his friend's quarters; and he eyed the dingy, windowless structure with curiosity, and gazed round with a distasteful sense of strangeness as he crossed the theatre, once crowded with eager students and now lying gaunt and silent, the tables laden with chemical apparatus, the floor strewn with crates and littered with packing straw, and the light falling dimly through the foggy cupola. At the further end, a flight of stairs mounted to a door covered with red baize; and through this, Mr. Utterson was at last received into the doctor's cabinet. It was a large room, fitted round with glass presses, furnished, among other things, with a cheval-glass and a business table, and looking out upon the court by three dusty windows barred with iron. A fire burned in the grate; a lamp was set lighted on the chimney shelf, for even in the houses the fog began to lie thickly; and there, close up to the warmth, sat Dr. Jekyll, looking deadly sick. He did not rise to meet his visitor, but held out a cold hand and bade him welcome in a changed voice.

"And now," said Mr. Utterson, as soon as Poole had left them, "you have heard the news?"

The doctor shuddered. "They were crying it in the square," he said. "I heard them in my dining-room."

"One word," said the lawyer. "Carew was my client, but so are you, and I want to know what I am doing. You have not been mad enough to hide this fellow?"

"Utterson, I swear to God," cried the doctor, "I swear to God I will never set eyes on him again. I bind my honour to you that I am done with him in this world. It is all at an end. And indeed he does not want my help; you do not know him as I do; he is safe, he is quite safe; mark my words, he will never more be heard of."

The lawyer listened gloomily; he did not like his friend's feverish manner. "You seem pretty sure of him," said he; "and for your sake, I hope you may be right. If it came to a trial, your name might appear."

"I am quite sure of him," replied Jekyll; "I have grounds for certainty that I cannot share with anyone. But there is one thing on which you may advise me. I have—I have received a letter; and I am at a loss whether I should show it to the police. I should like to leave it in your hands, Utterson; you would judge wisely, I am sure; I have so great a trust in you."

"You fear, I suppose, that it might lead to his detection?" asked the lawyer.

"No," said the other. "I cannot say that I care what becomes of Hyde; I am quite done with him. I was thinking of my own character, which this hateful business has rather exposed."

Utterson ruminated awhile; he was surprised at his friend's selfishness, and yet relieved by it. "Well," said he, at last, "let me see the letter."

The letter was written in an odd, upright hand and signed "Edward Hyde": and it signified, briefly enough, that the writer's benefactor, Dr. Jekyll, whom he had long so unworthily repaid for a thousand generosities, need labour under no alarm for his safety, as he had means of escape on which he placed a sure dependence. The lawyer liked this letter well enough; it put a better colour on the intimacy than he had looked for; and he blamed himself for some of his past suspicions.

"Have you the envelope?" he asked.

"I burned it," replied Jekyll, "before I thought what I was about. But it bore no postmark. The note was handed in."

"Shall I keep this and sleep upon it?" asked Utterson.

"I wish you to judge for me entirely," was the reply. "I have lost confidence in myself."

"Well, I shall consider," returned the lawyer. "And now one word more: it was Hyde who dictated the terms in your will about that disappearance?"

The doctor seemed seized with a qualm of faintness; he shut his mouth tight and nodded.

"I knew it," said Utterson. "He meant to murder you. You have had a fine escape."

"I have had what is far more to the purpose," returned the doctor solemnly: "I have had a lesson—O God, Utterson, what a lesson I have had!" And he covered his face for a moment with his hands.

On his way out, the lawyer stopped and had a word or two with Poole. "By the bye," said he, "there was a letter handed in to-day: what was the messenger like?" But Poole was positive nothing had come except by post; "and only circulars by that," he added.

This news sent off the visitor with his fears renewed. Plainly the letter had come by the laboratory door; possibly, indeed, it had been written in the cabinet; and if that were so, it must be differently judged, and handled with the more caution. The newsboys, as he went, were crying themselves hoarse along the footways: "Special edition. Shocking murder of an M. P." That was the funeral oration of one friend and client; and he could not help a certain apprehension lest the good name of another should be sucked down in the

eddy of the scandal.  It was, at least, a ticklish decision
that he had to make; and self-reliant as he was by habit,
he began to cherish a longing for advice.  It was not to
be had directly; but perhaps, he thought, it might be
fished for.

Presently after, he sat on one side of his own hearth,
with Mr. Guest, his head clerk, upon the other, and midway between, at a nicely calculated distance from the fire,
a bottle of a particular old wine that had long dwelt un-
sunned in the foundations of his house.  The fog still
slept on the wing above the drowned city, where the
lamps glimmered like carbuncles; and through the
muffle and smother of these fallen clouds, the procession of the town's life was still rolling in through the
great arteries with a sound as of a mighty wind.  But
the room was gay with firelight.  In the bottle the acids
were long ago resolved; the imperial dye had softened
with time, as the colour grows richer in stained windows;
and the glow of hot autumn afternoons on hillside vine-
yards, was ready to be set free and to disperse the fogs
of London.  Insensibly the lawyer melted.  There was
no man from whom he kept fewer secrets than Mr.
Guest; and he was not always sure that he kept as
many as he meant.  Guest had often been on business
to the doctor's; he knew Poole; he could scarce have
failed to hear of Mr. Hyde's familiarity about the house;
he might draw conclusions: was it not as well, then,
that he should see a letter which put that mystery to
rights? and above all since Guest, being a great student
and critic of handwriting, would consider the step natural
and obliging?  The clerk, besides, was a man of counsel; he would scarce read so strange a document without dropping a remark; and by that remark Mr. Utterson might shape his future course.

"This is a sad business about Sir Danvers," he said.

"Yes, sir, indeed. It has elicited a great deal of public feeling," returned Guest. "The man, of course, was mad."

"I should like to hear your views on that," replied Utterson. "I have a document here in his handwriting; it is between ourselves, for I scarce know what to do about it; it is an ugly business at the best. But there it is; quite in your way: a murderer's autograph."

Guest's eyes brightened, and he sat down at once and studied it with passion. "No, sir," he said: "not mad; but it is an odd hand."

"And by all accounts a very odd writer," added the lawyer.

Just then the servant entered with a note.

"Is that from Dr. Jekyll, sir?" inquired the clerk. "I thought I knew the writing. Anything private, Mr. Utterson?"

"Only an invitation to dinner. Why? Do you want to see it?"

"One moment. I thank you, sir;" and the clerk laid the two sheets of paper alongside and sedulously compared their contents. "Thank you, sir," he said at last, returning both; "it's a very interesting autograph."

There was a pause, during which Mr. Utterson struggled with himself. "Why did you compare them, Guest?" he inquired suddenly.

"Well, sir," returned the clerk, "there's a rather singular resemblance; the two hands are in many points identical: only differently sloped."

"Rather quaint," said Utterson.

"It is, as you say, rather quaint," returned Guest.

"I wouldn't speak of this note, you know," said the master.

"No, sir," said the clerk. "I understand."

But no sooner was Mr. Utterson alone that night than

he locked the note into his safe, where it reposed from that time forward. "What!" he thought. "Henry Jekyll forge for a murderer!" And his blood ran cold in his veins.

### REMARKABLE INCIDENT OF DR. LANYON

Time ran on; thousands of pounds were offered in reward, for the death of Sir Danvers was resented as a public injury; but Mr. Hyde had disappeared out of the ken of the police as though he had never existed. Much of his past was unearthed, indeed, and all disreputable: tales came out of the man's cruelty, at once so callous and violent; of his vile life, of his strange associates, of the hatred that seemed to have surrounded his career; but of his present whereabouts not a whisper. From the time he had left the house in Soho on the morning of the murder, he was simply blotted out; and gradually, as time drew on, Mr. Utterson began to recover from the hotness of his alarm, and to grow more at quiet with himself. The death of Sir Danvers was, to his way of thinking, more than paid for by the disappearance of Mr. Hyde. Now that that evil influence had been withdrawn, a new life began for Dr. Jekyll. He came out of his seclusion, renewed relations with his friends, became once more their familiar guest and entertainer; and whilst he had always been known for charities, he was now no less distinguished for religion. He was busy, he was much in the open air, he did good; his face seemed to open and brighten, as if with an inward consciousness of service; and for more than two months, the doctor was at peace.

On the 8th of January Utterson had dined at the doctor's with a small party; Lanyon had been there; and the face of the host had looked from one to the other as in the old days when the trio were inseparable friends. On the 12th, and again on the 14th, the door was shut against the lawyer. "The doctor was confined to the house," Poole said, "and saw no one." On the 15th, he tried again, and was again refused; and having now been used for the last two months to see his friend almost daily, he found this return of solitude to weigh upon his spirits. The fifth night he had in Guest to dine with him; and the sixth he betook himself to Dr. Lanyon's.

There at least he was not denied admittance; but when he came in, he was shocked at the change which had taken place in the doctor's appearance. He had his death-warrant written legibly upon his face. The rosy man had grown pale; his flesh had fallen away; he was visibly balder and older; and yet it was not so much these tokens of a swift physical decay that arrested the lawyer's notice, as a look in the eye and quality of manner that seemed to testify to some deep-seated terror of the mind. It was unlikely that the doctor should fear death; and yet that was what Utterson was tempted to suspect. "Yes," he thought; "he is a doctor, he must know his own state and that his days are counted; and the knowledge is more than he can bear." And yet when Utterson remarked on his ill-looks, it was with an air of great firmness that Lanyon declared himself a doomed man.

"I have had a shock," he said, "and I shall never recover. It is a question of weeks. Well, life has been pleasant; I liked it; yes, sir, I used to like it. I sometimes think if we knew all, we should be more glad to get away."

"Jekyll is ill, too," observed Utterson. "Have you seen him?"

But Lanyon's face changed, and he held up a trembling hand. "I wish to see or hear no more of Dr.

Jekyll," he said in a loud, unsteady voice. "I am quite done with that person; and I beg that you will spare me any allusion to one whom I regard as dead."

"Tut-tut," said Mr. Utterson; and then after a considerable pause, "Can't I do anything?" he inquired. "We are three very old friends, Lanyon; we shall not live to make others."

"Nothing can be done," returned Lanyon; "ask himself."

"He will not see me," said the lawyer.

"I am not surprised at that," was the reply. "Some day, Utterson, after I am dead, you may perhaps come to learn the right and wrong of this. I cannot tell you. And in the meantime, if you can sit and talk with me of other things, for God's sake, stay and do so; but if you cannot keep clear of this accursed topic, then, in God's name, go, for I cannot bear it."

As soon as he got home, Utterson sat down and wrote to Jekyll, complaining of his exclusion from the house, and asking the cause of this unhappy break with Lanyon; and the next day brought him a long answer, often very pathetically worded, and sometimes darkly mysterious in drift. The quarrel with Lanyon was incurable. "I do not blame our old friend," Jekyll wrote, "but I share his view that we must never meet. I mean from henceforth to lead a life of extreme seclusion; you must not be surprised, nor must you doubt my friendship, if my door is often shut even to you. You must suffer me to go my own dark way. I have brought on myself a punishment and a danger that I cannot name. If I am the chief of sinners, I am the chief of sufferers also. I could not think that this earth contained a place for sufferings and terrors so unmanning; and you can do but one thing, Utterson, to lighten this destiny, and that is to respect my silence." Utterson was amazed; the dark influence of Hyde had been withdrawn, the doctor had returned to his old tasks and amities; a week ago, the prospect had smiled with every promise of a cheerful and an honoured age; and now in a moment, friendship, and peace of mind, and the whole tenor of his life were wrecked. So great and unprepared a change pointed to madness; but in view cf Lanyon's manner and words, there must lie for it some deeper ground.

A week afterwards Dr. Lanyon took to his bed, and in something less than a fortnight he was dead. The night after the funeral, at which he had been sadly affected, Utterson locked the door of his business room, and sitting there by the light of a melancholy candle, drew out and set before him an envelope addressed by the hand and sealed with the seal of his dead friend. "PRIVATE: for the hands of G. J. Utterson ALONE, and in case of his predecease *to be destroyed unread*," so it was emphatically superscribed; and the lawyer dreaded to behold the contents. "I have buried one friend to-day," he thought: "what if this should cost me another?" And then he condemned the fear as a disloyalty, and broke the seal. Within there was another enclosure, likewise sealed, and marked upon the cover as "not to be opened till the death or disappearance of Dr. Henry Jekyll." Utterson could not trust his eyes. Yes, it was disappearance; here again, as in the mad will which he had long ago restored to its author, here again were the idea of a disappearance and the name of Henry Jekyll bracketted. But in the will, that idea had sprung from the sinister suggestion of the man Hyde; it was set there with a purpose all too plain and horrible. Written by the hand of Lanyon, what should it mean? A great curiosity came on the trustee, to disregard the prohibition and dive at once to the bottom of these mysteries; but professional honour and faith to his dead friend were stringent obligations; and the packet slept in the inmost corner of his private safe.

It is one thing to mortify curiosity, another to conquer it; and it may be doubted if, from that day forth, Utterson desired the society of his surviving friend with the same eagerness. He thought of him kindly; but his thoughts were disquieted and fearful. He went to call indeed; but he was perhaps relieved to be denied admittance; perhaps, in his heart, he preferred to speak with Poole upon the doorstep and surrounded by the air and sounds of the open city, rather than to be admitted into that house of voluntary bondage, and to sit and speak with its inscrutable recluse. Poole had, indeed, no very pleasant news to communicate. The doctor, it appeared, now more than ever confined himself to the cabinet over the laboratory, where he would sometimes even sleep; he was out of spirits, he had grown very silent, he did not read; it seemed as if he had something on his mind. Utterson became so used to the unvarying character of these reports, that he fell off little by little in the frequency of his visits.

### INCIDENT AT THE WINDOW

It chanced on Sunday, when Mr. Utterson was on his usual walk with Mr. Enfield, that their way lay once again through the by-street; and that when they came in front of the door, both stopped to gaze on it.

"Well," said Enfield, "that story's at an end at least. We shall never see more of Mr. Hyde."

"I hope not," said Utterson. "Did I ever tell you that I once saw him, and shared your feeling of repulsion?"

"It was impossible to do the one without the other," returned Enfield. "And by the way, what an ass you must have thought me, not to know that this was a back way to Dr. Jekyll's! It was partly your own fault that I found it out, even when I did."

"So you found it out, did you?" said Utterson. "But if that be so, we may step into the court and take a look at the windows. To tell you the truth, I am uneasy about poor Jekyll; and even outside, I feel as if the presence of a friend might do him good."

The court was very cool and a little damp, and full of premature twilight, although the sky, high up overhead, was still bright with sunset. The middle one of the three windows was half way open; and sitting close beside it, taking the air with an infinite sadness of mien, like some disconsolate prisoner, Utterson saw Dr. Jekyll.

"What! Jekyll!" he cried. "I trust you are better."

"I am very low, Utterson," replied the doctor, drearily, "very low. It will not last long, thank God."

"You stay too much indoors," said the lawyer. "You should be out, whipping up the circulation like Mr. Enfield and me. (This is my cousin—Mr. Enfield—Dr. Jekyll.) Come now; get your hat and take a quick turn with us."

"You are very good," sighed the other. "I should like to very much; but no, no, no, it is quite impossible; I dare not. But indeed, Utterson, I am very glad to see you; this is really a great pleasure; I would ask you and Mr. Enfield up, but the place is really not fit."

"Why then," said the lawyer, good-naturedly, "the best thing we can do is to stay down here and speak with you from where we are."

"That is just what I was about to venture to propose," returned the doctor with a smile. But the words were hardly uttered, before the smile was struck out of his face and succeeded by an expression of such abject terror and despair, as froze the very blood of the two gentlemen below. They saw it but for a glimpse, for the window was instantly thrust down; but that glimpse had been sufficient, and they turned and left the court without a word. In silence, too, they traversed the by-street; and it was not until they had come into a neighbouring thoroughfare, where even upon a Sunday there were still some stirrings of life, that Mr. Utterson at last turned and looked at his companion. They were both pale; and there was an answering horror in their eyes.

"God forgive us, God forgive us," said Mr. Utterson.

But Mr. Enfield only nodded his head very seriously, and walked on once more in silence.

### THE LAST NIGHT

Mr. Utterson was sitting by his fireside one evening after dinner, when he was surprised to receive a visit from Poole.

"Bless me, Poole, what brings you here?" he cried; and then taking a second look at him, "What ails you?" he added; "is the doctor ill?"

"Mr. Utterson," said the man, "there is something wrong."

"Take a seat, and here is a glass of wine for you," said the lawyer. "Now, take your time, and tell me plainly what you want."

"You know the doctor's ways, sir," replied Poole, "and how he shuts himself up. Well, he's shut up again in the cabinet; and I don't like it, sir—I wish I may die if I like it. Mr. Utterson, sir, I'm afraid."

"Now, my good man," said the lawyer, "be explicit. What are you afraid of?"

"I've been afraid for about a week," returned Poole, doggedly disregarding the question, "and I can bear it no more."

The man's appearance amply bore out his words; his manner was altered for the worse; and except for the moment when he had first announced his terror, he had not once looked the lawyer in the face. Even now, he sat with the glass of wine untasted on his knee, and his eyes directed to a corner of the floor. "I can bear it no more," he repeated.

"Come," said the lawyer, "I see you have some good reason, Poole; I see there is something seriously amiss. Try to tell me what it is."

"I think there's been foul play," said Poole, hoarsely.

"Foul play!" cried the lawyer, a good deal frightened and rather inclined to be irritated in consequence. "What foul play? What does the man mean?"

"I daren't say, sir," was the answer; "but will you come along with me and see for yourself?"

Mr. Utterson's only answer was to rise and get his hat and great coat; but he observed with wonder the greatness of the relief that appeared upon the butler's face, and perhaps with no less, that the wine was still untasted when he set it down to follow.

It was a wild, cold, seasonable night of March, with a pale moon, lying on her back as though the wind had tilted her, and a flying wrack of the most diaphanous and lawny texture. The wind made talking difficult, and flecked the blood into the face. It seemed to have swept the streets unusually bare of passengers, besides; for Mr. Utterson thought he had never seen that part of London so deserted. He could have wished it otherwise; never in his life had he been conscious of so sharp a wish to see and touch his fellow-creatures; for struggle as he might, there was borne in upon his mind a crushing anticipation of calamity. The square, when they got there, was all full of wind and dust, and the thin trees in the garden were lashing themselves along the railing. Poole.

who had kept all the way a pace or two ahead, now
pulled up in the middle of the pavement, and in spite of
the biting weather, took off his hat and mopped his
brow with a red pocket-handkerchief. But for all the
hurry of his coming, these were not the dews of exertion
that he wiped away, but the moisture of some strangling
anguish; for his face was white and his voice, when he
spoke, harsh and broken.

"Well, sir," he said, "here we are, and God grant
there be nothing wrong."

"Amen, Poole," said the lawyer.

Thereupon the servant knocked in a very guarded
manner; the door was opened on the chain; and a voice
asked from within, "Is that you, Poole?"

"It's all right," said Poole. "Open the door."

The hall, when they entered it, was brightly lighted
up; the fire was built high; and about the hearth the
whole of the servants, men and women, stood huddled
together like a flock of sheep. At the sight of Mr.
Utterson, the housemaid broke into hysterical whimper-
ing; and the cook, crying out "Bless God! it's Mr.
Utterson," ran forward as if to take him in her arms.

"What, what? Are you all here?" said the lawyer
peevishly. "Very irregular, very unseemly; your master would be far from pleased."

"They're all afraid," said Poole.

Blank silence followed, no one protesting; only the
maid lifted up her voice and now wept loudly.

"Hold your tongue!" Poole said to her, with a ferocity of accent that testified to his own jangled nerves;
and indeed, when the girl had so suddenly raised the note
of her lamentation, they had all started and turned
towards the inner door with faces of dreadful expectation. "And now," continued the butler, addressing the
knife-boy, "reach me a candle, and we'll get this through

hands at once." And then he begged Mr. Utterson to follow him, and led the way to the back garden.

"Now, sir," said he, "you come as gently as you can. I want you to hear, and I don't want you to be heard. And see here, sir, if by any chance he was to ask you in, don't go."

Mr. Utterson's nerves, at this unlooked-for termination, gave a jerk that nearly threw him from his balance; but he recollected his courage and followed the butler into the laboratory building and through the surgical theatre, with its lumber of crates and bottles, to the foot of the stair. Here Poole motioned him to stand on one side and listen; while he himself, setting down the candle and making a great and obvious call on his resolution, mounted the steps and knocked with a somewhat uncertain hand on the red baize of the cabinet door.

"Mr. Utterson, sir, asking to see you," he called; and even as he did so, once more violently signed to the lawyer to give ear.

A voice answered from within: "Tell him I cannot see anyone," it said complainingly.

"Thank you, sir," said Poole, with a note of something like triumph in his voice; and taking up his candle, he led Mr. Utterson back across the yard and into the great kitchen, where the fire was out and the beetles were leaping on the floor.

"Sir," he said, looking Mr. Utterson in the eyes, "was that my master's voice?"

"It seems much changed," replied the lawyer, very pale, but giving look for look.

"Changed? Well, yes, I think so," said the butler. "Have I been twenty years in this man's house, to be deceived about his voice? No, sir; master's made away with; he was made away with, eight days ago, when we heard him cry out upon the name of God; and *who's* in there instead of him, and *why* it stays there, is a thing tha* cries to Heaven, Mr. Utterson!"

"This is a very .t, .nge tale, Poole; this is rather a wild tale, my mar," said Mr. Utterson, biting his finger. "Supp se it were as you suppose, supposing Dr. Jekyll to have been—well, murdered, what could induce the murderer to stay? That won't hold water; it doesn't commend itself to reason."

"Well, Mr. Utterson, you are a hard man to satisfy, but I'll do it yet," said Poole. "All this last week (you must know) him, or it, or whatever it is that lives in that cabinet, has been crying night and day for some sort of medicine and cannot get it to his mind. It was sometimes his way—the master's, that is—to write his orders on a sheet of paper and throw it on the stair. We've had nothing else this week back; nothing but papers, and a closed door, and the very meals left there to be smuggled in when nobody was looking. Well, sir, every day, ay, and twice and thrice in the same day, there have been orders and complaints, and I have been sent flying to all the wholesale chemists in town. Every time I brought the stuff back, there would be another paper telling me to return it, because it was not pure, and another order to a different firm. This drug is wanted bitter bad, sir, whatever for."

"Have you any of these papers?" asked Mr. Utterson.

Poole felt in his pocket and handed out a crumpled note, which the lawyer, bending nearer to the candle, carefully examined. Its contents ran thus: "Dr. Jekyll presents his compliments to Messrs. Maw. He assures them that their last sample is impure and quite useless for his present purpose. In the year 18—, Dr. J. purchased a somewhat large quantity from Messrs. M. He now begs them to search with the most sedulous care, and should any of the same quality be left, to forward it to him at once. Expense is no consideration. The importance of this to Dr. J. can hardly be exaggerated." So far the letter had run composedly enough, but here with a sudden splutter of the pen, the writer's emotion had broken loose. "For God's sake," he had added, "find me some of the old."

"This is a strange note," said Mr. Utterson; and then sharply, "How do you come to have it open?"

"The man at Maw's was main angry, sir, and he threw it back to me like so much dirt," returned Poole.

"This is unquestionably the doctor's hand, do you know?" resumed the lawyer.

"I thought it looked like it," said the servant rather sulkily; and then, with another voice, "But what matters hand of write?" he said. "I 've seen him!"

"Seen him?" repeated Mr. Utterson. "Well?"

"That 's it!" said Poole. "It was this way. I came suddenly into the theatre from the garden. It seems he had slipped out to look for this drug or whatever it is; for the cabinet door was open; and there he was at the far end of the room digging among the crates. He looked up when I came in, gave a kind of cry, and whipped upstairs into the cabinet. It was but for one minute that I saw him, but the hair stood upon my head like quills. Sir, if that was my master, why had he a mask upon his face? If it was my master, why did he cry out like a rat, and run from me? I have served him long enough. And then . . ." The man paused and passed his hand over his face.

"These are all very strange circumstances," said Mr. Utterson, "but I think I begin to see daylight. Your master, Poole, is plainly seized with one of those maladies that both torture and deform the sufferer; hence, for aught I know, the alteration of his voice; hence the mask and the avoidance of his friends; hence his eagerness to find this drug, by means of which the poor soul retains some hope of ultimate recovery—God grant that he be not deceived! There is my explanation; it is sad enough, Poole, ay, and appalling to consider; but it is plain and natural, hangs well together, and delivers us from all exorbitant alarms."

"Sir," said the butler, turning to a sort of mottled pallor, "that thing was not my master, and there's the truth. My master"—here he looked round him and began to whisper—"is a tall, fine build of a man, and this was more of a dwarf." Utterson attempted to protest. "O, sir," cried Poole, "do you think I do not know my master after twenty years? Do you think I do not know where his head comes to in the cabinet door, where I saw him every morning of my life? No, sir, that thing in the mask was never Dr. Jekyll—God knows what it was, but it was never Dr. Jekyll; and it is the belief of my heart that there was murder done."

"Poole," replied the lawyer, "if you say that, it will become my duty to make certain. Much as I desire to spare your master's feelings, much as I am puzzled by this note which seems to prove him to be still alive, I shall consider it my duty to break in that door."

"Ah, Mr. Utterson, that's talking!" cried the butler.

"And now comes the second question," resumed Utterson: "Who is going to do it?"

"Why, you and me," was the undaunted reply.

"That's very well said," returned the lawyer; "and whatever comes of it I shall make it my business to see you are no loser."

"There is an axe in the theatre," continued Poole; "and you might take the kitchen poker for yourself."

The lawyer took that rude but weighty instrument into his hand, and balanced it. "Do you know, Poole," he said, looking up, "that you and I are about to place ourselves in a position of some peril?"

"You may say so, sir, indeed," returned the butler.

"It is well, then, that we should be frank," said the other. "We both think more than we have said; let us make a clean breast. This masked figure that you saw, did you recognise it?"

"Well, sir, it went so quick, and the creature was so doubled up, that I could hardly swear to that," was the answer. "But if you mean, was it Mr. Hyde?—why, yes, I think it was! You see, it was much of the same bigness; and it had the same quick, light way with it; and then who else could have got in by the laboratory door? You have not forgot, sir, that at the time of the murder he had still the key with him? But that's not all. I don't know, Mr. Utterson, if ever you met this Mr. Hyde?"

"Yes," said the lawyer, "I once spoke with him."

"Then you must know as well as the rest of us that there was something queer about that gentleman— something that gave a man a turn—I don't know rightly how to say it, sir, beyond this: that you felt it in your marrow kind of cold and thin."

"I own I felt something of what you describe," said Mr. Utterson.

"Quite so, sir," returned Poole. "Well, when that masked thing like a monkey jumped from among the chemicals and whipped into the cabinet, it went down my spine like ice. O, I know it's not evidence, Mr. Utterson; I'm book-learned enough for that; but a man has his feelings, and I give you my bible-word it was Mr. Hyde!"

"Ay, ay," said the lawyer. "My fears incline to the same point. Evil, I fear, founded—evil was sure to come—of that connection. Ay, truly, I believe you; I believe poor Harry is killed; and I believe his murderer (for what purpose, God alone can tell) is still lurking in his victim's room. Well, let our name be vengeance. Call Bradshaw."

The footman came at the summons, very white and nervous.

"Pull yourself together, Bradshaw," said the lawyer. "This suspense, I know, is telling upon all of you; but it is now our intention to make an end of it. Poole, here, and I are going to force our way into the cabinet. If all is well, my shoulders are broad enough to bear the blame. Meanwhile, lest anything should really be amiss, or any malefactor seek to escape by the back, you and the boy must go round the corner with a pair of good sticks and take your post at the laboratory door. We give you ten minutes to get to your stations."

As Bradshaw left, the lawyer looked at his watch. "And now, Poole, let us get to ours," he said; and taking the poker under his arm, led the way into the yard. The scud had banked over the moon, and it was now quite dark. The wind, which only broke in puffs and draughts into that deep well of building, tossed the light of the candle to and fro about their steps, until they came into the shelter of the theatre, where they sat down silently to wait. London hummed solemnly all around; but nearer at hand, the stillness was only broken by the sounds of a footfall moving to and fro along the cabinet floor.

"So it will walk all day, sir," whispered Poole; "ay, and the better part of the night. Only when a new sample comes from the chemist, there's a bit of a break. Ah, it's an ill-conscience that's such an enemy to rest! Ah, sir, there's blood foully shed in every step of it! But hark again, a little closer—put your heart in your ears, Mr. Utterson, and tell me, is that the doctor's foot?"

The steps fell lightly and oddly, with a certain swing, for all they went so slowly; it was different indeed from the heavy creaking tread of Henry Jekyll. Utterson sighed. "Is there never anything else?" he asked.

Poole nodded. "Once," he said. "Once I heard it weeping!"

"Weeping? how that?" said the lawyer, conscious of a sudden chill of horror.

"Weeping like a woman or a lost soul," said the butler. "I came away with that upon my heart, that I could have wept too."

But now the ten minutes drew to an end. Poole disinterred the axe from under a stack of packing straw; the candle was set upon the nearest table to light them to the attack; and they drew near with bated breath to where that patient foot was still going up and down, up and down, in the quiet of the night.

"Jekyll," cried Utterson, with a loud voice, "I demand to see you." He paused a moment, but there came no reply. "I give you fair warning, our suspicions are aroused, and I must and shall see you," he resumed; "if not by fair means, then by foul—if not of your consent, then by brute force!"

"Utterson," said the voice, "for God's sake, have mercy!"

"Ah, that's not Jekyll's voice—it's Hyde's!" cried Utterson. "Down with the door, Poole!"

Poole swung the axe over his shoulder; the blow shook the building, and the red baize door leaped against the lock and hinges. A dismal screech, as of mere animal terror, rang from the cabinet. Up went the axe again, and again the panels crashed and the frame bounded; four times the blow fell; but the wood was tough and the fittings were of excellent workmanship; and it was not until the fifth, that the lock burst in sunder and the wreck of the door fell inwards on the carpet.

The besiegers, appalled by their own riot and the stillness that had succeeded, stood back a little and peered in. There lay the cabinet before their eyes in the quiet lamplight, a good fire glowing and chattering on the hearth, the kettle singing its thin strain, a drawer or two open, papers neatly set forth on the business table, and nearer the fire, the things laid out for tea: the quietest room, you would have said, and, but for the glazed presses full of chemicals, the most commonplace that night in London.

Right in the midst there lay the body of a man sorely contorted and still twitching. They drew near on tiptoe, turned it on its back and beheld the face of Edward Hyde. He was dressed in clothes far too large for him, clothes of the doctor's bigness; the cords of his face still moved with a semblance of life, but life was quite gone: and by the crushed phial in the hand and the strong smell of kernels that hung upon the air, Utterson knew that he was looking on the body of a self-destroyer.

"We have come too late," he said sternly, "whether to save or punish. Hyde is gone to his account; and it only remains for us to find the body of your master."

The far greater proportion of the building was occupied by the theatre, which filled almost the whole ground story and was lighted from above, and by the cabinet, which formed an upper story at one end and looked upon the court. A corridor joined the theatre to the door on the by-street; and with this the cabinet communicated separately by a second flight of stairs. There were besides a few dark closets and a spacious cellar. All these they now thoroughly examined. Each closet needed but a glance, for all were empty, and all, by the dust that fell from their doors, had stood long unopened.

The cellar, indeed, was filled with crazy lumber, mostly dating from the times of the surgeon who was Jekyll's predecessor; but even as they opened the door they were advertised of the uselessness of further search, by the fall of a perfect mat of cobweb which had for years sealed up the entrance. Nowhere was there any trace of Henry Jekyll, dead or alive.

Poole stamped on the flags of the corridor. "He must be buried here," he said, hearkening to the sound.

"Or he may have fled," said Utterson, and he turned to examine the door in the by-street. It was locked; and lying near by on the flags, they found the key, already stained with rust.

"This does not look like use," observed the lawyer.

"Use!" echoed Poole. "Do you not see, sir, it is broken? much as if a man had stamped on it."

"Ay," continued Utterson, "and the fractures, too, are rusty." The two men looked at each other with a scare. "This is beyond me, Poole," said the lawyer. "Let us go back to the cabinet."

They mounted the stair in silence, and still with an occasional awestruck glance at the dead body, proceeded more thoroughly to examine the contents of the cabinet. At one table, there were traces of chemical work, various measured heaps of some white salt being laid on glass saucers, as though for an experiment in which the unhappy man had been prevented.

"That is the same drug that I was always bringing him," said Poole; and even as he spoke, the kettle with a startling noise boiled over.

This brought them to the fireside, where the easy-chair was drawn cosily up, and the tea things stood ready to the sitter's elbow, the very sugar in the cup. There were several books on a shelf; one lay beside the tea things open, and Utterson was amazed to find it a copy

of a pious work, for which Jekyll had several times
expressed a great esteem, annotated, in his own hand,
with startling blasphemies.

Next, in the course of their review of the chamber, the
searchers came to the cheval glass, into whose depths
they looked with an involuntary horror. But it was so
turned as to show them nothing but the rosy glow playing on the roof, the fire sparkling in a hundred repetitions
along the glazed front of the presses, and their own pale
and fearful countenances stooping to look in.

"This glass have seen some strange things, sir,"
whispered Poole.

"And surely none stranger than itself," echoed the
lawyer in the same tones. "For what did Jekyll"—he
caught himself up at the word with a start, and then
conquering the weakness—"what could Jekyll want
with it?" he said.

"You may say that!" said Poole.

Next they turned to the business table. On the desk,
among the neat array of papers, a large envelope was
uppermost, and bore, in the doctor's hand, the name of
Mr. Utterson. The lawyer unsealed it, and several en-
closures fell to the floor. The first was a will, drawn in
the same eccentric terms as the one which he had returned six months before, to serve as a testament in case
of death, and as a deed of gift in case of disappearance;
but in place of the name of Edward Hyde, the lawyer,
with indescribable amazement, read the name of Gabriel
John Utterson. He looked at Poole, and then back at
the paper, and last of all at the dead malefactor stretched
upon the carpet.

"My head goes round," he said. "He has been all
these days in possession; he had no cause to like me;
he must have raged to see himself displaced; and he
has not destroyed this document."

He caught up the next paper; it was a brief note in the doctor's hand and dated at the top. "O Poole!" the lawyer cried, "he was alive and here this day. He cannot have been disposed of in so short a space; he must be still alive, he must have fled! And then, why fled? and how? and in that case, can we venture to declare this suicide? O, we must be careful. I foresee that we may yet involve your master in some dire catastrophe."

"Why don't you read it, sir?" asked Poole.

"Because I fear," replied the lawyer solemnly. "God grant I have no cause for it!" And with that he brought the paper to his eyes and read as follows:

"MY DEAR UTTERSON,—When this shall fall into your hands, I shall have disappeared, under what circumstances I have not the penetration to foresee, but my instinct and all the circumstances of my nameless situation tell me that the end is sure and must be early. Go then, and first read the narrative which Lanyon warned me he was to place in your hands; and if you care to hear more, turn to the confession of

"Your unworthy and unhappy friend,
"HENRY JEKYLL."

"There was a third enclosure?" asked Utterson.

"Here, sir," said Poole, and gave into his hands a considerable packet sealed in several places.

The lawyer put it in his pocket. "I would say nothing of this paper. If your master has fled or is dead, we may at least save his crédit. It is now ten; I must go home and read these documents in quiet; but I shall be back before midnight, when we shall send for the police."

They went out, locking the door of the theatre behind them; and Utterson, once more leaving the servants gathered about the fire in the hall, trudged back to his office to read the two narratives in which this mystery was now to be explained.

### DR. LANYON'S NARRATIVE

On the ninth of January, now four days ago, I received by the evening delivery a registered envelope, addressed in the hand of my colleague and old school-companion, Henry Jekyll. I was a good deal surprised by this; for we were by no means in the habit of correspondence; I had seen the man, dined with him, indeed, the night before; and I could imagine nothing in our intercourse that should justify formality of registration. The contents increased my wonder; for this is how the letter ran:

"10th December, 18–

"DEAR LANYON,—You are one of my oldest friends; and although we may have differed at times on scientific questions, I cannot remember, at least on my side, any break in our affection. There was never a day when, if you had said to me, 'Jekyll, my life, my honour, my reason, depend upon you,' I would not have sacrificed my left hand to help you. Lanyon, my life, my honour, my reason, are all at your mercy; if you fail me to-night I am lost. You might suppose, after this preface, that I am going to ask you for something dishonourable to grant. Judge for yourself.

"I want you to postpone all other engagements for to-night—ay, even if you were summoned to the bedside of an emperor; to take a cab, unless your carriage should be actually at the door; and with this letter in your hand for consultation, to drive straight to my house. Poole, my butler, has his orders; you will find him waiting your arrival with a locksmith. The door of my cabinet is then to be forced: and you are to go in alone; to open the glazed press (letter E) on the left hand, breaking the lock if it be shut; and to draw out, *with all its contents as they stand*, the fourth drawer from the top or (which is the same thing) the third from the bottom. In my extreme distress of mind, I have a morbid fear of misdirecting you; but even if I am in error, you may know the right drawer by its contents: some powders, a phial and a paper book. This drawer I beg of you to carry back with you to Cavendish Square exactly as it stands.

"That is the first part of the service: now for the second. You should be back, if you set out at once on the receipt of this, long before midnight; but I will leave you that amount of margin, not only in the fear of one of those obstacles that can neither be prevented nor foreseen, but because an hour when your servants are in bed is to be preferred for what will then remain to do. At midnight, then, I have to ask you to be alone in your consulting room, to admit with your own hand into the house a man who will present himself in my name, and to place in his hands the drawer that you will have brought with you from my cabinet. Then you will have played your part and earned my gratitude completely. Five minutes afterwards, if you insist upon an explanation, you will have understood that these arrangements are of capital importance; and that by the neglect of one of them, fantastic as they must appear, you might have charged your conscience with my death or the shipwreck of my reason.

"Confident as I am that you will not trifle with this appeal, my heart sinks and my hand trembles at the bare thought of such a possibility. Think of me at this hour, in a strange place, labouring under a blackness of distress that no fancy can exaggerate, and yet well aware that, if you will but punctually serve me, my troubles will roll away like a story that is told. Serve me, my dear Lanyon, and save

"Your friend,
"H. J.

"P. S.—I had already sealed this up when a fresh terror struck upon my soul. It is possible that the post-office may fail me, and this letter not come into your hands until to-morrow morning. In that case, dear Lanyon, do my errand when it shall be most convenient for you in the course of the day; and once more expect my messenger at midnight. It may then already be too late; and if that night passes without event, you will know that you have seen the last of Henry Jekyll."

Upon the reading of this letter, I made sure my colleague was insane; but till that was proved beyond the possibility of doubt, I felt bound to do as he requested. The less I understood of this farrago, the less I was in a position to judge of its importance; and an appeal so worded could not be set aside without a grave responsibility. I rose accordingly from table, got into a hansom, and drove straight to Jekyll's house. The butler was awaiting my arrival; he had received by the same post as mine a registered letter of instruction, and had sent at once for a locksmith and a carpenter. The tradesmen came while we were yet speaking; and we moved in a body to old Dr. Denman's surgical theatre, from which (as you are doubtless aware) Jekyll's private cabinet is most conveniently entered. The door was very strong, the lock excellent; the carpenter avowed he would have great trouble and have to do much damage, if force were to be used; and the locksmith was near despair. But this last was a handy fellow, and after two hours' work, the door stood open. The press marked E was unlocked; and I took out the drawer, had it filled up with straw and tied in a sheet, and returned with it to Cavendish Square.

Here I proceeded to examine its contents. The powders were neatly enough made up, but not with the nicety of the dispensing chemist; so that it was plain they were of Jekyll's private manufacture: and when I opened one of the wrappers I found what seemed to me a simple crystalline salt of a white colour. The phial, to which I next turned my attention, might have been about half full of a blood-red liquor, which was highly pungent to the sense of smell and seemed to me to contain phosphorus and some volatile ether. At the other ingredients I could make no guess. The book was an ordinary version book and contained little but a series of dates. These covered a period of many years, but I observed that the entries ceased nearly a year ago and quite abruptly. Here and there a brief remark was appended to a date, usually no more than a single word: "double" occurring perhaps six times in a total of several hundred entries; and once very early in the list and followed by several marks of exclamation, "total failure!!!" All this, though it whetted my curiosity, told me little that was definite. Here were a phial of some tincture, a paper of some salt, and the record of a series of experi-

ments that had led (like too many of Jekyll's investiga-
tions) to no end of practical usefulness. How could the
presence of these articles in my house affect either the
honour, the sanity, or the life of my flighty colleague?
If his messenger could go to one place, why could he not
go to another? And even granting some impediment,
why was this gentleman to be received by me in secret?
The more I reflected the more convinced I grew that I
was dealing with a case of cerebral disease; and though
I dismissed my servants to bed, I loaded an old revolver,
that I might be found in some posture of self-defence.

Twelve o'clock had scarce rung out over London, ere
the knocker sounded very gently on the door. I went
myself at the summons, and found a small man crouching against the pillars of the portico.

"Are you come from Dr. Jekyll?" I asked.

He told me "yes" by a constrained gesture; and when
I had bidden him enter, he did not obey me without a
searching backward glance into the darkness of the
square. There was a policeman not far off, advancing
with his bull's eye open; and at the sight, I thought my
visitor started and made greater haste.

These particulars struck me, I confess, disagreeably;
and as I followed him into the bright light of the consulting room, I kept my hand ready on my weapon.
Here, at last, I had a chance of clearly seeing him. I
had never set eyes on him before, so much was certain.
He was small, as I have said; I was struck besides with
the shocking expression of his face, with his remarkable
combination of great muscular activity and great apparent debility of constitution, and—last but not least—
with the odd, subjective disturbance caused by his
neighbourhood. This bore some resemblance to incipient rigour,[1] and was accompanied by a marked sinking

[1] The first stages of a nervous chill.

of the pulse. At the time, I set it down to some idio-syncratic, personal distaste, and merely wondered at the acuteness of the symptoms; but I have since had reason to believe the cause to lie much deeper in the nature of man, and to turn on some nobler hinge than the principle of hatred.

This person (who had thus, from the first moment of his entrance, struck in me what I can only describe as a disgustful curiosity) was dressed in a fashion that would have made an ordinary person laughable; his clothes, that is to say, although they were of rich and sober fabric, were enormously too large for him in every measure-ment—the trousers hanging on his legs and rolled up to keep them from the ground, the waist of the coat below his haunches, and the collar sprawling wide upon his shoulders. Strange to relate, this ludicrous accoutre-ment was far from moving me to laughter. Rather, as there was something abnormal and misbegotten in the very essence of the creature that now faced me—some-thing seizing, surprising and revolting—this fresh dis-parity seemed but to fit in with and to reinforce it; so that to my interest in the man's nature and character, there was added a curiosity as to his origin, his life, his fortune and status in the world.

These observations, though they have taken so great a space to be set down in, were yet the work of a few seconds. My visitor was, indeed, on fire with sombre excitement.

"Have you got it?" he cried. "Have you got it?" And so lively was his impatience that he even laid his hand upon my arm and sought to shake me.

I put him back, conscious at his touch of a certain icy pang along my blood. "Come, sir," said I. "You forget that I have not yet the pleasure of your acquaint-ance. Be seated, if you please." And I showed him an example, and sat down myself in my customary seat and with as fair an imitation of my ordinary manner to a patient, as the lateness of the hour, the nature of my preoccupations, and the horror I had of my visitor, would suffer me to muster.

"I beg your pardon, Dr. Lanyon," he replied civilly enough. "What you say is very well founded; and my impatience has shown its heels to my politeness. I come here at the instance of your colleague, Dr. Henry Jekyll, on a piece of business of some moment, and I understood . . ." He paused and put his hand to his throat, and I could see, in spite of his collected manner, that he was wrestling against the approaches of the hysteria— "I understood, a drawer . . ."

But here I took pity on my visitor's suspense, and some perhaps on my own growing curiosity.

"There it is, sir," said I, pointing to the drawer, where it lay on the floor behind a table and still covered with the sheet.

He sprang to it, and then paused, and laid his hand upon his heart: I could hear his teeth grate with the convulsive action of his jaws; and his face was so ghastly to see that I grew alarmed both for his life and reason.

"Compose yourself," said I.

He turned a dreadful smile to me, and as if with the decision of despair, plucked away the sheet. At sight of the contents, he uttered one loud sob of such immense relief that I sat petrified. And the next moment, in a voice that was already fairly well under control, "Have you a graduated glass?" he asked.

I rose from my place with something of an effort and gave him what he asked.

He thanked me with a smiling nod, measured out a few minims of the red tincture and added one of the powders. The mixture, which was at first of a reddish hue, began, in proportion as the crystals melted, to brighten in colour, to effervesce audibly, and to throw off small fumes of vapour. Suddenly and at the same moment, the ebullition ceased and the compound changed to a dark purple, which faded again more slowly to a watery green. My visitor, who had watched these metamorphoses with a keen eye, smiled, set down the glass upon the table, and then turned and looked upon me with an air of scrutiny.

"And now," said he, "to settle what remains. Will you be wise? will you be guided? will you suffer me to take this glass in my hand and to go forth from your house without further parley? or has the greed of curiosity too much command of you? Think before you answer, for it shall be done as you decide. As you decide, you shall be left as you were before, and neither richer nor wiser, unless the sense of service rendered to a man in mortal distress may be counted as a kind of riches of the soul. Or, if you shall so prefer to choose, a new province of knowledge and new avenues to fame and power shall be laid open to you, here, in this room, upon the instant; and your sight shall be blasted by a prodigy to stagger the unbelief of Satan."

"Sir," said I, affecting a coolness that I was far from truly possessing, "you speak enigmas, and you will perhaps not wonder that I hear you with no very strong impression of belief. But I have gone too far in the way of inexplicable services to pause before I see the end."

"It is well," replied my visitor. "Lanyon, you remember your vows: what follows is under the seal of our profession. And now, you who have so long been bound to the most narrow and material views, you who have denied the virtue of transcendental medicine, you who have derided your superiors—behold!"

He put the glass to his lips and drank at one gulp. A

cry followed; he reeled, staggered, clutched at the table and held on, staring with injected eyes, gasping with open mouth; and as I looked there came, I thought, a change—he seemed to swell—his face became suddenly black and the features seemed to melt and alter—and the next moment, I had sprung to my feet and leaped back against the wall, my arm raised to shield me from that prodigy, my mind submerged in terror.

"O God!" I screamed, and "O God!" again and again; for there before my eyes—pale and shaken, and half fainting, and groping before him with his hands, like a man restored from death—there stood Henry Jekyll!

What he told me in the next hour, I cannot bring my mind to set on paper. I saw what I saw, I heard what I heard, and my soul sickened at it; and yet now when that sight has faded from my eyes, I ask myself if I believe it, and I cannot answer. My life is shaken to its roots; sleep has left me; the deadliest terror sits by me at all hours of the day and night; I feel that my days are numbered, and that I must die; and yet I shall die incredulous. As for the moral turpitude that man unveiled to me, even with tears of penitence, I cannot, even in memory, dwell on it without a start of horror. I will say but one thing, Utterson, and that (if you can bring your mind to credit it) will be more than enough. The creature who crept into my house that night was, on Jekyll's own confession, known by the name of Hyde and hunted for in every corner of the land as the murderer of Carew.

HASTIE LANYON.

### HENRY JEKYLL'S FULL STATEMENT OF THE CASE

I was born in the year 18— to a large fortune, endowed besides with excellent parts, inclined by nature to industry, fond of the respect of the wise and good

among my fellow-men, and thus, as might have been
supposed, with every guarantee of an honourable and
distinguished future. And indeed the worst of my
faults was a certain impatient gaiety of disposition, such
as has made the happiness of many, but such as I found
it hard to reconcile with my imperious desire to carry
my head high, and wear a more than commonly grave
countenance before the public. Hence it came about
that I concealed my pleasures; and that when I reached
years of reflection, and began to look round me and take
stock of my progress and position in the world, I stood
already committed to a profound duplicity of life.
Many a man would have even blazoned such irregular-
ities as I was guilty of; but from the high views that I
had set before me, I regarded and hid them with an
almost morbid sense of shame. It was thus rather the
exacting nature of my aspirations than any particular
degradation in my faults, that made me what I was,
and, with even a deeper trench than in the majority of
men, severed in me those provinces of good and ill
which divide and compound man's dual nature. In this
case, I was driven to reflect deeply and inveterately on
that hard law of life, which lies at the root of religion
and is one of the most plentiful springs of distress.
Though so profound a double-dealer, I was in no sense
a hypocrite; both sides of me were in dead earnest; I
was no more myself when I laid aside restraint and
plunged in shame, than when I laboured, in the eye of
day, at the furtherance of knowledge or the relief of
sorrow and suffering. And it chanced that the direction
of my scientific studies, which led wholly towards the
mystic and the transcendental, reäcted and shed a strong
light on this consciousness of the perennial war among
my members. With every day, and from both sides of
my intelligence, the moral and the intellectual, I thus

drew steadily nearer to that truth, by whose partial discovery I have been doomed to such a dreadful shipwreck: that man is not truly one, but truly two. I say two, because the state of my own knowledge does not pass beyond that point. Others will follow, others will outstrip me on the same lines; and I hazard the guess that man will be ultimately known for a mere polity of multifarious, incongruous and independent denizens. I for my part, from the nature of my life, advanced infallibly in one direction and in one direction only. It was on the moral side, and in my own person, that I learned to recognise the thorough and primitive duality of man; I saw that, of the two natures that contended in the field of my consciousness, even if I could rightly be said to be either, it was only because I was radically both; and from an early date, even before the course of my scientific discoveries had begun to suggest the most naked possibility of such a miracle, I had learned to dwell with pleasure, as a beloved day-dream, on the thought of the separation of these elements. If each, I told myself, could but be housed in separate identities, life would be relieved of all that was unbearable; the unjust might go his way, delivered from the aspirations and remorse of his more upright twin; and the just could walk steadfastly and securely on his upward path, doing the good things in which he found his pleasure, and no longer exposed to disgrace and penitence by the hands of this extraneous evil. It was the curse of mankind that these incongruous faggots were thus bound together— that in the agonised womb of consciousness, these polar twins should be continuously struggling, How, then, were they dissociated?

I was so far in my reflections when, as I have said, a side light began to shine upon the subject from the laboratory table. I began to perceive more deeply than it

has ever yet been stated, the trembling immateriality
the mist-like transience, of this seemingly so solid body
in which we walk attired. Certain agents I found to
have the power to shake and to pluck back that fleshly
vestment, even as a wind might toss the curtains of a
pavilion. For two good reasons, I will not enter deeply
into this scientific branch of my confession. First, because I have been made to learn that the doom and
burthen of our life is bound forever on man's shoulders,
and when the attempt is made to cast it off, it but returns upon us with more unfamiliar and more awful
pressure. Second, because, as my narrative will make,
alas! too evident, my discoveries were incomplete.
Enough, then, that I not only recognised my natural
body for the mere aura and effulgence of certain of the
powers that made up my spirit, but managed to compound a drug by which these powers should be de-
throned from their supremacy, and a second form and
countenance substituted, none the less natural to me
because they were the expression, and bore the stamp,
of lower elements in my soul.

I hesitated long before I put this theory to the test of
practice. I knew well that I risked death; for any
drug that so potently controlled and shook the very fortress of identity, might by the least scruple of an over-
dose or at the least inopportunity in the moment of
exhibition, utterly blot out that immaterial tabernacle
which I looked to it to change. But the temptation of
a discovery so singular and profound, at last overcame
the suggestions of alarm. I had long since prepared my
tincture; I purchased at once, from a firm of wholesale
chemists, a large quantity of a particular salt which I
knew, from my experiments, to be the last ingredient
required; and late one accursed night, I compounded
the elements, watched them boil and smoke together in

the glass, and when the ebullition had subsided, with a strong glow of courage, drank off the potion.

The most racking pangs succeeded: a grinding in the bones, deadly nausea, and a horror of the spirit that cannot be exceeded at the hour of birth or death. Then these agonies began swiftly to subside, and 1 came to myself as if out of a great sickness. There was something strange in my sensations, something indescribably new and, from its very novelty, incredibly sweet. I felt younger, lighter, happier in body; within I was conscious of a heady recklessness, a current of disordered sensual images running like a mill race in my fancy, a solution of the bonds of obligation, an unknown but not an innocent freedom of the soul. I knew myself, at the first breath of this new life, to be more wicked, tenfold more wicked, sold a slave to my original evil; and the thought, in that moment, braced and delighted me like wine. I stretched out my hands, exulting in the freshness of these sensations; and in the act, I was suddenly aware that I had lost in stature.

There was no mirror, at that date, in my room; that which stands beside me as I write, was brought there later on and for the very purpose of these transformations. The night, however, was far gone into the morning—the morning, black at it was, was nearly ripe for the conception of the day—the inmates of my house were locked in the most rigorous hours of slumber; and I determined, flushed as I was with hope and triumph, to venture in my new shape as far as to my bedroom. I crossed the yard, wherein the constellations looked down upon me, I could have thought, with wonder, the first creature of that sort that their unsleeping vigilance had yet disclosed to them; I stole through the corridors, a stranger in my own house; and coming to my room, I saw for the first time the appearance of Edward Hyde.

I must here speak by theory alone, say.ng not that which I know, but that which I suppose to be most probable. The evil side of my nature, to which I had now transferred the stamping efficacy, was less robust and less developed than the good which I had just deposed. Again, in the course of my life, which had been, after all, nine-tenths a life of effort, virtue and control, it had been much less exercised and much less exhausted. And hence, as I think, it came about that Edward Hyde was so much smaller, slighter and younger than Henry Jekyll. Even as good shone upon the countenance of the one, evil was written broadly and plainly on the face of the other. Evil besides (which I must still believe to be the lethal [1] side of man) had left on that body an imprint of deformity and decay. And yet when I looked upon that ugly idol in the glass, I was conscious of no repugnance, rather of a leap of welcome. This, too, was myself. It seemed natural and human. In my eyes it bore a livelier image of the spirit, it seemed more express and single, than the imperfect and divided countenance I had been hitherto accustomed to call mine. And in so far I was doubtless right. I have observed that when I wore the semblance of Edward Hyde, none could come near to me at first without a visible misgiving of the flesh. This, as I take it, was because all human beings, as we meet them, are commingled out of good and evil: and Edward Hyde, alone in the ranks of mankind, was pure evil.

I lingered but a moment at the mirror: the second and conclusive experiment had yet to be attempted; it yet remained to be seen if I had lost my identity beyond redemption and must flee before daylight from a house that was no longer mine; and hurrying back to my cabinet, I once more prepared and drank the cup, once

[1] Deadly, causing death.

more suffered the pangs of dissolution, and came to myself once more with the character, the stature and the
face of Henry Jekyll.

That night I had come to the fatal cross roads.  Had
I approached my discovery in a more noble spirit, had I
risked the experiment while under the empire of generous
or pious aspirations, all must have been otherwise, and
from these agonies of death and birth, I had come forth
an angel instead of a fiend.  The drug had no discriminating action; it was neither diabolical nor divine; but it
shook the doors of the prison-house of my disposition;
and like the captives of Philippi, that which stood within
ran forth.  At that time my virtue slumbered; my evil,
kept awake by ambition, was alert and swift to seize the
occasion; and the thing that was projected was Edward
Hyde.  Hence, although I had now two characters as
well as two appearances, one was wholly evil, and the
other was still the old Henry Jekyll, that incongruous
compound of whose reformation and improvement I
had already learned to despair.  The movement was
thus wholly towards the worse.

Even at that time, I had not yet conquered my aver-
sion to the dryness of a life of study.  I would still be
merrily disposed at times; and as my pleasures were
(to say the least) undignified, and I was not only well
known and highly considered, but growing towards the
elderly man, this incoherency of my life was daily growing more unwelcome.  It was on this side that my new
power tempted me until I fell in slavery.  I had but to
drink the cup, to doff at once the body of the noted professor, and to assume, like a thick cloak, that of Edward
Hyde.  I smiled at the notion; it seemed to me at the
time to be humourous; and I made my preparations
with the most studious care.  I took and furnished that
house in Soho, to which Hyde was tracked by the police;
and engaged as housekeeper a creature whom I well

knew to be silent and unscrupulous. On the other side, I announced to my servants that a Mr. Hyde (whom I described) was to have full liberty and power about my house in the square; and to parry mishaps, I even called and made myself a familiar object, in my second character. I next drew up that will to which you so much objected; so that if anything befell me in the person of Dr. Jekyll, I could enter on that of Edward Hyde without pecuniary loss. And thus fortified, as I supposed, on every side, I began to profit by the strange immunities of my position.

Men have before hired bravos to transact their crimes, while their own person and reputation sat under shelter. I was the first that ever did so for his pleasures. I was the first that could thus plod in the public eye with a load of genial respectability, and in a moment, like a schoolboy, strip off these lendings and spring headlong into the sea of liberty. But for me, in my impenetrable mantle, the safety was complete. Think of it—I did not even exist! Let me but escape into my laboratory door, give me but a second or two to mix and swallow the draught that I had always standing ready; and whatever he had done, Edward Hyde would pass away like the stain of breath upon a mirror; and there in his stead, quietly at home, trimming the midnight lamp in his study, a man who could afford to laugh at suspicion, would be Henry Jekyll.

The pleasures which I made haste to seek in my disguise were, as I have said, undignified; I would scarce use a harder term. But in the hands of Edward Hyde, they soon began to turn towards the monstrous. When I would come back from these excursions, I was often plunged into a kind of wonder at my vicarious depravity. This familiar that I called out of my own soul, and sent forth alone to do his good pleasure, was a being inherently malign and villainous; his every act and thought centered on self; drinking pleasure with bestial avidity from any degree of torture to another; relentless like a man of stone. Henry Jekyll stood at times aghast before the acts of Edward Hyde; but the situation was apart from ordinary laws, and insidiously relaxed the grasp of conscience. It was Hyde, after all, and Hyde alone, that was guilty. Jekyll was no worse; he woke again to his good qualities seemingly unimpaired; he would even make haste, where it was possible, to undo the evil done by Hyde. And thus his conscience slumbered.

Into the details of the infamy at which I thus connived (for even now I can scarce grant that I committed it) I have no design of entering; I mean but to point out the warnings and the successive steps with which my chastisement approached. I met with one accident which, as it brought on no consequence, I shall no more than mention. An act of cruelty to a child aroused against me the anger of a passer-by, whom I recognised the other day in the person of your kinsman; the doctor and the child's family joined him; there were moments when I feared for my life; and at last, in order to pacify their too just resentment, Edward Hyde had to bring them to the door, and pay them in a cheque drawn in the name of Henry Jekyll. But this danger was easily eliminated from the future, by opening an account at another bank in the name of Edward Hyde himself; and when, by sloping my own hand backward, I had supplied my double with a signature, I thought I sat beyond the reach of fate.

Some two months before the murder of Sir Danvers, I had been out for one of my adventures, had returned at a late hour, and woke the next day in bed with somewhat odd sensations. It was in vain I looked about me·

in vain I saw the decent furniture and tall proportions of my room in the square, in vain that I recognised that pattern of the bed curtains and the design of the mahogany frame; something still kept insisting that I was not where I was, that I had not wakened where I seemed to be, but in the little room in Soho where I was accustomed to sleep in the body of Edward Hyde. I smiled to myself, and, in my psychological way began lazily to inquire into the elements of this illusion, occasionally, even as I did so, dropping back into a comfortable morning doze. I was still so engaged when, in one of my more wakeful moments, my eyes fell upon my hand. Now the hand of Henry Jekyll (as you have often remarked) was professional in shape and size: it was large, firm, white and comely. But the hand which I now saw, clearly enough, in the yellow light of a mid-London morning, lying half shut on the bed clothes, was lean, corded, knuckly, of a dusky pallor and thickly shaded with a swart growth of hair. It was the hand of Edward Hyde.

I must have stared upon it for near half a minute, sunk as I was in the mere stupidity of wonder, before terror woke up in my breast as sudden and startling as the crash of cymbals; and bounding from my bed, I rushed to the mirror. At the sight that met my eyes, my blood was changed into something exquisitely thin and icy. Yes, I had gone to bed Henry Jekyll, I had awakened Edward Hyde. How was this to be explained? I asked myself; and then, with another bound of terror—how was it to be remedied? It was well on in the morning; the servants were up; all my drugs were in the cabinet—a long journey down two pair of stairs, through the back passage, across the open court and through the anatomical theatre, from where I was then standing horror-struck. It might indeed be possible to cover my face; but of what use was that, when

I was unable to conceal the alteration in my stature? And then with an overpowering sweetness of relief, it came back upon my mind that the servants were already used to the coming and going of my second self. I had soon dressed, as well as I was able, in clothes of my own size: had soon passed through the house, where Bradshaw stared and drew back at seeing Mr. Hyde at such an hour and in such a strange array; and ten minutes later, Dr. Jekyll had returned to his own shape and was sitting down, with a darkened brow, to make a feint of breakfasting.

Small indeed was my appetite. This inexplicable incident, this reversal of my previous experience, seemed, like the Babylonian finger on the wall, to be spelling out the letters of my judgment; and I began to reflect more seriously than ever before on the issues and possibilities of my double existence. That part of me which I had the power of projecting, had lately been much exercised and nourished; it had seemed to me of late as though the body of Edward Hyde had grown in stature, as though (when I wore that form) I were conscious of a more generous tide of blood; and I began to spy a danger that, if this were much prolonged, the balance of my nature might be permanently overthrown, the power of voluntary change be forfeited, and the character of Edward Hyde become irrevocably mine. The power of the drug had not been always equally displayed. Once, very early in my career, it had totally failed me; since then I had been obliged on more than one occasion to double, and once, with infinite risk of death, to treble the amount; and these rare uncertainties had cast hitherto the sole shadow on my contentment. Now, however, and in the light of that morning's accident, I was led to remark that whereas, in the beginning, the difficulty had been to throw off the body of Jekyll, it had of late gradually but decidedly transferred itself to the other side. All things therefore seemed to point to this: that I was slowly losing hold of my original and better self, and becoming slowly incorporated with my second and worse.

Between these two, I now felt I had to choose. My two natures had memory in common, but all other faculties were most unequally shared between them. Jekyll (who was composite) now with the most sensitive apprehensions, now with a greedy gusto, projected and shared in the pleasures and adventures of Hyde; but Hyde was indifferent to Jekyll, or but remembered him as the mountain bandit remembers the cavern in which he conceals himself from pursuit. Jekyll had more than a father's interest; Hyde had more than a son's indifference. To cast in my lot with Jekyll, was to die to those appetites which I had long secretly indulged and had of late begun to pamper. To cast it in with Hyde, was to die to a thousand interests and aspirations, and to become, at a blow and forever, despised and friendless. The bargain might appear unequal; but there was still another consideration in the scales; for while Jekyll would suffer smartingly in the fires of abstinence, Hyde would be not even conscious of all that he had lost. Strange as my circumstances were, the terms of this debate are as old and commonplace as man; much the same inducements and alarms cast the die for any tempted and trembling sinner; and it fell out with me, as it falls with so vast a majority of my fellows, that I chose the better part and was found wanting in the strength to keep to it.

Yes, I preferred the elderly and discontented doctor, surrounded by friends and cherishing honest hopes; and bade a resolute farewell to the liberty, the comparative youth, the light step, leaping impulses and secret pleasures, that I had enjoyed in the disguise of Hyde. I made this choice perhaps with some unconscious reservation, for I neither gave up the house in Soho, nor destroyed the clothes of Edward Hyde, which still lay ready in my cabinet. For two months, however, I was true to my determination; for two months I led a life of such severity as I had never before attained to, and enjoyed the compensations of an approving conscience. But time began at last to obliterate the freshness of my alarm; the praises of conscience began to grow into a thing of course; I began to be tortured with throes and longings, as of Hyde, struggling after freedom; and at last, in an hour of moral weakness, I once again compounded and swallowed the transforming draught.

I do not suppose that, when a drunkard reasons with himself upon his vice, he is once out of five hundred times affected by the dangers that he runs through his brutish, physical insensibility; neither had I, long as I had considered my position, made enough allowance for the complete moral insensibility and insensate readiness to evil, which were the leading characters of Edward Hyde. Yet it was by these that I was punished. My devil had been long caged, he came out roaring. I was conscious, even when I took the draught, of a more unbridled, a more furious propensity to ill. It must have been this, I suppose, that stirred in my soul that tempest of impatience with which I listened to the civilities of my unhappy victim; I declare, at least before God, no man morally sane could have been guilty of that crime upon so pitiful a provocation; and that I struck in no more reasonable spirit than that in which a sick child may break a plaything. But I had voluntarily stripped myself of all those balancing instincts by which even the worst of us continues to walk with some degree of steadiness among temptations; and in my case, to be tempted, however slightly, was to fall.

Instantly the spirit of hell awoke in me and raged. With a transport of glee, I mauled the unresisting body, tasting delight from every blow, and it was not til' weariness had begun to succeed, that I was suddenly, in the top fit of my delirium, struck through the heart by a cold thrill of terror. A mist dispersed; I saw my life to be forfeit; and fled from the scene of these excesses, at once glorifying and trembling, my lust of evil gratified and stimulated, my love of life screwed to the topmost peg. I ran to the house in Soho, and (to make assurance doubly sure) destroyed my papers; thence I set out through the lamplit streets, in the same divided ecstasy of mind, gloating on my crime, light-headedly devising others in the future, and yet still hastening and still hearkening in my wake for the steps of the avenger. Hyde had a song upon his lips as he compounded the draught, and as he drank it, pledged the dead man. The pangs of transformation had not done tearing him, before Henry Jekyll, with streaming tears of gratitude and remorse, had fallen upon his knees and lifted his clasped hands to God. The veil of self-indulgence was rent from head to foot. I saw my life as a whole: I followed it up from the days of childhood, when I had walked with my father's hand, and through the self-denying toils of my professional life, to arrive again and again, with the same sense of unreality, at the damned horrors of the evening. I could have screamed aloud; I sought with tears and prayers to smother down the crowd of hideous images and sounds with which my memory swarmed against me; and still, between the petitions, the ugly face of my iniquity stared into my soul. As the acuteness of this remorse began to die away, it was succeeded by a sense of joy. The problem of my conduct was solved. Hyde was thenceforth impossible; whether I would or not, I was now confined to the better part of my existence; and O, how I rejoiced to think it! with what willing humility, I embraced anew the restrictions of natural life! with what sincere renunciation, I locked the door by which I had so often gone and come, and ground the key under my heel!

The next day, came the news that the murder had been overlooked, that the guilt of Hyde was patent to the world, and that the victim was a man high in public estimation. It was not only a crime, it had been a tragic folly. I think I was glad to know it; I think I was glad to have my better impulses thus buttressed and guarded by the terrors of the scaffold. Jekyll was now my city of refuge; let but Hyde peep out an instant, and the hands of all men would be raised to take and slay him.

I resolved in my future conduct to redeem the past; and I can say with honesty that my resolve was fruitful of some good. You know yourself how earnestly in the last months of last year, I laboured to relieve suffering; you know that much was done for others, and that the days passed quietly, almost happily for myself. Nor can I truly say that I wearied of this beneficent and innocent life; I think instead that I daily enjoyed it more completely; but I was still cursed with my duality of purpose; and as the first edge of my penitence wore off, the lower side of me, so long indulged, so recently chained down, began to growl for license. Not that I dreamed of resuscitating Hyde; the bare idea of that would startle me to frenzy: no, it was in my own person, that I was once more tempted to trifle with my conscience; and it was as an ordinary secret sinner, that I at last fell before the assaults of temptation.

There comes an end to all things; the most capacious measure is filled at last; and this brief condescension to my evil finally destroyed the balance of my soul. And yet I was not alarmed; the fall seemed natural, like a return to the old days before I had made my discovery. It was a fine, clear, January day, wet under foot where the frost had melted, but cloudless overhead; and the Regent's Park was full of winter chirrupings and sweet with spring odours. I sat in the sun on a bench; the animal within me licking the chops of memory; the spiritual side a little drowsed, promising subsequent penitence, but not yet moved to begin. After all, I reflected, I was like my neighbours; and then I smiled, comparing myself with other men, comparing my active goodwill with the lazy cruelty of their neglect. And at the very moment of that vain-glorious thought, a qualm came over me, a horrid nausea and the most deadly shuddering. These passed away, and left me faint; and then as in its turn the faintness subsided, I began to be aware of a change in the temper of my thoughts, a greater boldness, a contempt of danger, a solution of the bonds of obligation. I looked down; my clothes hung formlessly on my shrunken limbs; the hand that lay on my knee was corded and hairy. I was once more Edward Hyde. A moment before I had been safe of all men's respect, wealthy, beloved—the cloth laying for me in the dining-room at home; and now I was the common quarry of mankind, hunted, houseless, a known murderer, thrall to the gallows.

My reason wavered, but it did not fail me utterly. I have more than once observed that, in my second character, my faculties seemed sharpened to a point and my spirits more tensely elastic; thus it came about that, where Jekyll perhaps might have succumbed, Hyde rose to the importance of the moment. My drugs were in one of the presses of my cabinet; how was I to reach them? That was the problem that (crushing my temples in my hands) I set myself to solve. The laboratory door I had closed. If I sought to enter by the house my own servants would consign me to the gallows. I saw I must employ another hand, and thought of Lanyon. How was he to be reached? how persuaded? Supposing that I escaped capture in the streets, how was I to make my way into his presence? and how should I, an unknown and displeasing visitor, prevail on the famous physician to rifle the study of his colleague, Dr. Jekyll? Then I remembered that of my original character, one part remained to me: I could write my own hand; and once I had conceived that kindling spark, the way that I must follow became lighted up from end to end.

Thereupon, I arranged my clothes as best I could, and summoning a passing hansom, drove to an hotel in Portland Street, the name of which I chanced to remember. At my appearance (which was indeed comical enough, however tragic a fate these garments covered) the driver could not conceal his mirth. I gnashed my teeth upon him with a gust of devilish fury; and the smile withered from his face—happily for him—yet more happily for myself, for in another instant I had certainly dragged him from his perch. At the inn, as I entered, I looked about me with so black a countenance as made the attendants tremble; not a look did they exchange in my presence; but obsequiously took my orders, led me to a private room, and brought me wherewithal to write. Hyde in danger of his life was a creature new to me; shaken with inordinate anger, strung to the pitch of murder, lusting to inflict pain. Yet the creature was astute; mastered his fury with a great effort of the will; composed his two important letters, one to Lanyon and one to Poole; and that he might receive actual evidence of their being posted, sent them out with directions that they should be registered.

Thenceforward, he sat all day over the fire in the private room, gnawing his nails; there he dined, sitting alone with his fears, the waiter visibly quailing before his eye; and thence, when the night was fully come, he set forth in the corner of a closed cab, and was driven to and fro about the streets of the city. He, I say—I cannot say, I. That child of Hell had nothing human; nothing lived in him but fear and hatred. And when at last, thinking the driver had begun to grow suspicious, he discharged the cab and ventured on foot, attired in his misfitting clothes, an object marked out for observation, into the midst of the nocturnal passengers, these two base passions raged within him like a tempest. He walked fast, hunted by his fears, chattering to himself, skulking through the less frequented thoroughfares, counting the minutes that still divided him from midnight. Once a woman spoke to him, offering, I think, a box of lights. He smote her in the face, and she fled.

When I came to myself at Lanyon's, the horror of my old friend perhaps affected me somewhat; I do not know; it was at least but a drop in the sea to the abhorrence with which I looked back upon these hours. A change had come over me. It was no longer the fear of the gallows, it was the horror of being Hyde that racked me. I received Lanyon's condemnation partly in a dream; it was partly in a dream that I came home to my own house and got into bed. I slept after the prostration of the day, with a stringent and profound slumber which not even the nightmares that wrung me could avail to break. I awoke in the morning shaken, weakened, but refreshed. I still hated and feared the thought of the brute that slept within me, and I had not of course forgotten the appalling dangers of the day before; but I was once more at home, in my own house and close to my drugs; and gratitude for my escape shone so strong in my soul that it almost rivalled the brightness of hope.

I was stepping leisurely across the court after breakfast, drinking the chill of the air with pleasure, when I was seized again with those indescribable sensations that heralded the change; and I had but the time to gain the shelter of my cabinet, before I was once again raging and freezing with the passions of Hyde. It took on this occasion a double dose to recall me to myself; and alas! six hours after, as I sat looking sadly in the fire, the pangs returned, and the drug had to be readministered. In short, from that day forth it seemed only by a great effort as of gymnastics, and only under the immediate stimulation of the drug, that I was able to wear the countenance of Jekyll. At all hours of the day and night, I would be taken with the premonitory shudder; above all, if I slept, or even dozed for a moment in my chair, it was always as Hyde that I awakened. Under the strain of this continually impending doom and by the sleeplessness to which I now condemned myself, ay, even beyond what I had thought possible to man, I became, in my own person, a creature eaten up and emptied by fever, languidly weak both in body and mind, and solely occupied by one thought: the horror of my other self. But when I slept, or when the virtue of the medicine wore off, I would leap almost without transition (for the pangs of transformation grew daily less marked) into the possession of a fancy brimming with images of terror, a soul boiling with causeless hatreds, and a body that seemed not strong enough to contain the raging energies of life. The powers of Hyde seemed to have grown with the sickliness of Jekyll. And certainly the hate that now divided them was equal on each side. With Jekyll, it was a thing of vital instinct. He had now seen the full deformity of that creature that shared with

him some of the phenomena of consciousness, and was
co-heir with him to death: and beyond these links of
community, which in themselves made the most poignant
part of his distress, he thought of Hyde, for all his energy
of life, as of something not only hellish but inorganic.
This was the shocking thing; that the slime of the pit
seemed to utter cries and voices; that the amorphous
dust gesticulated and sinned; that what was dead, and
had no shape, should usurp the offices of life. And this
again, that that insurgent horror was knit to him closer
than a wife, closer than an eye; lay caged in his flesh,
where he heard it mutter and felt it struggle to be born;
and at every hour of weakness, and in the confidence of
slumber, prevailed against him, and deposed him out of
life. The hatred of Hyde for Jekyll, was of a different
order. His terror of the gallows drove him continually
to commit temporary suicide, and return to his subordi-
nate station of a part instead of a person; but he loathed
the necessity, he loathed the despondency into which
Jekyll was now fallen, and he resented the dislike with
which he was himself regarded. Hence the apelike
tricks that he would play me, scrawling in my own hand
blasphemies on the pages of my books, burning the
letters and destroying the portrait of my father; and
indeed, had it not been for his fear of death, he would
long ago have ruined himself in order to involve me in
the ruin. But his love of life is wonderful; I go further:
I, who sicken and freeze at the mere thought of him,
when I recall the abjection and passion of this attach-
ment, and when I know how he fears my power to cut
him off by suicide, I find it in my heart to pity him.

It is useless, and the time awfully fails me, to prolong
this description; no one has ever suffered such torments,
let that suffice; and yet even to these, habit brought—
no, not alleviation—but a certain callousness of soul, a

certain acquiescence of despair; and my punishment might have gone on for years, but for the last calamity which has now fallen, and which has finally severed me from my own face and nature. My provision of the salt, which had never been renewed since the date of the first experiment, began to run low. I sent out for a fresh supply, and mixed the draught; the ebullition followed, and the first change of colour, not the second; I drank it and it was without efficiency. You will learn from Poole how I have had London ransacked; it was in vain; and I am now persuaded that my first supply was impure, and that it was that unknown impurity which lent efficacy to the draught.

About a week has passed, and I am now finishing this statement under the influence of the last of the old powders. This, then, is the last time, short of a miracle, that Henry Jekyll can think his own thoughts or see his own face (now how sadly altered!) in the glass. Nor must I delay too long to bring my writing to an end; for if my narrative has hitherto escaped destruction, it has been by a combination of great prudence and great good luck. Should the throes of change take me in the act of writing it, Hyde will tear it in pieces; but if some time shall have elapsed after I have laid it by, his wonderful selfishness and circumscription to the moment will probably save it once again from the action of his apelike spite. And indeed the doom that is closing on us both, has already changed and crushed him. Half an hour from now, when I shall again and forever reindue that hated personality, I know how I shall sit shuddering and weeping in my chair, or continue, with the most strained and fearstruck ecstasy of listening, to pace up and down this room (my last earthly refuge) and give ear to every sound of menace. Will Hyde die upon the scaffold? or will he find courage to release himself at the